Models in Hydraulic Engineering
Physical Principles and Design Applications

P Novak
University of Newcastle upon Tyne

and

J Čábelka
Czech Technical University, Prague

𝛑

Pitman Advanced Publishing Program
Boston · London · Melbourne

PITMAN PUBLISHING LIMITED
39 Parker Street, London WC2B 5PB

PITMAN PUBLISHING INC
1020 Plain Street, Marshfield, Massachusetts

Associated Companies
Pitman Publishing Pty Ltd, Melbourne
Pitman Publishing New Zealand Ltd, Wellington
Copp Clark Pitman, Toronto

© P. Novak and J. Čábelka 1981

Library of Congress Cataloging in Publication Data

Novák, Pavel
  Models in hydraulic engineering.

  (Monographs and surveys in water resources engineering; 4)
  A revised translation of the authors' Modelový výzkum, which
  was published in 1964 as V. 1 of Hydrotechnický výzkum.
  Includes bibliographical references and index.
  I. Hydraulic models. II. Čábelka, Jaroslav, 1906–, joint author.
  II. Title. III. Series.
  TC 163.N73 627'.0228 80–22383

  ISBN 0-273-08436-4

Text set at The Universities Press (Belfast) Ltd.
Printed and bound in Great Britain at The Pitman Press, Bath.

To Eli

Contents

Preface

The main aim of this book is to give the reader not only a survey of the theory of models and similarity in hydraulics but also of the methods, results and application of hydraulic research. A major part of the book, therefore, is concerned both with a thorough treatment of the similarity criteria for various types of models and the determination of their scales and with the practical use of models and the results achieved in the solution of important hydrodynamic problems associated with the design, construction and operation of hydraulic structures. The chapters dealing with the actual construction of models and their instrumentation are necessarily fairly brief and general, but the reader requiring further information is given a list of references at the end of each chapter of the book. Although the book deals primarily with scale models, a brief chapter on analogue models and on hydraulic measurements in the field has been included.

The omission of a deeper treatment of mathematical models is intentional as a reasonably comprehensive coverage of this subject would make the text too long and, further, the book is part of a series where the subject is covered in other volumes (on computational hydraulics).

This is neither a textbook on hydraulics nor a treatise on hydraulic engineering; indeed basic knowledge of these disciplines is assumed. It is primarily intended for final year undergraduates, postgraduate students and hydraulic engineers working in research laboratories and engaged in the design and operation of hydraulic structures.

The book is loosely based on *Hydrotechnický výzkum 1—Modelový výzkum* (*Hydraulic Research 1—Research on Models*) by J. Čábelka and P. Novák, and published by SNTL, Prague in 1964. The text has been completely revised and new chapters added. The authors have, however, preserved substantial parts of the original approach based on the sometimes lesser known central and eastern European outlook and references and on examples frequently taken from their own experience. At the same time it has, of course, been their endeavour to present a text which is valid and of use to hydraulic engineers anywhere.

Professor Čábelka is the author of Chapters 3 and 8, major parts of Chapters 7 and 12 and Sections 5.2 to 5.4. The rest of the book was written by Professor Novak who also revised the whole text.

1981   P. Novak
                                                                       J. Čábelka

List of notations

		Dimension
a	acceleration; pressure wave velocity	LT^{-2}; LT^{-1}
A	coefficient in the Prandtl–Karman equation; area	$-$, L^2
b	width	L
B	coefficient in the Prandtl–Karman equation	$-$
c	coefficient; wave celerity	$-$, LT^{-1}
C	coefficient in Chezy's equation	$L^{1/2}T^{-1}$
C'	concentration of suspended sediment	$MT^{-2}L^{-2}$
Ca	Cauchy number	$-$
d	(sediment) diameter	L
$\bar{d}$	average grain diameter	L
d_s	equivalent grain diameter	L
d_{90}	diameter at 90% grain distribution curve	L
D	pipe diameter; diffusion coefficient	L, L^2T^{-1}
e	work	ML^2T^{-2}
E	specific energy	L
Eu	Euler number	$-$
f	function	$-$
F	function	
Fr	Froude number	$-$
g	acceleration due to gravity	LT^{-2}
g_s	specific sediment discharge	MT^{-3}
G_s	sediment discharge	MLT^{-3}
h	depth; head	L
H	head	L
k	roughness size; permeability coefficient	L, LT^{-1}
K	compressibility coefficient	$ML^{-1}T^{-2}$
K'	coefficient in Strickler's equation	$L^{1/3}T^{-1}$
Ka	Karman number	$-$
l	length	L
L	length (dimension)	
L	wave length	L

Dimension

La	Lagrange number	–
m	index denoting model	–
M	mass (dimension)	
Ma	Mach number	–
M_x	scale of x (x prototype/x model)	–
n	Manning's coefficient	$TL^{-1/3}$
N	power	ML^2T^{-3}
Ne	Newton number	–
p	pressure intensity; index denoting prototype	$ML^{-1}T^{-2}$, –
P	force; wetted perimeter	MLT^{-2}, L
q	specific discharge	L^2T^{-1}
Q	discharge	L^3T^{-1}
r	pipe radius	L
R	hydraulic radius	L
Re	Reynolds number	–
S	slope	–
S_0	bed slope	–
S_e	slope of energy line	–
Sh	Strouhal number	–
t	time	T
T	time (dimension)	
T	wave period	T
u	instantaneous local velocity	LT^{-1}
$\bar{u}$	time mean local velocity	LT^{-1}
u'	($\bar{u}-u$) difference between mean and instantaneous velocity	LT^{-1}
v	mean (cross-sectional) velocity	LT^{-1}
V	volume	L^3
w	settling velocity	LT^{-1}
We	Weber number	–
X	coordinate	L
y	depth below water level; height above bed	L
Y	coordinate	L
z	height above datum	L
Z	coordinate	L
α	Coriolis number	–
δ	boundary layer thickness	L
δ'	laminar sub-layer thickness	L
ϕ	function; shape of sediment	–
γ	specific weight	$ML^{-2}T^{-2}$
γ_s	specific weight of sediment	$ML^{-2}T^{-2}$
γ_s'	specific weight of sediment under water	$ML^{-2}T^{-2}$
κ	Karman's universal constant	–

Dimension

λ	coefficient of friction head loss $\left(=\dfrac{2gDS}{v^2}\right)$	–
λ_R	coefficient of friction head loss $\left(=\dfrac{2gRS}{v^2}=\dfrac{\lambda}{4}\right)$	–
μ	coefficient of dynamic viscosity	$ML^{-1}T^{-1}$
ν	coefficient of kinematic viscosity	L^2T^{-1}
ρ	specific mass (density)	ML^{-3}
ρ_s	specific mass of sediment	ML^{-3}
σ	coefficient of surface tension	MT^{-2}
σ_c	cavitation number	–
σ_s	*MRS*	–
τ	shear stress	$ML^{-1}T^{-2}$
τ_0	wall shear stress	$ML^{-1}T^{-2}$
ω	angular velocity	T^{-1}
ξ	velocity head coefficient (local losses)	–
ε	relative roughness; coefficient of eddy viscosity	$-, ML^{-1}T^{-1}$
η	efficiency	

Selected List of Abbreviations

ANSSR	Academy of Sciences of the USSR, Moscow (Akademia nauk SSSR).
ASCE	American Society of Civil Engineers, New York.
ASME	American Society of Mechanical Engineers, New York.
BHRA	British Hydromechanics Research Association, Cranfield (BHRA Fluid Engineering).
BSI	British Standards Institution, London.
ČSAV	Czechoslovak Academy of Sciences, Prague (Československá akademie věd).
HRS	Hydraulics Research Station, Wallingford.
IAHR/AIRH	International Association for Hydraulic Research, Delft.
ICE	Institution of Civil Engineers, London.
ISO	International Standards Organisation, Geneva.
HMSO	Her Majesty's Stationery Office, London.
PIANC	Permanent International Association for Navigation Congresses, Brussels.
SAV	Slovak Academy of Sciences, Bratislava (Slovenská akademia vied).
SNTL	State Publishing House for Technical Literature, Prague (Statní nakladatelství technické literatury).
VÚV	Water Resources Research Institute, Prague and Bratislava (Výzkumny ústav vodohospodářský).
VÚVH	Water Resources Research Institute, Bratislava (formerly VÚV Bratislava, Výzkumný ústav vodného hospodárstva).

1 Introduction

The hydraulic engineer is concerned with the motion of liquids in the widest sense. The liquid is usually, but not exclusively, water—a viscous slightly compressible fluid. The science of hydraulics thus works with the real liquids of engineering interest although it owes much to the laws derived in theoretical hydromechanics for ideal (homogeneous, incompressible, non-viscous) liquids.

The subject has been marked by an extraordinary development of experimental methods: the complexity of most cases of liquid flow and our still-limited analytical abilities permit the strict application of basic flow equations only in certain schematized situations and experimental methods are needed in most other cases. Almost every analytical solution of fluid motion requires the situation to be idealized to a certain extent and in all but the simplest cases the effect of the simplifications introduced must be tested by experiment. In the analysis of the more complicated cases of turbulent flow, the difficulties and shortcomings connected with a theoretical solution are further increased: a mathematical treatment, if at all possible, may be extremely laborious and produce results which can only be used safely after verification by experiment and experience. In consequence, research into hydraulic engineering has increasingly come to rely on experimental methods, including the use of scale and analogue models.

The term *model* is used in hydraulics to describe the simulation of a 'prototype', i.e. field size, situation. The hydraulic engineer uses models to predict the effect of a proposed design or scheme; they are tools for producing technically and economically optimal solutions to engineering problems. In other words, a model is a system which will convert a given input (geometry, boundary conditions, force, etc.), into an output (flow rates, levels, pressures, etc.), to be used in civil engineering design and operation.

The design of any hydraulic structure can be approached in three ways: by theory and reasoning; by experience derived from similar structures; or by testing the proposed design on a model. Unfortunately experience may be lacking, usually due to the uniqueness of the design and circumstance. Furthermore many problems of non-uniform and unsteady flow, sediment motion, dispersion, density currents and cases with complicated geometry still defy full (or even partial) theoretical treatment. Thus experimental work on *scale models* is often the most efficient and sometimes indeed the only method of solving the problem.

One of the first to use scale models in hydraulic engineering was Osborne Reynolds who designed and operated a tidal model of the Upper Mersey in 1885 at Manchester University. In 1898 Hubert Engels established the first River Hydraulics Laboratory at Dresden. Then followed a gradual and, after 1920, an accelerating expansion of laboratories for the study of hydraulic engineering problems using scale models.

It is self-evident that the basic requirement of any model is that it should reproduce correctly the behaviour of the situation being modelled. The success of the solution depends on the accurate formulation of the problem and on the correct identification of the main parameters influencing the phenomena under investigation. This may lead to an intentional suppression of forces and influences whose role in the prototype is, in the light of experience, only of secondary importance. A possible pitfall here is that the magnitude of forces neglected in the analysis may assume a disproportionately large significance in the model, so introducing a discrepancy usually referred to as a scale effect. The appreciation of similarity laws and of limits of their validity is therefore particularly important if scale effects are to be avoided. All these considerations influence the selection of appropriate methods and techniques of simulation.

As we are primarily concerned with the reproduction of present or future full-size behaviour, obtaining relevant field data is an important and integral part of the modelling process. Information on this aspect will be found in Chapter 12 and elsewhere.

Although it forms the main subject of this book, direct simulation by the use of scale models is not the only method available for simulating the real situation. Semi-direct methods of simulation include electrical, mechanical or hydrodynamic analogues and indirect methods make use of theoretical analysis including mathematical models:

An *analogue model* is a system reproducing a prototype situation in a physically different medium. This technique is dependent on the equations representing the prototype and model being mathematically identical. Thus torsional vibrations of a bar may represent the water-level oscillations of a simple surge tank, and both can be simulated by the voltage changes in an electric circuit, i.e. by an electrical analogue.

A *mathematical model* is a series of equations defining, in a simplified form, the system we are dealing with. The application of mathematical models in hydraulics is mainly in the treatment of diffusion and dispersion phenomena and of transients in unsteady flow in open channels and in pipelines. The rapid development of digital computers and of computer programming has naturally played a substantial part in the growth and application of such modelling techniques. They can only be used successfully, however, in cases where the correct equations representing the process are known or can be established. Thus the introduction of computers can never fully displace experimental techniques. On the contrary it is often found that a combination of methods may result in an efficient approach to the required solution.

Hydraulic research cannot be disassociated from theory if it is to be fully effective. The purely experimental approach to the solution of a problem without any theoretical analysis, even if restricted to a dimensional analysis, is likely to be wasteful of effort. Systematic experiments require theoretical guide-lines in the absence of which they show only a certain relationship of observed hydraulic parameters within the range of the experiments undertaken. If the physical principles depicted by an empirical function are not elucidated, then the function can neither be safely extrapolated nor generalized for other similar cases of flow.

In hydraulic research it is almost impossible to draw a clear dividing line between basic and applied research, as both intermingle in the solution of hydraulic problems connected with engineering design. The field of hydraulic research also extends beyond hydraulic engineering into other branches of engineering and science.

References

Novak, P. (1971). *The Hydraulic Engineer and his Models*, (Inaugural Lecture), University of Newcastle Upon Tyne.

Vinje, J. J. (1977). *Recent Developments in Hydraulic Research*, Publication No. 183, Delft Hydraulics Laboratory, Delft.

2 Theory of Similarity

2.1 General Considerations

Research on scale models is based on the theory of similarity between the model and prototype. The theory of similarity shows:

(a) how the model experiment should be theoretically founded and methodologically prepared;
(b) what requirements the model must fulfil to depict reality on a reduced scale as faithfully as possible;
(c) which parameters should be measured during the experiment;
(d) how the research results must be processed;
(e) to what phenomenon the obtained results may be applied and what is the extent of their validity.

The theory of similarity today is generally elaborated in two directions. The first determines the criteria of similarity from a system of basic homogeneous (differential) equations, which mathematically express the investigated physical phenomena. This method is most suitable for various technical disciplines, physical chemistry, etc., and in some cases also for hydraulic research. Here, however, we often lack the differential equations of the system which we intend to study, in particular when dealing with problems of sediment transport, river processes, high velocities with cavitation, aerated flow, etc. In these cases the second path—dimensional analysis—may be taken as the basis for determining the conditions of similarity of the phenomena. Its use requires a careful preliminary appraisal of the physical basis of each phenomenon and the determination of parameters which influence it; this is often verified with the aid of separate experiments. The combined use of physical and dimensional analyses is usually successful in various technical disciplines and therefore also in hydraulic research.

2.2 Dimensional Analysis

2.2.1 System of units

In mechanics several basic systems of units may be used:

(a) The physical (practical) system, better known as Système International d'Unités or SI system, with the basic units of length, mass and time, the metre (m), the kilogram (kg) and the second (s) respectively. The unit of force is one newton $(N) \equiv kgm/s^2$ (from the second law of Newton, force = mass × acceleration). As the SI system has been internationally agreed as the only system to be used in the future, wherever possible it is used throughout this book; since 1970 it has replaced the 'British System' (*see* (d) below) in UK publications.

(b) The physical (absolute) system used mainly by physicists and, before the widespread adoption of SI units, based on smaller units of length and mass, the centimetre and gram respectively, and denoted sometimes as the CGS system. The unit of force is $1 \text{ dyne} \equiv g \, cm/s^2$. 1 newton is therefore 10^5 dynes.

(c) The technical system used prior to 1960 in many European countries with basic units of length, time and force, the metre, second and kilopond (or kg* or kilogram force) respectively, and known as the system MKpS, where 1 kilopond is 980665 dynes = 9.80665 newtons.

(d) The British system based on units for length, mass and time, the foot (ft) (= 0.3048 m), the pound (lb) (= 0.4536 kg) and the second (s). Two units of force were used: the pound force (lbf) where $1 \text{ lbf} = 32.174 \text{ lb ft/s}^2$ (as acceleration due to gravity is 32.174 ft/s^2) and the poundal (pdl) where $1 \text{ pdl} = \text{lb ft/s}^2$; thus $1 \text{ lbf} = 32.174 \text{ pdl} = 4.448 \text{ N}$. (*See also* note in (a) above).

(e) The American technical system based on ft–lb–s with the pound as a unit of force (lb_f). In the slug-mass system (1 slug = 14.59 kg) one pound force (lb_f) accelerates 1 slug mass 1 ft/s^2 $(1 \, lb_f = 1 \text{ slug ft/s}^2)$.

If we denote mass as M, length as L and time as T, we can express the physical dimensions of almost all parameters used in hydraulics with these symbols; e.g. velocity has the dimension LT^{-1}, specific mass (mass/volume) ML^{-3}, the coefficient of dynamic viscosity $ML^{-1}T^{-1}$. These dimensions are easily derived from the definitions of the above quantities and from the physical laws which characterize them. For example velocity is defined as the increase in distance during a unit of time

$$u = \frac{dx}{dt} = \frac{L}{T}$$

The coefficient of viscosity is characterized by the equation

$$\tau = \mu \frac{du}{dy}$$

where τ is the tangential stress.

Stress has the dimension of force acting on a unit area; therefore $MLT^{-2}L^{-2} = ML^{-1}T^{-2}$. From the above equation we thus obtain

$$ML^{-1}T^{-2} \equiv \mu LT^{-1}L^{-1}$$

and therefore

$$\mu \equiv ML^{-1}T^{-1}$$

In the list of symbols the physical dimensions in the units mass–length–time are given for each parameter.

Expressing the parameter in physical dimensions permits safe transformation from one unit system to another. For example the unit of the coefficient of viscosity in a centimetre–gram–second (CGS) system is poise. This is to be expressed in the ft–lb–s system, where we regard the pound, lb_f, as the unit of force (system e):

$$1 \text{ poise} = 1 \text{ g/cm} \equiv ML^{-1}T^{-1}$$

If we introduce for the unit of force $P = MLT^{-2}$ then

$$ML^{-1}T^{-1} = PL^{-1}T^2L^{-1}T^{-1} = PTL^{-2}$$

therefore

$$1 \text{ poise} = \frac{30.48^2}{980.665 \times 453.6} \text{ lb}_f/\text{ft}^2 = 0.002088 \text{ lb}_f/\text{ft}^2$$

($1 \text{ lb}_f = 453.6 \times 980.665$ dynes, $1 \text{ ft} = 30.48$ cm)

2.2.2 Principles of dimensional analysis and its use in hydraulic research

Dimensional analysis provides some basic information about the investigated phenomenon on the assumption that it can be expressed by a dimensionally correct equation containing the variables influencing it. Thus we obtain a certain grouping of variables, reduce their total number and allow for a wider application and interpretation of the experimental results.

An equation is dimensionally homogeneous if it is independent of the basic units used. For example in the well-known form of Bazin's equation for discharge Q over a rectangular notch

$$Q = m\sqrt{(2g)}bH^{3/2}$$

where H is the head, b the length of the notch and g the acceleration due to gravity. The coefficient m is independent of the units used to measure b, H, g and Q as long as the same units of length (cm, m, ft, etc.) are being used throughout. This is so because in the dimensional form both sides of the equation are identical: $Q - L^3 T^{-1}$; $g - LT^{-2}$; $b - L$; $H - L$

$$L^3 T^{-1} \equiv L^{1/2} T^{-1} L L^{3/2}$$

therefore

$$L^3 T^{-1} \equiv L^3 T^{-1}$$

On the other hand we must not assume that every equation we are trying to establish in its general form will be dimensionally homogeneous. This is only the case if the equation contains all variables, as it would in an analytical derivation. Thus in the application of dimensional analysis the basic step is the correct choice of variables that might influence the phenomenon under observation.

In hydraulic research the mutual relationship of variables any one of which may be dependent on the others is experimentally investigated on a physical model. In most cases all quantities are easily independently controlled with the exception of one which becomes the dependent variable. In the choice of variables we often introduce a parameter which under the conditions investigated is in fact constant, but which in connection with different variables forms a dimensionless number; thus in analysis we often introduce, e.g. acceleration due to gravity.

The inclusion of more than one dependent variable into the investigated relationship is almost as serious a mistake as omitting some of the participating quantities. On the other hand it is not detrimental to introduce quantities which do not influence the investigated problem, because they mostly eliminate themselves in further analysis. To make a correct choice of variables we must, first of all, formulate a certain theory about the phenomenon under consideration and accordingly assess which independent variables must be taken into account. This means that we must at least know, either from experience or by analogy, why the phenomenon might be influenced by a particular variable.

Three kinds of variables participate in hydraulic research; they describe either the geometry of the model, the flow in it, or the properties of the fluid used. In scale models with preserved geometric similarity it suffices to introduce into the experimentally investigated relationship a single variable for the determination of the linear scale (model scale) on which the other dimensions depend. Usually only two or three fluid properties are chosen which may play an important part in the case under investigation (e.g., specific mass, viscosity, surface tension). Nearly every flow characteristic comes within the group of dependent variables, but always one only can be considered, according to the type of acting force.

Greatest simplicity must be observed in the choice of variables included in the investigated relationships. Thus, of the three mutually dependent variables, length, velocity and discharge, it is usually more suitable to include length and velocity than velocity and discharge ($Q = vA = vl^2$).

Two related methods of dimensional analysis are of greatest importance in hydraulics: Rayleigh's method and Buckingham's method (π theorem).

In conclusion it must be stressed that even though dimensional analysis is often justly applied in hydraulic research, its use must not be exaggerated and regarded as a replacement for, rather than a primary aid to, the analytical solution of differential equations. The correct use of dimensional analysis is always linked with knowledge and experience in the field and previous critical analysis of the investigated phenomenon. A deeper knowledge of dimensional analysis, in particular of its use for the choice of dimensionless numbers and the determination of others, requires more profound study and the use of matrices.

2.2.3 Rayleigh's method

Rayleigh's method is based on the fact that in each dimensionally homogeneous equation the exponent of every dimension on the left side of the equation must be equal to the sum of the exponents of the corresponding dimension on the right. If the equation expressing a dependent variable p contains n independent variables and if the dependent variable contains r basic dimensions, we can write r equations for n unknown exponents; from them it is possible to calculate r exponents for arbitrary values of the remaining $(n-r)$ exponents and the result can be expressed as a general function containing r independent variables with known exponents and $(n-r)$ dimensionless arguments with unknown exponents. This unknown function is then determined on the basis of experimental results. Let the general expression for the dependent variable p given by equation

$$p = a^x b^y c^z d^u e^v \tag{2.1}$$

where a, b, c, d, e are independent variables and x, y, z, u, v are unknown exponents. On the assumption that the dimensions of quantities p, a, b, c, d, e, are P, A, B, C, D, E, equation

$$P = A^x B^y C^z D^u E^v \tag{2.2}$$

is valid. If we substitute for P, A, B, C, D, E the corresponding dimensions M, L, T, we obtain three homogeneous linear equations for the exponents of the dimensions M, L, T, from which three unknown exponents may be calculated, for example, x, y, z expressed by means of the remaining exponents u and v. The result may then be expressed by the equation

$$p = a^{x_1} b^{y_1} c^{z_1} \pi_1^u \pi_2^v \tag{2.3}$$

where x, y, z are integers or fractions calculated from the equations for the exponents of M, L, T and π_1, π_2 are dimensionless arguments. Equation (2.3) is, however, only a special form of the general equation

$$p = a^{x_1} b^{y_1} c^{z_1} \left(\sum_1^\infty k_n \pi_1^n \right) \left(\sum_1^\infty k_m \pi_2^m \right) \tag{2.4}$$

where k_n and k_m are dimensionless constants. Since the series in Equation (2.4) are general functions of π_1 and π_2 it can be written as

$$p = a^{x_1} b^{y_1} c^{z_1} f(\pi_1, \pi_2) \tag{2.5}$$

Rayleigh's method may best be illustrated on the following example. Let us consider the equation for the determination of resistance $P(\text{MLT}^{-2})$ of a sphere diameter $D(\text{L})$ moving with a velocity $u(\text{LT}^{-1})$ in an incompressible and unlimited medium of specific mass $\rho(\text{ML}^{-3})$ and coefficient of viscosity $\mu(\text{ML}^{-1}\text{T}^{-1})$. The equation will have the following form

$$P = f(D, u, \rho, \mu) \tag{2.6}$$

or

$$P = D^a u^b \rho^c \mu^d \tag{2.6'}$$

where a, b, c, d are constants. If we rewrite Equation (2.6') dimensionally, we obtain

$$\text{MLT}^{-2} = \text{L}^a, \text{L}^b \text{T}^{-b}, \text{M}^c \text{L}^{-3c}, \text{M}^d \text{L}^{-d} \text{T}^{-d} \tag{2.6''}$$

For this equation to be dimensionally homogeneous the exponents for M, L, T on both sides of the equation must be identical. Therefore for

$$\left.\begin{array}{lll} \text{M} & 1 = c + d \\ \text{L} & 1 = a + b - 3c - d \\ \text{T} & -2 = -b - d \end{array}\right\} \tag{2.7}$$

We have three equations for four unknowns and can therefore express three of them by means of the fourth. From the equation for M

$$c = 1 - d$$

from the equation for T

$$b = 2 - d$$

and from the equation for L,

$$a = 1 - b + 3c + d = 1 - 2 + d + 3 - 3d + d = 2 - d$$

Substituting into Equation (2.6′) we obtain

$$P = D^{2-d}u^{2-d}\rho^{1-d}\mu^d = \rho D^2 u^2 \left(\frac{\mu}{uD\rho}\right)^d \tag{2.8}$$

or according to Equation (2.5)

$$P = \rho D^2 u^2 f\left(\frac{uD}{\nu}\right) \tag{2.8′}$$

thus

$$\frac{P}{\rho D^2 u^2} = f\left(\frac{uD}{\nu}\right) \tag{2.8″}$$

In Equation (2.8″) both sides are dimensionless numbers:

$$\frac{P}{\rho D^2 u^2} = \frac{MLT^{-2}}{ML^{-3}L^2 L^2 T^{-2}} = \text{dimensionless number (Newton Number)}$$

$$\frac{uD}{\nu} = \frac{uD\rho}{\mu} = \frac{LT^{-1}LML^{-3}}{ML^{-1}T^{-1}} = \text{dimensionless number (Reynolds Number).}$$

We shall return later to these dimensionless numbers and their names.

The area of the projection of the sphere is $A = \frac{1}{4}\pi D^2$; we can therefore rewrite Equation (2.8′) into the form

$$P = \frac{1}{2}C_D \rho u^2 A \tag{2.9}$$

where the resistance coefficient C_D is

$$C_D = \frac{8}{\pi} f\left(\frac{uD}{\nu}\right) \tag{2.10}$$

Equation (2.9) is the generally used form of the equation for the resistance of a sphere moving in an incompressible medium, where Equation (2.10) has to be investigated experimentally. To obtain the same result without dimensional analysis we would have to plot and use many graphs to show the mutual influence of the variables u, D, ρ, μ.

The correct result in the derivation of Equations (2.9) and (2.10) naturally depended also on the choice of the unknown in Equation (2.7) which we used to express the other three unknowns. Here use was made of the fact known from analysis that a force can best be expressed from the given four variables by the use of ρ, D, u, because

$$P = ma = \rho l^3 \frac{l}{t^2} = \rho l^2 \frac{l^2}{t^2} = \rho l^2 u^2$$

where l represents a length.

2.2.4 Buckingham's method (π theorem)

The basis of the application of the π theorem lies in the transformation of the relationship describing the investigated problem in terms of variables $a, b, c, \ldots$

$$f(a, b, c, \ldots, n) = 0 \tag{2.1'}$$

into another relatively simpler relationship between a smaller number of variable dimensionless arguments $\pi_1 \pi_2 \ldots$ which are established from the variables participating in the problem

$$F(\pi_1, \pi_2, \pi_3 \ldots) = 0 \tag{2.11}$$

If n independent variables $a, b, c \ldots n$ participate in a problem and their dimensions $A, B, C \ldots N$ can be expressed with the aid of r basic magnitudes, it is usually possible to establish $(n - r)$ dimensionless arguments $\pi_1, \pi_2, \pi_3, \ldots, \pi_{n-r}$. When these arguments are regarded as new variables, instead of Equation (2.1') introducing the original relation between the n participating variables, a new dimensionally homogeneous relationship (2.11) with $(n - r)$ variables can be written. The investigation of this second function is much simpler since the reduction of the number of variables by r also reduces the number of experiments necessary for the experimental solution of the problem. The closer the number of participating quantities n to the number of basic dimensions r, the simpler the solution.

The number of basic magnitudes helping to express the dimensions of independent variables participating in the investigated problem is $r \leqslant 3$ as there are three basic units, length, mass and time. If, therefore, all three participate in the problem—the most frequent case in practice—then $r = 3$.

The dimensionless arguments $\pi_1, \pi_2, \ldots, \pi_{n-r}$, are products of various powers of variables participating in the problem

$$\left.\begin{array}{l} \pi_1 = a^{x_1} b^{y_1} c^{z_1} \\ \pi_2 = a^{x_2} b^{y_2} c^{z_2} \text{ etc.} \end{array}\right\} \tag{2.12}$$

In every argument π there should be $(r + 1)$ of these variables. In the choice of the variables which are to occur in every dimensionless argument two conditions must be fulfilled; these recurring variables must together include all the basic dimensions and they must not in themselves form a dimensionless argument. In the general case $(r = 3)$ these conditions are complied with in such a way that among four variables three will be repeated in every argument, i.e. the characteristic length, velocity and specific mass. The fourth variable will differ in every argument (with the exponent ± 1) so that in the solution all n variables that influence the problem might be applied.

In general the dimensionless arguments π are simple numbers. Therefore

$$[\pi] = [A]^x [B]^y [C]^z \ldots [N]^v = 1 \tag{2.13}$$

If the dimensions A, B, etc., of the variables participating in the problem contained in every dimensionless argument π_1, π_2, π_3, etc., are now expressed with the aid of the basic dimensions (for example L, M, T) we can add the exponents of the same basic dimension for each dimensionless argument. The sum of the exponents of each basic dimension is then equal to zero since the product of the various powers of the dimension from which we set out was equal to one. Thus we obtain r equations for the unknown exponents $x, y, z, \ldots, v$. The remaining unknown exponents are chosen by experience, and thus the expressions for all dimensionless arguments are determined and we can proceed with the experimental solution of the problem.

In practice certain dimensionless arguments are already introduced as normal, so that the investigation of unknown exponents and thus also of dimensionless arguments is directed and simplified to a considerable degree.

When dealing with a greater number of dimensionless arguments and lacking sufficient experience in the choice of suitable exponents, it is possible arbitrarily to combine various dimensionless arguments (raise to a power, multiply or divide) so that we obtain for example the relation

$$F'\left(\pi_1^2, \frac{\pi_2}{\pi_1^2}, \pi_1 \pi_2 \pi_3 \ldots\right) = 0 \tag{2.14}$$

All these combinations of arguments are again dimensionless numbers. However, their number must be the same as before, i.e. $(n - r)$ (and all the original arguments must be used). This procedure usually aims at cancelling out some of the variables common to two or more combined arguments.

The use of Buckingham's method of dimensional analysis is again best demonstrated on a simple example.

One of the oldest tasks of experimental hydrodynamics is the determination, with the aid of a geometrically similar reduced model, of the resistance of a body (ship) moving with a steady velocity on an unlimited surface of an ideal (non-viscous) liquid of unlimited depth. Effect of viscosity is omitted to simplify the problem, as only a method of dimensional analysis is being demonstrated; for further treatment of the subject *see* Section 2.11. The following variables are involved: resistance $P(\mathrm{MLT^{-2}})$, velocity $v(\mathrm{LT^{-1}})$, gravitational acceleration $g(\mathrm{LT^{-2}})$, specific mass of the liquid $\rho(\mathrm{ML^{-3}})$ and a basic dimension (for example length of the vessel) $l(\mathrm{L})$, i.e. altogether five variables $(n = 5)$. Their dimensions may be expressed by three $(r = 3)$ basic dimensions $(\mathrm{M, L, T})$, so that

$(n - r)$, i.e. two dimensionless arguments may be established, according to the principles stated above.

$$\pi_1 = l^{x_1} v^{y_1} \rho^{z_1} g^1$$
$$\pi_2 = l^{x_2} v^{y_2} \rho^{z_2} P^1$$

(2.15)

The variables are now expressed in terms of the basic dimensions L, M, T, and the exponents of the same basic dimension added:

$$\pi_1 = L^{x_1} \left(\frac{L}{T}\right)^{y_1} \left(\frac{M}{L^3}\right)^{z_1} \left(\frac{L}{T^2}\right)^1$$

For

L	$x_1 + y_1 - 3z_1 + 1 = 0$
T	$-y_1 - 2 \qquad = 0$
M	$z_1 \qquad = 0$

Therefore $x_1 = 1$, $y_1 = -2$, $z_1 = 0$

$$\pi_1 = \frac{gl}{v^2} \text{ (reciprocal of the square of Froude number } Fr^2),$$

$$\pi_2 = L^{x_2} \left(\frac{L}{T}\right)^{y_2} \left(\frac{M}{L^3}\right)^{z_2} \left(\frac{ML}{T^2}\right)^1$$

For

L	$x_2 + y_2 - 3z_2 + 1 = 0$
T	$-y_2 - 2 = 0$
M	$z_2 + 1 = 0$

Therefore $x_2 = -2$, $y_2 = -2$, $z_2 = -1$, $\pi_2 = P/(l^2 v^2 \rho)$ (Newton number Ne). The relation between the two dimensionless arguments

$$F\left(\frac{P}{l^2 v^2 \rho}, \frac{gl}{v^2}\right) = 0$$

(2.16)

may be found experimentally, e.g. in such a way that a model of known size is dragged along the surface of the (ideal) fluid with a varying velocity v and the resistance P is measured. For pairs of measured values v and P the corresponding pairs of numbers Ne and Fr^2 are calculated; these represent points on the graph of the investigated correlation $F(Ne, Fr) = 0$.

If the resistance of a geometrically similar body of length l_p dragged at velocity v_p over the surface of an ideal fluid is to be determined, the Froude number Fr_p (or $Fr_p^2 = v_p^2/gl_p$) is calculated and from the graph of $F(Ne, Fr)$ the corresponding value of Newton's Number Ne_p is read. The resistance against the movement of this body on the surface of an ideal liquid is then represented by the relation

$$P_p = N e_p l_p^2 v_p^2 \rho$$

From the above it will be seen that there is no fundamental difference between the two methods of dimensional analysis. The advantage of Buckingham's method is that it avoids the use of infinite series—Equation (2.4)—the introduction of which is part of the derivation of Rayleigh's method. In practice, however, this step can be omitted without difficulty and we change over from equation type (2.1) with a numerical coefficient by analysis to an equation of the type (2.5).

The above examples demonstrate sufficiently clearly the advantages of the use of dimensional analysis in the study of hydraulic phenomena.

2.3 Basic Concepts and Definitions in the Theory of Similarity

If a reduced model of any object is built so that its shape corresponds exactly to prototype and all dimensions are reduced in the same scale and the corresponding angles are the same, then this is referred to as *geometric similarity* of the model and prototype. In geometry corresponding points of two formations (which need not necessarily be geometrically similar) are called *homologous points*. Homologous parts of a model and prototype are thus parts composed of homologous points.

The ratio of a certain quantity in prototype and the corresponding quantity on the model, e.g. l_p/l_m is called the *module* (of lengths) or *scale* (of lengths) and will be referred to throughout this book as M.

Let us now consider two formations, e.g. the real formation and its model, in motion and let us observe the routes described by the homologous points. If the homologous points of both formations lie on the homologous points of their routes in proportional (i.e. homologous) times, this is referred to as *kinematic similarity*. The proportionality of times means that the ratio of times in prototype and on the model $(t_p/t_m = M_t)$, in which the homologous points travel a homologous part of their routes is constant. Kinematic similarity thus assumes the similarity of the corresponding components of velocity and acceleration.

For the ratio of lengths in three coordinates

$$\frac{l_{px}}{l_{mx}} = M_{lx}; \qquad \frac{l_{py}}{l_{my}} = M_{ly}; \qquad \frac{l_{pz}}{l_{mz}} = M_{lz}$$

we can write for velocities

$$M_{ux} = \frac{u_{px}}{u_{mx}} = \frac{M_{lx}}{M_t}; \qquad M_{uy} = \frac{u_{py}}{u_{my}} = \frac{M_{ly}}{M_t}; \qquad M_{uz} = \frac{u_{pz}}{u_{mz}} = \frac{M_{lz}}{M_t} \qquad (2.17)$$

and for acceleration

$$M_{ax} = \frac{a_{px}}{a_{mx}} = \frac{M_{lx}}{M_t^2} \qquad M_{ay} = \frac{a_{py}}{a_{my}} = \frac{M_{ly}}{M_t^2} \qquad M_{az} = \frac{a_{pz}}{a_{mz}} = \frac{M_{lz}}{M_t^2} \qquad (2.18)$$

If in Equations (2.17) and (2.18) M_{ux}, M_{uy}, M_{uz} and M_{ax}, M_{ay}, M_{az} are constants, the expression of kinematic similarity is obtained. Further, if the formations are geometrically similar, i.e. $M_{lx} = M_{ly} = M_l$, this results in the equality of the velocity scales $M_{ux} = M_{uy} = M_{uz} = M_l/M_t$ and of the acceleration scales $M_{ax} = M_{ay} = M_{az} = M_l/M_t^2$. In this special case the streamlines passing through homologous points of the two formations are also geometrically similar.

Lastly, when the homologous parts of the model and prototype are exposed to proportional total forces, this is referred to as *dynamic similarity*. Since, according to Newton's law, force = mass × acceleration, the following equation may be written for prototype and the model

$$\left. \begin{array}{lll} P_{px} = m_p a_{px} & P_{py} = m_p a_{py} & P_{pz} = m_p a_{pz} \\ P_{mx} = m_m a_{mx} & P_{my} = m_m a_{my} & P_{mz} = m_m a_{mz} \end{array} \right\} \qquad (2.19)$$

Writing the ratio of forces we obtain for kinematic similarity

$$\frac{P_{px}}{P_{mx}} = \frac{m_p l_{px} t_m^2}{m_m l_{mx} t_p^2} \qquad \frac{P_{py}}{P_{my}} = \frac{m_p l_{py} t_m^2}{m_m l_{my} t_p^2} \qquad \frac{P_{pz}}{P_{mz}} = \frac{m_p l_{pz} t_m^2}{m_m l_{mz} t_p^2} \qquad (2.20)$$

If the ratio of forces in reality and on the model is denoted by M_p Equation (2.20) can be further rewritten as

$$M_{px} = \frac{M_m M_{lx}}{M_t^2} \qquad M_{py} = \frac{M_m M_{ly}}{M_t^2} \qquad M_{pz} = \frac{M_m M_{lz}}{M_t^2} \qquad (2.20')$$

For geometric similarity of both formations

$$(M_{lx} = M_{ly} = M_{lz} = M_l)$$

it is valid that

$$M_p = \frac{M_m M_l}{M_t^2} \qquad (2.20'')$$

If we substitute for $M_m = M_\rho M_V = M_\rho M_l^3$ we obtain from Equation (2.20'')

$$M_p = M_\rho \frac{M_l^4}{M_t^2} \qquad (2.21)$$

or after substituting for $M_v = M_l/M_t$, the equation:

$$M_p = M_\rho M_l^2 M_v^2 \qquad (2.22)$$

If in Equation (2.20') M_{px}, M_{py} and M_{pz} are constants (condition of proportionality of total forces) the expression for dynamic similarity is obtained, which then apart from kinematic similarity also contains proportionality of the distribution of mass m in both formations. If both formations are geometrically similar, Equations (2.20″), (2.21) or (2.22) express their *mechanical similarity*, which includes their geometric, kinematic and dynamic similarity.

Mechanical similarity may therefore be defined as follows: two formations (prototype, p and model, m) are mechanically similar if they are geometrically similar and if, for proportional masses of homologous points, their paths described in proportional times are also geometrically similar. The definition based on Newton's law thus includes geometric similarity of the two formations, the proportionality of times and the geometric similarity of the paths travelled (kinematic similarity) as well as the proportionality of masses, and thus also of forces (dynamic similarity). Thus for geometric similarity M_l is a constant; M_{lx}, M_{ly}, M_{lz} and M_t are constants for kinematic similarity and M_m as well as M_{px}, M_{py} and M_{pz} are constants for dynamic similarity; for mechanical similarity $M_{px} = M_{py} = M_{pz}$ and $M_{lx} = M_{ly} = M_{lz}$ and further M_t and M_m are naturally constants.

It must be stressed that *mechanical similarity* always includes dynamic (and thus also kinematic) and geometric similarity, whereas dynamic similarity always includes kinematic but not necessarily geometric similarity. This is particularly important in hydrodynamics where, e.g. in models of rivers, geometric similarity cannot always be adhered to; this, however, does not exclude the possibility of attaining dynamic similarity.

2.4 General Law of Mechanical Similarity in Hydrodynamics

2.4.1 Derivation of the law of mechanical similarity by dimensional analysis

The motion of fluids under various conditions, the motion of solid bodies in fluids, or the motion and interaction of both may be investigated on scale models. The physical parameters which in a general case may influence the body and fluid motion are: *for the body*—a characteristic length d (e.g. diameter of sediment) and its specific mass ρ_s; *for the fluid*—the specific mass ρ, the coefficient of viscosity μ, the coefficient of surface tension σ, the bulk modulus K, the mean velocity of flow v; acceleration due to gravity must also be taken into consideration. Lastly the entire phenomenon occurs in a medium of length l, width b and depth h (e.g. river channel).

The force acting on the body in the fluid flow can be expressed by the equation

$$P = c'\mu^a\rho^c K^e\sigma^f v^i b^k l^n h^p d^x \rho_s^y g^z \qquad (2.23)$$

where c' is a constant and $a \ldots z$ are unknowns.

The dimensions of the above quantities in the basic system of physical units L, M, T, are

$$P - MLT^{-2} \qquad\qquad \sigma - MT^{-2}$$
$$\mu - ML^{-1}T^{-1} \qquad\qquad v - LT^{-1}$$
$$\rho', \rho - ML^{-3} \qquad\qquad h, b, l, d - L$$
$$K - ML^{-1}T^{-2} \qquad\qquad g - LT^{-2}$$

Rewriting Equation (2.23) in terms of dimensions we obtain

$$MLT^{-2} = M^aL^{-a}T^{-a}M^cL^{-3c}M^eL^{-e}T^{-2e}M^fT^{-2f}L^iT^{-i}L^kL^nL^p$$
$$L^xM^yL^{-3y}L^zT^{-2z} \qquad (2.23')$$

To make this equation dimensionally homogeneous, the exponents for M, L, T on both sides of the equation must be identical.

For M $\qquad 1 = a + c + e + f + y$

for L $\qquad 1 = -a - 3c - e + i + k + n + p + x - 3y + z$

for T $\qquad -2 = -a - 2e - 2f - i - 2z$

We have three equations for eleven unknowns and can therefore express three of them by means of the remaining eight. To make the equation soluable and because again

$$P = ma = \rho l^3 \frac{l}{t^2} = \rho l^2 \frac{l^2}{t^2} = \rho l^2 v^2$$

we choose for the calculation the unknowns c, i, n;

from the equation for M $\qquad c = 1 - a - e - f - y$

from the equation for T $\qquad i = 2 - a - 2e - 2f - 2z$

from the equation for L $\qquad n = 1 + a + 3c + e - i - k - p - x + 3y - z$

After substituting for c and i from the first two equations into the third we obtain:

$$n = 1 + a + 3 - 3a - 3e - 3f - 3y + e - 2 + a + 2e + 2f + 2z - k - p - x$$
$$+ 3y - z$$
$$n = 2 - a - f + z - k - p - x$$

After substitution into Equation (2.23) we obtain

$$P = c'\rho l^2 v^2 \left(\frac{\mu}{\rho l v}\right)^a \left(\frac{K}{\rho v^2}\right)^e \left(\frac{\sigma}{\rho v^2 l}\right)^f \left(\frac{gl}{v^2}\right)^z \left(\frac{h}{l}\right)^p \left(\frac{b}{l}\right)^k \left(\frac{d}{l}\right)^x \left(\frac{\rho_s}{\rho}\right)^y \qquad (2.24)$$

or

$$P = \rho l^2 v^2 \phi \left(\frac{v^2}{gl}, \frac{\rho l v}{\mu}, \frac{\rho v^2 l}{\sigma}, \frac{\rho v^2}{K}, \frac{h}{l}, \frac{b}{l}, \frac{d}{l}, \frac{\rho_s}{\rho}\right) \qquad (2.25)$$

Equation (2.25) is the general equation for the force acting on a body in a fluid during their relative motion, in prototype and on the model. It follows from the manner of deriving Equation (2.25) that all expressions in brackets are dimensionless numbers; this can be easily verified by substituting the dimensions of the various parameters.

Since it has been shown that according to Newton's law $P = \rho l^2 v^2$ and since for mechanical similarity Equation (2.22) is valid ($M_p = M\rho M_l^2 M_v^2$) it follows that for mechanical similarity between the model and prototype the ratio of all corresponding dimensionless numbers in Equation (2.25) for prototype and the model must be equal to one.

The condition

$$\frac{M_h}{M_l} = \frac{M_b}{M_l} = \frac{M_d}{M_l} = 1$$

and therefore

$$M_h = M_b = M_d = M_l$$

expresses the condition of geometric similarity. The condition

$$\frac{M_{\rho_s}}{M_\rho} = 1$$

and therefore

$$M_{\rho_s} = M_\rho$$

contains the condition of the proportionality of masses.

Further dimensionless numbers occurring in Equation (2.25) are:

(a) $\dfrac{P}{\rho l^2 v^2}$ Newton number (Ne).

Since $P/l^2 = p$, i.e. specific pressure, Ne can be written in the form $p/\rho v^2$ which is the Euler number (Eu). (Sometimes the square root of half the reciprocal value is also used as Euler number)

$$\sqrt{\left(\frac{\rho v^2}{2p}\right)} = \left(\frac{v}{\sqrt{(2p/\rho)}}\right)$$

(b) $\dfrac{v}{\sqrt{(gl)}}$ Froude number (Fr).

The same name and notation (*Fr*) is sometimes used for the square of this ratio (v^2/gl), particularly in Russian and east European literature.

(c) $\dfrac{\rho l v}{\mu} = \dfrac{l v}{\nu}$ Reynolds number (*Re*).

(d) $\dfrac{\rho v^2 l}{\sigma}$ Weber number (*We*).

Again the square root of *We* is sometimes quoted as the Weber number.

(e) $\dfrac{\rho v^2}{K}$ Cauchy number (*Ca*).

The square root, which is called the Mach number (*Ma*), is more often used in its place (sometimes also referred to as Bairstow–Booth or Majevskij number).

Equation (2.25) can therefore be written as

$$Ne = \phi\left(Fr, Re, We, Ma, \frac{h}{l}, \frac{b}{l}, \frac{d}{l}, \frac{\rho_s}{\rho}\right) \tag{2.25'}$$

The condition of mechanical similarity may now be expressed from Equation (2.25) by a system of nine equations:

$$M_{Ne} = M_{Fr} = M_{Re} = M_{We} = M_{Ma} = \frac{M_h}{M_l} = \frac{M_b}{M_l} = \frac{M_d}{M_l} = \frac{M_{\rho_s}}{M_\rho} = 1.$$

Equation

$$M_{Fr} = 1 \tag{2.26}$$

or

$$Fr = idem \tag{2.26'}$$

expresses the Froude law of mechanical similarity valid for an ideal fluid under the exclusive action of gravity.

Equation

$$M_{Re} = 1 \tag{2.27}$$

or

$$Re = idem \tag{2.27'}$$

expresses the Reynolds law of mechanical similarity under the exclusive action of internal friction (viscosity) of the fluid.

Equation

$$M_{We} = 1 \tag{2.28}$$

or

$$We = idem \tag{2.28'}$$

expresses the Weber law of mechanical similarity under the exclusive action of surface tension.

Equation

$$M_{Ma} = 1 \tag{2.29}$$

or

$$Ma = idem \tag{2.29'}$$

possibly

$$M_{Ca} = 1 \tag{2.29''}$$

or

$$Ca = idem \tag{2.29'''}$$

expresses the law of mechanical similarity under the exclusive effect of compressibility.

It follows from Equation (2.25) that for full mechanical similarity in hydraulics in all cases and for a real fluid, i.e. under the simultaneous effect of all types of forces, all Equations (2.26) to (2.29) must be fulfilled together with geometric similarity and proportionality of masses. Only under these conditions is Equation (2.22) fulfilled, and therefore also

$$M_{Ne} = M_{Eu} = 1 \tag{2.22'}$$

or

$$Ne = idem \tag{2.22''}$$

or

$$Eu = idem \tag{2.22'''}$$

(equality of Newton or Euler number on the model and in prototype).

2.4.2 Derivation of the law of mechanical similarity in hydrodynamics from the basic Navier–Stokes equations

The Navier–Stokes differential equations are the most general equations of three-dimensional motion of a real, i.e. viscous, incompressible fluid, and express the balance between the three components of inertia forces and the difference of the corresponding components of volumetric forces (in a general force field) and the pressure forces, increased by the components of the force due to the viscosity of the fluid.

The mathematical expression in the explicit form is

$$\frac{\partial u}{\partial t}+u\frac{\partial u}{\partial x}+v\frac{\partial u}{\partial y}+w\frac{\partial u}{\partial z} = X-\frac{1}{\rho}\frac{\partial p}{\partial x}+\frac{\mu}{\rho}\left(\frac{\partial^2 u}{\partial x^2}+\frac{\partial^2 u}{\partial y^2}+\frac{\partial^2 u}{\partial z^2}\right)$$

$$\frac{\partial v}{\partial t}+u\frac{\partial v}{\partial x}+v\frac{\partial v}{\partial y}+w\frac{\partial v}{\partial z} = Y-\frac{1}{\rho}\frac{\partial p}{\partial y}+\frac{\mu}{\rho}\left(\frac{\partial^2 v}{\partial x^2}+\frac{\partial^2 v}{\partial y^2}+\frac{\partial^2 v}{\partial z^2}\right) \qquad (2.30)$$

$$\frac{\partial w}{\partial t}+u\frac{\partial w}{\partial x}+v\frac{\partial w}{\partial y}+w\frac{\partial w}{\partial z}= Z-\frac{1}{\rho}\frac{\partial p}{\partial z}+\frac{\mu}{\rho}\left(\frac{\partial^2 w}{\partial x^2}+\frac{\partial^2 w}{\partial y^2}+\frac{\partial^2 w}{\partial z^2}\right)$$

or more concisely

$$\left.\begin{aligned}
\frac{du}{dt} &= X-\frac{1}{\rho}\frac{\partial p}{\partial x}+\nu\,\Delta u, \\[2mm]
\frac{dv}{dt} &= Y-\frac{1}{\rho}\frac{\partial p}{\partial y}+\nu\,\Delta v, \\[2mm]
\frac{dw}{dt} &= Z-\frac{1}{\rho}\frac{\partial p}{\partial z}+\nu\,\Delta w,
\end{aligned}\right\} \quad [\text{m/s}^2] \qquad (2.30')$$

where ρX, ρY, ρZ are the components of volumetric forces, $\partial p/\partial x$, $\partial p/\partial y$, $\partial p/\partial z$ are the components of pressure forces, and $\mu\Delta u$, $\mu\Delta v$, $\mu\Delta w$ are the components of viscous forces acting in the direction of the axes x, y, z (X, Y, Z are the components of the acceleration due to gravity g, if we consider the normal case of the external force being gravity).

Equations (2.30) and (2.30') are valid both for the prototype and the model. If Equation (2.30) is now rewritten with the use of the corresponding scales, we obtain for gravity and x axis the equation:

$$\frac{M_v}{M_t}\frac{\partial u}{\partial t}+\frac{M_v^2}{M_l}\left(u\frac{\partial u}{\partial x}+v\frac{\partial u}{\partial y}+w\frac{\partial u}{\partial z}\right)$$

$$= M_g X-\frac{M_p}{M_\rho M_l}\frac{1}{\rho}\frac{\partial p}{\partial x}+\frac{M_\mu M_v}{M_\rho M_l^2}\frac{\mu}{\rho}\left(\frac{\partial^2 u}{\partial x^2}+\frac{\partial^2 u}{\partial y^2}+\frac{\partial^2 u}{\partial z^2}\right)$$

A similar equation would be obtained for the y and z axes.

If the above equation is divided by M_v^2/M_l we obtain

$$\frac{M_l}{M_v M_t}\frac{\partial u}{\partial t}+u\frac{\partial u}{\partial x}+v\frac{\partial u}{\partial y}+w\frac{\partial u}{\partial z}$$

$$= \frac{M_g M_l}{M_v^2}X-\frac{M_p}{M_\rho M_v^2}\frac{1}{\rho}\frac{\partial p}{\partial x}+\frac{M_\mu}{M_\rho M_v M_l}\frac{\mu}{\rho}\left(\frac{\partial^2 u}{\partial x^2}+\frac{\partial^2 u}{\partial y^2}+\frac{\partial^2 u}{\partial x^2}\right) \quad (2.31)$$

Similar equations would be valid for the y and z axes.

Equation (2.31) is a differential equation valid for all groups of similar phenomena. On the other hand, we arrived at it from Equation (2.30); if Equations (2.30) and (2.31) are to represent the model and prototype both must be identical for the law of mechanical similarity to be valid. This also requires all the multiples of the corresponding members of both equations to be equal to one. By comparing Equations (2.30) and (2.31) we obtain therefore conditions

$$\frac{M_l}{M_v M_t} = \frac{M_g M_l}{M_v^2} = \frac{M_p}{M_\rho M_v^2} = \frac{M_\mu}{M_\rho M_v M_l} = 1$$

Equation

$$\frac{M_v}{\sqrt{(M_g M_l)}} = M_{Fr} = 1 \tag{2.26}$$

is the already derived Froude law of mechanical similarity,

$$\frac{M_\rho M_v M_l}{M_\mu} = \frac{M_v M_l}{M_\nu} = M_{Re} = 1 \tag{2.27}$$

is the already derived Reynolds law of mechanical similarity and

$$\frac{M_p}{M_\rho M_v^2} = M_{Eu} = 1 \tag{2.22}$$

is the already derived condition of equality of the Euler number on the model and prototype.

By the above procedure we did not derive the Weber and Cauchy numbers as before, because the Navier–Stokes equations do not take into account surface tension and are valid for an incompressible fluid. However, by comparing Equations (2.30) and (2.31) we obtain a further equation

$$\frac{M_l}{M_v M_t} = 1 \tag{2.32}$$

$l/(vt)$ is another dimensionless number, referred to as Strouhal number (Sh). Equation (2.32) may be written in the form

$$Sh = idem \tag{2.32'}$$

For steady flow

$$\frac{\partial u}{\partial t} = \frac{\partial v}{\partial t} = \frac{\partial w}{\partial t} = 0$$

thus Equation (2.32) may be omitted. Therefore the Strouhal number takes on the character of the criterion for unsteady flow and processes. In this case t in the Strouhal number denotes a certain time interval in the unsteady process, (e.g. time of one rotation of a propeller); the Strouhal number may therefore also be written in the form $(nl)/v$, where n is the number of revolutions, angular velocity or frequency. (In the study of wake train formation the square of this number, with n denoting the frequency of the wake, is sometimes referred to as the Richardson number of the wake train.)

For the sake of completeness a few remarks must be added to the above derivation of the criteria of similarity: when using the Navier–Stokes equations it must be realized that they are equally valid for the flow past any body as well as for the flow of liquid in a pipe or channel. The system of differential equations thus expresses a whole class of phenomena and possesses an infinitely large number of solutions. However, dimensionless numbers obtained in the above manner from the condition of identity of Equations (2.30) and (2.31) can only be the criteria of similarity if the initial equations have an unambiguous solution. This can only be attained if the differential equations are limited by certain conditions so that, after solution, they give values of variables characterizing the given phenomenon. The boundary conditions that must be added to the differential equations thus attain the character of conditions of unambiguity of solution. These conditions take into account the geometry and dimensions of the space in which the given phenomenon occurs, the physical properties of the medium and, lastly, the initial conditions determining the values of the variables at the limits of the system and at the beginning of the observed phenomenon. If the various phenomena within the limited group now differ from one another only in scale, then they fulfil the main presuppositions of the theory of similarity.

Returning once more to the Navier–Stokes equations let us consider the case that inertia and external forces may be neglected. Equation (2.30′) would then read for the x axis

$$0 = -\frac{1}{\rho}\frac{\partial p}{\partial x} + \nu\Delta u$$

By a similar process as before we obtain

$$-\frac{M_p}{M_\rho M_l}\frac{1}{\rho}\frac{\partial p}{\partial x} + \frac{M_\mu M_v}{M_\rho M_l^2}\frac{\mu}{\rho}\Delta\mu = 0$$

and after dividing by $(M_\mu M_v/M_\rho M_l^2)$ the equation

$$\frac{M_p M_l}{M_\mu M_v} = 1 \tag{2.33}$$

In the theory of similarity the dimensionless number $pl/\mu v$ is referred to as Lagrange number (La). Equation (2.33) may therefore be rewritten as

$$\frac{pl}{\mu v} = La = idem \tag{2.33′}$$

The Lagrange criterion is in fact the consequence of the existence of similarity and therefore Equation (2.33) will refer to a group of phenomena in a region which is characterized by the possibility of neglecting the influence of the forces of inertia and the external force (e.g. gravity) in the Navier–Stokes equation. For example, the well-known equation (Hagen–Poiseuille law) for the distribution of velocity u in laminar flow through a pipe of radius r and pressure head loss $(p_1 - p_2)$ over length l is

$$u = \frac{(p_1 - p_2)}{4\mu l} (r^2 - y^2)$$

and is an example of the equation $La = \text{const.}$

Generally the case where the influence of all other forces, except that due to viscosity of the liquid can be neglected, may be expressed as follows from Equation (2.31):

$$Eu = f(Re) \tag{2.34}$$

If we put as a special but frequent case in Equation (2.34):

$$f(Re) = c \frac{1}{Re} \qquad (c \text{ is constant})$$

we obtain

$$Eu = \frac{c}{Re}$$

or

$$\frac{p}{\rho v^2} = \frac{c}{v l \rho / \mu}$$

and from this the previously given equation

$$\frac{pl}{v\mu} = La = \text{const.} \tag{2.33''}$$

Let us now investigate the second limiting case assuming that the viscous forces are negligible in comparison with inertia, simultaneously neglecting the influence of volumetric forces. For steady flow we obtain from Equation (2.30)

$$u\frac{\partial u}{\partial x} + v\frac{\partial u}{\partial y} + w\frac{\partial u}{\partial z} = -\frac{1}{\rho}\frac{\partial p}{\partial x} \text{ for the } x \text{ axis.}$$

By a similar process as before we obtain

$$\frac{M_v^2}{M_l}\left(u\frac{\partial u}{\partial x} + v\frac{\partial u}{\partial y} + w\frac{\partial u}{\partial z}\right) = -\frac{M_p}{M_\rho M_l}\frac{1}{\rho}\frac{\partial p}{\partial x}$$

From this follows the condition

$$\frac{M_p}{M_\rho M_v^2} = M_{Eu} = 1 \tag{2.22'}$$

This equation represents again another limiting case and a further auto-modelling region. It is also another special case of Equation (2.34) where $f(Re) = $ constant.

Equation (2.34) expresses the relationship between variables which characterize the steady flow of an homogeneous incompressible viscous liquid without the influence of volumetric forces and is therefore valid for a group of similar phenomena. In this group there exist two limiting automodelling regions in which the phenomena are characterized by the values of the variables given by the equation $La = $ constant or $Eu = $ constant (*see* examples in Chapters 5 and 6).

Most practical cases deal with turbulent flow. It is not the purpose of this chapter (nor the book) to deal with the theory of turbulence, but it will be useful to note briefly to what extent the previous derivations of the general law of mechanical similarity with the aid of Navier–Stokes equations apply to the case of similarity of turbulent flow.

Turbulent flow is accompanied by rapid changes of velocity, both in magnitude and direction, and thus the original Navier–Stokes equations do not give a solution. However, we can use transformed equations with the temporal mean values of the variables. It can be proved that under these conditions we obtain from Equation (2.30)

$$\frac{\partial \bar{u}}{\partial t} + \bar{u}\frac{\partial \bar{u}}{\partial x} + \bar{v}\frac{\partial \bar{u}}{\partial y} + \bar{w}\frac{\partial \bar{u}}{\partial z} = X - \frac{1}{\rho}\frac{\partial \bar{p}}{\partial x} + \frac{\mu}{\rho}\Delta\bar{u}$$
$$- \left[\frac{\partial(\overline{u'u'})}{\partial x} + \frac{\partial(\overline{u'v'})}{\partial y} + \frac{\partial(\overline{u'w'})}{\partial z}\right] \tag{2.35}$$

(where $u = \bar{u} + u'$, $\bar{u} = $ temporal mean velocity).

In the same manner as before, i.e. by introducing scales, we obtain the same equations

$$M_{Sh} = M_{Fr} = M_{Eu} = M_{Re} = 1$$

but from the last member of Equation (2.35) we obtain a further equation:

$$\frac{M_{v'}^2}{M_{\bar{v}}^2} = 1 \tag{2.36}$$

In the theory of similarity the dimensionless number $v'/\bar{v}$ is referred to as Karman number (Ka) and Equation (2.36) may thus be written

$$Ka = idem. \tag{2.36'}$$

Equation (2.36) introduces the criterion of constant velocity scale for mechanical similarity in turbulent flow, i.e. scale of velocity pulsation equal to scale of mean velocities. Present knowledge of turbulence as well as experimental results indicate that this criterion will generally be observed if the other conditions and criteria of similarity are satisfied.

2.4.3 Approximate mechanical similarity

Let us investigate further the condition of complete mechanical similarity requiring that while using real fluids all Equations (2.26) to (2.29) should be simultaneously satisfied. We shall find that it is practically impossible to obtain fluids possessing the necessary physical properties that comply with the given conditions. If we choose the same liquid for the model as in prototype it is impossible to attain complete mechanical similarity, since for $M_g = 1$ (the same gravitational acceleration acts on the model as in prototype) we obtain from Equation (2.26) $M_v = \sqrt{M_l}$ and for $M_v = 1$ (the same liquid in the model and prototype) from equation (2.27) $M_v = 1/M_l$. Both these equations for M_v can be satisfied only for $M_l = 1$, i.e. a model of the same size as prototype.

Hydraulic models work thus only with *approximate mechanical similarity* based on the ratio of those forces which determine the type of motion.

Accordingly the Reech–Froude, Reynolds, Weber or Mach law is then chosen for the investigation. By working on the model according to one main and determining law and neglecting the others, errors occur due to *scale effect* and the reduction of the model against reality must be chosen to make this error in the given situation negligible. These limits of model reduction determine the *limits of similarity* or the limiting boundary conditions for scaling procedure (for a more detailed analysis *see* Section 2.8).

In conclusion let us elucidate in the light of the Navier–Stokes equations two possibilities of complete mechanical similarity for flow of an incompressible liquid exposed simultaneously to gravity and viscous forces. With regard to the structure of the Navier–Stokes equations the influence of surface tension and compressibility continues to be excluded, which is very often permissible in technical practice.

(a) Consider more closely in Equation (2.30′) the member

$$\Delta u = \frac{\partial^2 u}{\partial x^2} + \frac{\partial^2 u}{\partial y^2} + \frac{\partial^2 u}{\partial z^2}$$

The potential flow of a viscous fluid of a constant specific weight must be irrotational. After adding and subtracting

$$\frac{\partial^2 v}{\partial x \, \partial y} + \frac{\partial^2 w}{\partial x \, \partial z}$$

to Δu we obtain the equation:

$$\Delta u = \frac{\partial^2 u}{\partial x^2} + \frac{\partial}{\partial y}\left(\frac{\partial u}{\partial y} - \frac{\partial v}{\partial x}\right) - \frac{\partial}{\partial z}\left(\frac{\partial w}{\partial x} - \frac{\partial u}{\partial z}\right) + \frac{\partial}{\partial x}\left(\frac{\partial v}{\partial y} + \frac{\partial w}{\partial z}\right)$$

If in the last member we introduce from continuity

$$\frac{\partial v}{\partial y} + \frac{\partial w}{\partial z} = -\frac{\partial u}{\partial x}$$

and according to the definition of rotational flow write the equation for angular velocity

$$\omega_z = \frac{1}{2}\left(\frac{\partial v}{\partial x} - \frac{\partial u}{\partial y}\right)$$

$$\omega_y = \frac{1}{2}\left(\frac{\partial u}{\partial z} - \frac{\partial w}{\partial x}\right)$$

we obtain the equation

$$\Delta u = -2\left(\frac{\partial \omega_z}{\partial y} - \frac{\partial \omega_y}{\partial z}\right) \tag{2.37}$$

Similar equations can be obtained for the other axes y, z and Δv, Δw. For irrotational flow, however, $\omega_z = \omega_y = \omega_x = 0$ and therefore also $\Delta u, \Delta v, \Delta w = 0$. This means that the Reynolds number is eliminated from the criteria of similarity and only the Froude number (possibly also the Strouhal number for unsteady flow) remains as a criterion. For steady irrotational flow of a viscous liquid with a free surface, i.e. flow with a velocity potential, similarity is governed exclusively by the Froude law. Therefore equation

$$Eu = f(Fr) \tag{2.38}$$

is valid.

Potential motion may be attained at least approximately in practice, if the liquid flows between smooth walls sufficiently distant from each other so that their influence on the flow is negligible.

(b) In the case of viscous fluid flow under pressure, the influence of gravity may be included in the pressure differential and not connected physically with the mass of the fluid. Mathematically this assumption may easily be expressed in the Navier–Stokes equations by rewriting them for the force field of gravity with the z axis vertical and positive downwards. The third equation in system (2.30′) will then be

$$\frac{\mathrm{d}w}{\mathrm{d}t} = g - \frac{1}{\rho}\frac{\partial p}{\partial z} + \nu\Delta w = -\frac{1}{\rho}\frac{\partial(p - \rho g z)}{\partial z} + \nu\Delta w$$

$$= -\frac{1}{\rho}\frac{\partial p^*}{\partial z} + \nu\Delta w \tag{2.39}$$

equally

$$-\frac{1}{\rho}\frac{\partial p}{\partial x} = -\frac{1}{\rho}\frac{\partial(p-\rho gz)}{\partial x} = -\frac{1}{\rho}\frac{\partial p^*}{\partial x}$$

$$-\frac{1}{\rho}\frac{\partial p}{\partial y} = -\frac{1}{\rho}\frac{\partial(p-\rho gz)}{\partial y} = -\frac{1}{\rho}\frac{\partial p^*}{\partial y}$$

In these equations the pressure

$$p^* = p - \rho gz = p - p'$$

has been introduced.

In the above equation p is the pressure intensity at an arbitrary point of the cross-section during motion and $p' = \rho gz$ is the hydraulic pressure at the same point at rest under otherwise equal conditions. If we now apply the above-mentioned procedure with the introduction of scales into Equation (2.39) we find that only the Reynolds number (possibly also the Strouhal number for unsteady flow) remains as a criterion of similarity.

For steady flow of a viscous incompressible fluid under pressure, similarity is governed exclusively by the Reynolds law. Equation

$$Eu = f(Re) \tag{2.34}$$

is valid.

For the practical application of the above deductions it must be pointed out, however, that in the second automodelling region $f(Re) = $ const (*see* Sub-section 2.4.2, Equation (2.22′) and also Chapter 5); in this region therefore, it is not necessary, from the point of view of similarity, to maintain the identity of the Reynolds number.

Finally it must be pointed out that this chapter deals with the theory of similarity in general terms. The next chapters will not only give the application of these principles but also develop the theory in several more specialized fields, e.g. unsteady flow, sediment transport, stratified flow, etc.

2.5 Froude Law

The Froude law (first expressed by Reech and later independently by Froude and therefore sometimes also referred to as the Reech–Froude Law) represents the condition of dynamic similarity for flow in model and prototype exclusively governed by gravity. Other forces, such as frictional resistance of a viscous liquid, capillary forces, the forces of volumetric elasticity and cavitation phenomena, either do not affect the flow or their effect may be neglected. With certain limitations, e.g. for the choice of model scales, this is permissible especially for free surface flow as it occurs when modelling the discharge from orifices and over notches and weirs, the movement of larger surface waves and flow in short open channel sections (hydraulic jump, etc.). In the flow of a real (viscous) fluid, however, internal friction always acts simultaneously with gravity. If the model is geometrically similar to prototype and the boundary conditions are also similar (e.g., inflow or outflow condition, wall roughness, etc.), then similarity not only between forces due to gravity but also to a large extent between the resistances due to friction is ensured (*see* Chapters 6 and 7).

When investigating the similarity under the exclusive or overwhelming action of gravity we thus accept geometric similarity as the basis of mechanical similarity. The basic equation for this case was given by Equation (2.26); from this follow all necessary further relations. The basic equation can also be derived very simply by the following method.

If the force due to gravity is expressed by

$$P = \gamma V,$$

the ratio (scale) of the forces in prototype and the model is

$$M_p = \frac{P_p}{P_m} = \frac{\gamma_p V_p}{\gamma_m V_m} = M_\gamma M_l^3$$

By comparing this with the ratio of forces of inertia according to the Newton law (Equation (2.22)) we get

$$M_\gamma M_l^3 = M_\rho M_l^2 M_v^2$$

If we write $M_\gamma = M_g M_\rho$ this results in

$$\frac{M_v}{\sqrt{(M_g M_l)}} = M_{Fr} = 1 \qquad (2.26)$$

or

$$\frac{v_p}{\sqrt{(g_p^l)}} = \frac{v_m}{\sqrt{(g_m^l)}}$$

expressing the equality of the Froude numbers for prototype and its model.

Since the scale of acceleration $M_g = 1$ (g is the same on the model and in prototype) for a chosen length scale, M_l, the scale for the other parameters may easily be determined: for velocities

$$M_v = \frac{v_p}{v_m} = \sqrt{(M_l)}$$

for discharge

$$M_Q = \frac{Q_p}{Q_m} = \frac{A_p v_p}{A_m v_m} = M_l^2 \sqrt{(M_l)} = M_l^{5/2}$$

for time

$$M_t = \frac{M_l}{M_v} = \frac{M_l}{\sqrt{(M_l)}} = \sqrt{(M_l)}$$

for angular velocity and revolutions per minute

$$M_\omega = \frac{\omega_p}{\omega_m} = \frac{1}{M_t} = \frac{1}{\sqrt{(M_l)}}$$

and for forces

$$M_P = \frac{P_p}{P_m} = \frac{\gamma_p V_p}{\gamma_m V_m} = \frac{\rho_p g V_p}{\rho_m g V_m} = M_\rho M_l^3$$

When the same liquid (e.g. water of the same temperature) is used on the model as in the prototype the scale of specific weights is $M_\gamma = 1$. Then for specific pressures

$$M_P = \frac{P_p}{P_m} = M_l$$

for power

$$M_N = \frac{N_p}{N_m} = \frac{\gamma Q_p H_p}{\gamma Q_m H_m} = M_l^{5/2} M_l = M_l^{7/2}$$

and for work (energy)

$$M_e = M_N M_t = M_l^{7/2} M_l^{1/2} = M_l^4$$

Froude similarity is valid not only for the exclusive effect of gravity but also for other volumetric forces, e.g., for centrifugal force. Since the basic force determining motion in the majority of cases is gravity, the above relations are very important in modelling.

2.6 Reynolds Law

Reynolds law expresses the criterion of dynamic similarity of the motion of two incompressible viscous liquids under the exclusive effect of internal friction. It is valid, for example, in modelling flow round bodies submerged in the liquid without surface waves, etc. The basic equation has already been given (2.27) and it may also be very simply derived as follows.

Resistance during the flow of liquid depends exclusively on its viscosity, expressed by the coefficient of viscosity μ. For an area A and change in velocity along a perpendicular dv/dr the internal friction force is given by

$$P = \mu \frac{dv}{dr} A$$

The ratio of these forces in prototype and the model is expressed by

$$M_p = \frac{P_p}{P_m} = \frac{\mu_p(dv_p/dr_p)A_p}{\mu_m(dv_m/dr_m)A_m} = M_\mu M_v M_l$$

If the scale of the forces of internal friction is compared with that for the inertia forces (Equation (2.22)) we obtain

$$M_\mu M_v M_l = M_\rho M_l^2 M_v^2$$

Therefore

$$\frac{M_\rho M_l M_v}{M_\mu} = M_{Re} = 1 \qquad (2.27)$$

If the scales are replaced by the corresponding ratios and putting $v = \mu/\rho$ we obtain the relation

$$\frac{v_p l_p}{v_p} = \frac{v_m l_m}{v_m}$$

which expresses the equality of Reynolds numbers for flow in prototype and model.

The coefficient of kinematic viscosity v depends on temperature and pressure, and it decreases with increasing temperature in liquids and rises in gases. At a pressure of 760 mm Hg and a temperature of 0°, 10°, 20°, v for air is 0.133, 0.140, 0.149 cm²/s respectively and v for water is 0.018, 0.013, 0.0101 cm²/s respectively. Air compressed to 100 atms at 0°C has $v = 0.00133$ cm²/s and at 100°C $v = 0.00245$ cm²/s. At a temperature of 20°C v for mercury is 0.00177, petroleum 0.74, engine oil 3.8 and glycerine 6.8 cm²/s.

If the same liquid is used in the model as in prototype (e.g., water of the same temperature), the relation between the velocity scale and length scale is

$$M_v = M_l^{-1}$$

(because $M_\gamma = 1$, $M_\rho = 1$ and $M_\mu = 1$)

The scales for the other parameters for a chosen length scale are then given as follows:

for time $\qquad\qquad M_t = \dfrac{M_l}{M_v} = \dfrac{M_l}{M_l^{-1}} = M_l^2$

for discharges $\qquad M_Q = M_l^2 M_v = M_l^2 M_l^{-1} = M_l$

Table 2.1

Parameter	Symbol	Dimension	Scale for Froude	Scale for Reynolds
Length	l	L	M_l	M_l
Area	A	L^2	M_l^2	M_l^2
Volume	V	L^3	M^3	M_l^3
Time	t	T	$M_l^{1/2}$	$M_l^2 M_\nu^{-1}$
Velocity	v	LT^{-1}	$M_l^{1/2}$	$M_l^{-1}M_\nu$
Acceleration	a	LT^{-2}	1	$M_l^{-3}M_\nu^2$
Angular velocity	ω	T^{-1}	$M_l^{-1/2}$	$M_l^{-2}M_\nu$
Discharge	Q	L^3T^{-1}	$M_l^{5/2}$	$M_l M_\nu$
Specific discharge	q	L^2T^{-1}	$M_l^{3/2}$	M_ν
Mass	m	M	$M_l^3 M_\rho$	$M_l^3 M_\rho$
Force	P	MLT^{-2}	$M_l^3 M_\gamma$	$M_l^2 M_\rho^{-1}$
Specific pressure	p	$ML^{-1}T^{-2}$	$M_l M_\gamma$	$M_l^{-2}M_\mu^2 M_\rho^{-1}$
Impulse and momentum	i	MLT^{-1}	$M_l^{7/2}M_\rho$	$M_l^3 M_\mu$
Energy and work	e	ML^2T^{-2}	$M_l^4 M_\gamma$	$M_l M_\mu^2 M_\rho^{-1}$
Power	N	ML^2T^{-3}	$M_l^{7/2}M_\gamma$	$M_l^{-1}M_\mu^3 M_\rho^{-2}$

For $g_p = g_m = g$, $M_\gamma = M_\rho$.
For the same liquid in model and prototype $M_\gamma = M_\rho = M_\mu = M_\nu = 1$

for forces $\qquad M_P = M_l^2 M_v^2 = M_l^2 M_l^{-2} = M_l^0 = 1$

for specific pressures $\quad M_P = M_P M_l^{-2} = M_l^{-2}$

for work (energy) $\qquad M_e = M_P M_l = M_l$

and for power $\qquad M_N = M_e M_t^{-1} = M_l M_l^{-2} = M_l^{-1}$

If Froude and Reynolds similarity are compared it will be found that the modelling of motion according to Froude similarity is considerably simpler, since the velocities of flow on the model are smaller than in prototype ($M_v = \sqrt{(M_l)}$). On the other hand in Reynolds similarity the velocities on the model are greater than in the prototype ($M_v = M_l^{-1}$). Similarly unfavourable situations also exist for discharges, specific pressures, etc., and this often leads to great technical difficulties in modelling.

Table 2.1 summarizes the scales of various parameters for the Froude or Reynolds similarity laws and for the general case of differing liquids on the model and prototype.

2.7 Weber Law

The Weber law represents the condition of dynamic similarity for the exclusive or prevailing effect of capillary forces causing surface tension.

This surface tension manifests itself both on the liquid gas interface and on the interface between two different liquids by the formation of a kind of membrane due to the effect of molecular forces. The surface tension does not depend on the curvature of the surface and its value decreases with rising temperature. The curvature of the area dividing two different liquids obviously causes stresses in particles of the liquid on both sides of this surface.

Surface tension influences, e.g., the flow and shape of small nappes, formation of small free surface waves, etc. For greater overflow heights and longer waves the effect of gravity exceeds that of surface tension. Since different laws of similarity are valid for the two kinds of forces i.e. the Froude law for gravity and the Weber law for surface tension, in modelling spillways and waves according to the Froude law there is a limit to the model reduction lest the molecular forces of surface tension prevail (*see* Section 2.10).

The basic equation for similarity with the exclusive effect of capillary forces has already been derived (2.28). It can also be proved simply in the following way.

Surface tension is given by the force, the so-called capillary constant σ, which acts on the unit of length of the surface. For example, on a water surface above which there is air it attains 8.02 g cm/s^2 per 1 cm at a temperature of $21°C$. The corresponding force causing surface tension may therefore be expressed by the relation

$$P = \sigma l$$

The scale of forces of surface tension for prototype and the model is given by

$$M_P = \frac{P_p}{P_m} = \frac{\sigma_p l_p}{\sigma_m l_m} = M_\sigma M_l$$

If we compare this scale of forces of surface tension with that of inertia forces (2.22) we obtain

$$M_\sigma M_l = M_\rho M_l^2 M_v^2$$

Therefore

$$\frac{M_\rho M_v^2 M_l}{M_\sigma} = M_{We} = 1 \tag{2.28}$$

If we express the scales by the corresponding ratios, we obtain

$$\frac{\rho_p v_p^2 l_p}{\sigma_p} = \frac{\rho_m v_m^2 l_m}{\sigma_m}$$

This relation expresses the equality of Weber numbers for prototype and the model.

For the same liquid in the model and prototype ($\rho_p = \rho_m$; $\sigma_p = \sigma_m$; $M_\rho = 1$; $M_\sigma = 1$) we obtain the relation between the velocity scale and the length scale

$$M_v = M_l^{-1/2}$$

On the basis of this equation it is possible to derive the scales for other parameters similarly as in the preceding cases. Let us consider only the scale of time

$$M_t = \frac{M_l}{M_v} = \frac{M_l}{M_l^{-1/2}} = M_l^{3/2}$$

Comparing the velocity scale for the Weber and Froude laws it can be seen that, e.g., the celerity of small waves is governed by a different criterion than that of large, gravitational waves.

2.8   Mach Law

The Mach law expresses the criterion of dynamic similarity for the exclusive or prevailing effect of volumetric elasticity (compressibility) of the medium (liquid). The modulus of compressibility (bulk modulus) K of a liquid expresses the ratio of increase in stress to the reduction of volume which was caused by it. The reduction in volume causes an increase in specific mass (density). Thus

$$K = \rho \frac{\Delta p}{\Delta \rho}$$

Again as in the preceding cases the basic equation for this law of similarity, which has already been stated (2.25), is derived by comparing the forces caused by the compressibility and the forces of inertia. The acting force is expressed as the product of specific pressure and the corresponding area on which the pressure acts

$$P = KA$$

The scale of forces is given by the ratio

$$M_p = \frac{P_p}{P_m} = \frac{K_p A_p}{K_m A_m} = M_K M_l^2$$

By comparing it with the scale of the inertia forces (2.22) we obtain

$$M_K M_l^2 = M_\rho M_l^2 M_v^2$$

Therefore

$$M_v \sqrt{\left(\frac{M_\rho}{M_K}\right)} = M_{Ma} = 1 \tag{2.29}$$

If the scale is expressed by the corresponding ratios quantities, we obtain

$$\frac{\sqrt{(\rho_p)}v_p}{\sqrt{(K_p)}} = \frac{\sqrt{(\rho_m)}v_m}{\sqrt{(K_m)}}$$

or the equality of Mach numbers for the model and prototype.

If we use the same liquid on both

$$(\rho_p = \rho_m;\ K_p = K_m;\ M_\rho = 1;\ M_K = 1)$$

we obtain for the velocity scale

$$M_v = 1$$

and for the time scale

$$M_t = \frac{M_l}{M_v} = M_l$$

With the aid of these relations the scales of various parameters may be derived.

2.9 Cavitation Number

Cavitational phenomena occur as a result of the separation of water flowing with a high velocity over parts of hydraulic structures. At outlets and spillways it may occur downstream of gate grooves, on the lateral and rear faces of baffles and sills in stilling basins, etc. In pressure systems cavitation may occur at sudden changes of cross-section and downstream of protuberances. Cavitation occurs where the pressure drops to the value of pressure of saturated water vapour p_v at a given water temperature. At the points of separation the formed cavities are immediately filled by saturated vapour and partly also by gases excluded from the water due to the pressure drop. Bubbles of saturated water vapour are carried along the surfaces of the immersed bodies by the stream until they reach parts where the pressure is greater than p_v; there the vapour quickly condenses and its bubbles suddenly implode. The space formerly occupied by the imploded bubbles is filled by the surrounding water which causes violent impacts acting in quick succession with very high pressures on the surface of the body. This causes damage to the surface of the body (cavitation corrosion) and vibration which is usually very harmful to the whole structure.

In hydraulic research on models we are thus also sometimes faced with the task of investigating cavitation, the occurrence of which we are trying to prevent in prototype. For two flows to be similar also in cavitation it is necessary for the pressure in similarly situated points to sink to the value of saturated vapour pressure. It follows from this that (according to Bernoulli's equation) the ratio of the pressure head $(p - p_v)/\gamma$ and velocity head $v^2/2g$ must be the same on the model and prototype, i.e.

$$\frac{p - p_v}{\gamma} : \frac{v^2}{2g} = \frac{2g(p - p_v)}{\gamma v^2} = \frac{p - p_v}{\frac{1}{2}\rho v^2} = \text{const.}$$

Here p and v indicate the mean pressure and velocity of undisturbed flow, i.e. flow at a sufficient distance from the submerged body; for free water surface flow the pressure p is equal to atmospheric pressure p_0, acting on the water surface. The saturated water vapour pressure p_v depends on the temperature of the water and on the altitude above sea-level.

The dimensionless number

$$\frac{p - p_v}{\frac{1}{2}\rho v^2}$$

one of the forms of Euler's number, is called the cavitation number σ_c.

$$\sigma_c = \frac{p - p_v}{\frac{1}{2}\rho v^2} \tag{2.40}$$

With the aid of this number we usually characterize the moment of the occurrence of cavitation which begins as soon as its value attains a certain critical limit $\sigma_{c_{cr}}$. Above this limit this number has no influence on the flow, but below it the character of the phenomena is very dependent on it.

To prevent cavitation successfully it is necessary to ascertain experimentally on the model conditions at which cavitation occurs and especially the value of the critical limit of cavitation number $\sigma_{c_{cr}}$.

The similarity of cavitation phenomena on the model and in prototype exists with the equality of Froude numbers $Fr_p = Fr_m$ and of the critical cavitation numbers $\sigma_{c_{crp}} = \sigma_{c_{crm}}$ (for negligible influence of viscosity and surface tension).

Under laboratory conditions cavitation may be observed in two ways:

(a) The model is installed and tested in the normal manner under normal atmospheric pressure p_0 (i.e. atmospheric pressure is not reduced on the model).

(b) The model is installed in a special experimental rig from which air may be exhausted so that the pressure is lower than atmospheric.

In method (a), which is common in hydraulics, pressure must be measured at many points on the model in the zone where negative pressure or cavitation are expected in the prototype. Cavitation does not usually occur on the model due to lower velocities, but by recalculating the measured negative pressures for the prototype it may be roughly ascertained where cavitation will occur. In this way physically impossible negative pressures may naturally also be indicated, since the maximum possible negative pressure is $(p_0 - p_v) \simeq 10.33$ m of water. During measurements it is necessary to observe both constant and pulsating pressures which may attain values corresponding to cavitation, even if the mean value of the negative pressure might be permissible.

In method (b), which is usual for laboratory cavitation tests of hydraulic machines, cavitation occurs directly on the model at points corresponding to cavitation in the prototype, if the criteria of similarity are observed. This method enables us to register cavitation photographically, to ascertain its extent, and sometimes even its effect. However, it is more difficult, requires more costly research equipment, and is more time-consuming, since it does not offer a possibility of as rapid a comparison of several alternatives as the method of direct measurement of negative pressures. The simultaneous use of both methods is naturally the best.

During experiments with pressures lower than atmospheric, air is diluted in a closed experimental rig in such a way that the atmospheric pressure acting on the water surface is approximately reduced according to the model scale. For the same temperature and therefore for the same pressure of saturated water vapour p_v on the model and in prototype we can write

$$M_l = \frac{p_{0_p} - p_v}{p_{0_m} - p_v}$$

therefore,

$$p_{0_m} = \frac{p_{0_p}}{M_l} + \frac{M_l - 1}{M_l} p_v \tag{2.41}$$

where p_{0_m} is the reduced atmospheric pressure on the model and the atmospheric pressure in prototype is p_{0_p}. Since p_v is very small compared with p_{0_p} we may write approximately

$$p_{0_m} \simeq \frac{p_{0_p}}{M_l} \tag{2.41'}$$

Thus all pressures measured on a model with reduced atmospheric pressure and expressed by absolute values must be reduced by the value $((M_l - 1)/M_l)p_v$ before converting them into prototype (this does not, of course, refer to the measurement of relative pressures).

2.10 Limiting Conditions

Sections 2.4 to 2.8 discussed in detail both the general law of mechanical similarity in hydrodynamics and some separate laws of similarity. Already in the preceding analysis the need for adding to the various criteria of similarity conditions limiting their validity—in order to avoid scale effects—has been dealt with at several points. This section sums up the main conditions mentioned so far and discusses several more.

(a) It follows from the definition of mechanical similarity that it contains both dynamic and kinematic, as well as geometric similarity (Section 2.3). Geometric and dynamic similarity are thus pre-conditions of mechanical similarity. If geometric similarity is omitted, at the most dynamic (and thus also kinematic) similarity may be attained.

(b) Section 2.4 proved that in hydraulic research, because it is impossible to observe simultaneously all criteria of similarity (i.e. the identity of Froude, Reynolds, Weber and Mach numbers, and also of Strouhal number in unsteady flow), approximate similarity only is always used. Very good results may be obtained however, as long as the criterion of similarity is the law expressing the ratio of forces which determine the investigated phenomenon or which are decisive and prevail over all other types of forces. The limiting conditions in this case limit, above all, the geometric scale of the model so that on the model no force, other than the one according to which the phenomenon is modelled, should attain a magnitude which could influence it, since the basic assumption of similarity is that the flow on the model and in prototype is expressed by an identical system of differential equations.

(c) It was also shown in Sub-section 2.4.3 that if capillarity is neglected it is possible (from the analysis of the Navier–Stokes equations) in two cases to arrive at mechanical similarity of flow of a viscous liquid under the influence of gravity (and thus with the apparent simultaneous validity of Reynolds and Froude criteria without the predominance of either of them). Similarity is controlled exclusively by Froude law in the case of steady irrotational flow of a viscous liquid with a free surface (i.e. flow with a velocity potential), and exclusively by Reynolds law in the case of a steady flow of a viscous incompressible liquid under pressure (respectively in the automodelling region it is independent of Reynolds number). These conclusions do not apply to a thin boundary layer at rough or smooth walls of the conduits in which the flow takes place.

(d) In hydraulic research the main criteria of similarity are the Froude and Reynolds laws. In hydraulics the Mach or Weber laws are rarely decisive criteria.

Problems with the decisive effect of compressibility only occur at velocities greater than sound and are therefore applicable, e.g., in waterhammer problems and, above all, in aerodynamics. The forces caused by surface tension are very important in hydraulic models, but in the solution of practical engineering problems they are avoided by not reducing the model below a certain limit so that they are almost as insignificant on the model as in the majority of cases in prototype. Separate research has shown that if the influence of surface tension and capillarity is to be negligible, the following minimum limiting values must be observed on a model operated according to the Froude law:

(1) The head of a nappe on a sharp-edged notch must be $h \geqslant 60$ mm, for the measured shape of the nappe to be capable of extrapolation. For a head $H \leqslant 20$ mm the overflow parabola of the free jet due to the influence of capillary tension acting on both its sides is deformed almost into a straight line.

(2) The length of a surface wave on the model $\geqslant 17$ mm.

(3) The velocity at the water surface on the model $v \geqslant 230$ mm/s in order that gravity waves might occur (this is important especially for experiments with the resistance of piers and head losses for flow round various bodies). (Zegzhda, 1938).

(4) The depth of flow on the model $h > 15$ mm to eliminate the effect of capillary and surface tension. This condition can lead to distorted models (*see* Chapter 6).

Only if these conditions are satisfied will the surface tension on the model with water of normal temperature be negligible and not influence the observed flow.

The effect of capillary forces is also present in the flow of liquids considerably mixed with air bubbles as, e.g., in chutes, stilling basins and wherever water flows at great velocity. Chapter 7 treats the problem of similarity of aerated flows in greater detail.

(e) When modelling the flow under gates or from orifices gravity is the decisive force and Froude law the criterion of similarity. However, the orifices must not be smaller than a minimum limit, as for smaller dimensions the roughness of the upstream face of the gate or of the bottom and walls of the vessel influences the flow. Simultaneously in the case of these 'small' orifices there is a strong influence of surface tension on the discharge jet:

(1) For flow under a gate the smallest height a of the orifice for which the outflow jet and the coefficient of contraction may be extrapolated into prototype is $a \geqslant 60$ mm. The smallest head for which the shape of the outflowing jet is still independent of h is $h \geqslant 3,3a$ (Smetana, 1957).

(2) For the discharge from a circular orifice placed at the bottom or the wall of a vessel the smallest diameter D of the orifice, for which the shape of the jet and the discharge coefficient may be extrapolated into prototype, is $D = 70$ cm. The smallest head for which the shape of the jet from a sharp-edged circular orifice is still independent of h is $h \geqslant 6D$. (Lískovec, 1961).

(f) We have seen in the preceding paragraphs that when observing all necessary criteria and laws of similarity the Euler Number on the model and in prototype is also identical ($Eu = idem$). Simultaneously we have established one special case of the Euler Number, the cavitation number σ_c, which is an important criterion in the research of phenomena accompanied by negative pressure or even cavitation.

The negative pressure ($p_0 - p_v$) recalculated for prototype is thus a further limiting condition in hydraulic research on models. This limiting condition was expressed in Section 2.9 as the critical value of the cavitation number $\sigma_{c_{cr}}$, equally it was shown that work on the model proceeds in this case according to the Froude law. The influence of viscosity and surface tension is eliminated when both Weber and Reynolds model numbers have sufficiently great values, i.e. $v_m \sqrt{(l_m)} > 3 \sim 4 \text{ m}^{3/2}/\text{s}$ and $Re_m = (1 \text{ to } 2) \cdot 10^6$. For this reason large models are set up in special experimental rigs equipped to produce and regulate negative pressure on a free water surface.

(g) The condition of equal flow regime on the model and in prototype must be added to the analysis of similarity based on prevailing forces. From the view point of similarity, contrasting flow regimes are irrotational and rotational, laminar and turbulent.

The irrotational regime (velocity potential) makes possible the similarity of flow of viscous fluids according to the Froude law. The condition of irrotational flow has been mathematically defined by $\omega_z = \omega_y = \omega_x = 0$ (*see* Sub-section 2.4.3).

It is known from hydraulics that the energy loss in laminar and turbulent flow differs. In laminar flow the hydraulic gradient changes with the first power, but in fully developed turbulent flow with the square of velocity. This is why the same regime must be preserved on the model and in the prototype.

In the prototype flow is mostly turbulent and therefore the model must not be so small that the flow regime changes into laminar flow. The criterion for turbulent and laminar flow in pipes as well as open channels is the Reynolds number. Laminar flow in pipes occurs at Re smaller than the critical Reynolds number $Re_{cr} = 580$; in wide open channels $Re_{cr} \approx 800$. The limit for fully developed turbulent flow depends on the relative roughness and may be as high as $Re = 10^6$. Reynolds number is defined here as $Re = vR/\nu$ where R is the hydraulic radius. There is a transitional zone between these two values where the flow regime is first unstable and later turbulent, but the resistance coefficient is always a function of Reynolds number (and relative roughness); the exponent of the mean velocity in tne equation for loss of mechanical energy is thus still smaller than 2. Chapters 5 and 6 discuss this problem in greater detail. Here it suffices to realize that three regions exist in the relationship, $\lambda = f(Re)$, between the friction coefficient and the Reynolds number: the first, where for laminar flow $\lambda = kRe^{-1}$, limited by the critical value $Re_{cr} \leqslant 2300$ (pipe flow) ($Re = vD/v$); the second where the equation $\lambda = f(Re)$ is valid and which has an upper limit varying as a function of the relative roughness up to about $Re_{sq} \simeq 10^6$, $Re_{cr} < Re < Re_{sq}$; and the third, where $\lambda = $ constant (the magnitude of this constant again depends on the relative roughness), and where the flow is already fully turbulent. From the viewpoint of similarity it is thus important to ensure by a correct choice of the model scale that for fully turbulent flow in prototype $Re_m > Re_{sq}$ is also valid for the model and for transitional turbulent flow $Re_m > Re_{cr}$.

The first and third regions mentioned above are after all only a further example of the 'automodelling regions' mentioned earlier, as for the first it is valid that

$$La = \text{constant}, \tag{2.33''}$$

and for the third

$$Eu = \text{constant}. \tag{2.22'}$$

In open channel hydraulics we meet further subcritical and supercritical flow. Since the criterion of this flow regime is the Froude number (for subcritical flow $Fr < 1$ and for supercritical flow $Fr > 1$) and since flow in open channels is mainly modelled according to the Froude law of similarity ($Fr = idem$) the condition of an equal flow regime (in relation to the critical flow), is automatically observed. In the exceptional cases where the Froude criterion of similarity is not used the condition of equal flow regime on the model and prototype must be specially observed.

(h) The above mentioned conditions of similarity, in particular the need for an identical flow regime on the model and in prototype, sometimes mean that whilst keeping the basic laws of similarity it is impossible to obtain geometric similarity of the model. This occurs in particular in the case of models of open channel flow with fixed and movable bed, but also in modelling some structures forming part of a whole system, e.g., models of conduits with surge tanks, etc. The main reason why geometric similarity cannot be maintained is the fact that when preserving the criterion and conditions of similarity, the model would be too large and costly, due to the size of the prototype structure or the length of the river reach reproduced. Then one or more geometrical scales of the model are distorted, i.e. *distorted models* are used. Most often the scale of depth, as opposed to length and width, is decreased to produce a vertically distorted model ($M_h < M_l$). Models, however, may also be simultaneously or independently shortened (different scale for length and width), or inclined (change of slope as against prototype), or they can have a distorted bed load scale, distorted roughness, etc. In the case of models of rivers with movable bed the scale of the specific gravity of the bed load on the model is often changed to obtain similarity of incipient movement as well as discharge of the bed load.

In all these cases of model distortion, where geometric similarity is abandoned or where the scale of the specific gravity of sediment is changed, mechanical similarity is not kept but dynamic similarity is preserved; even this is only an approximate similarity according to the criteria of similarity for the prevailing force. A more detailed analysis of similarity for distorted models, together with their use, will be found in the following chapters and a detailed theoretical analysis is given in Chapter 6 which deals with the modelling of open channel flow.

(i) This section does not exhaust all limits of similarity, nor does it deal in detail with all limits mentioned. For special cases we shall return to the criteria and conditions of similarity later.

2.11 Methods of Dealing with Complex Phenomena

It is difficult in some cases to decide in advance whether the influence of the forces we want to eliminate as unimportant in the choice of criteria, is indeed negligible. Independent experimental work must then determine whether the model scale was chosen correctly or whether on the model (or in prototype) a complex phenomenon occurs influenced simultaneously by several types of forces.

The simplest method in this case is measuring the same phenomenon on two or more models of different size, i.e., a 'family' of models. If the results are then plotted (e.g. the relationship of discharge and head $Q = f(h)$) as converted to prototype from all models, we obtain a number of experimentally determined points. These may be joined by one curve where the scatter of points expresses the measurement errors, or the points obtained must be joined by two or more curves, always one for each model, which shows a systematic deviation signifying that similarity has not been obtained in the models. When preparing experiments on two models we must ensure, of course, that at least in part the experiments on both models include values of variables within the same limits after conversion to prototype.

If the experiment is carried out on three models of different size, and the systematic deviation appears only in the case of the smallest model, whereas for the other two the dispersion is within experimental errors, it may be concluded that in the smallest model the systematic error is caused only by exceeding the limit of model similarity. We then exclude the smallest model and continue working with one of the larger models. If the systematic deviation appears, however, in all results and does not decrease with an increase in the model size, we are faced in all likelihood with a complex phenomenon in prototype, where the safety of extrapolation from the model to prototype will be the smaller, the greater the systematic deviation.

If deviation is considerable, research into the phenomenon must be undertaken so that, as far as possible, the individual factors are investigated by separate experiments or attempts are made to determine the influence of one type of force by calculation and to introduce the result into the experimental procedure. Froude's method of investigating the resistance of a towed ship is an example of solving a complex phenomenon by model experiments.

In the resistance of a towed ship both gravity and viscosity apply, and neither of the resulting forces may be regarded as subordinate. Gravity influences the shape resistance of the ship which is proportional to the main rib section and the square of the velocity of the wave formed by the movement of the ship. Viscosity affects the frictional resistance of the water on the wetted surface of the ship. The total resistance P is thus made up of the shape resistance P_1 (Froude law) and frictional resistance P_2 (Reynolds law).

$$P = P_1 + P_2$$

During the towing of the model of the ship the total resistance of the model P_m may be ascertained for various shapes and draughts of the ship and different speeds of towing. Froude proved that the tangential resistance of the surface of the ship is practically the same as the resistance of a vertical towed board of the same surface area and roughness as the ship surface. The board must have a sharp leading edge and be thin enough for its shape resistance to be negligible. From the experiment with the board it is possible to obtain the frictional resistance for a unit of area experimentally and calculate P_2 for the model ship as well as for the prototype. Therefore

$$P_{1m} = P_m - P_{2m}$$

As the experiment has been carried out according to the Froude law

$$P_{1p} = M_l^3 P_{1m}$$

and for the total resistance of the prototype ship we obtain

$$P_p = M_l^3 (P_m - P_{2m}) + P_{2p} \tag{2.42}$$

In Equation (2.42) the values P_{2m} and P_{2p} are obtained by calculation and P_m experimentally.

Froude's method is only approximate since in prototype the frictional forces P_2 depend also on the shape and dimensions of the ship. But it indicates the possibilities of separate experimental investigation of the various parameters involved.

References

Allen, J. (1947). *Scale Models in Hydraulic Engineering*, Longmans, Green and Co., London.

Barenblatt, G. I. (1979). *Similarity, Self-similarity and Intermediate Asymptotics*, (translation from Russian), Plenum, New York.

Barr, D. I. H. and Smith, A. A. (1967). Application of similitude theory to correlation of uniform flow data, *Proc. ICE*, **37**, pp. 487–509.

British Standards Institution. (1964). *The International System (SI) Units*, BS3763, BSI, London.

Buckingham, E. (1915). Model experiments and the forms of empirical equations. *Trans. ASME*, **37**, pp. 263–296.

Čábelka, J. and Novak, P. (1964). *Hydraulic Research 1—Research on Models*, (in Czech), SNTL, Prague.

Comolet, R. (1958). *Introduction a l'Analyse Dimensionelle et aux Problèmes de Similitude en Mécanique des Fluides*, Masson et Cie, Paris.

Escande, L. and Camichel, C. (1938). *Similitude Hydrodynamique et Technique des Modèles Reduits*, Publications scientifiques et techniques No. 127, Ministère de l'Air, Toulouse.

Gukhmam, A. A. (1965). *Introduction to the Theory of Similarity*, Academic Press, New York, London.

Isaacson, E. de St. Q. and Isaacson, M. de St. Q. (1975). *Dimensional Methods in Engineering and Physics*, Edward Arnold, London.

Ivicsics, L. (1975). *Hydraulic Models*, VITUKI, Budapest.

Kline, S. J. (1965). *Similitude and Approximation Theory*, McGraw–Hill, New York.

Langhaar, H. L. (1951). *Dimensional Analysis and Theory of Models*, John Wiley and Sons, New York.

Levi, J. J. (1960). *Modelling of Hydraulic Phenomena*, (in Russian), Gosenergoizdat, Moscow.

Lískovec, L. (1961). *Study of Bottom Outlets*, (in Czech), Práce a štúdie No. 102, VÚV, Prague.

Novak, P. (1963). Erfahrungen bei der Anwendung der Ähnlichkeitsgesetze im wasserbaulichen Versuchswesen, *Wissenschaftliche Zeitschrift der Technischen Universität Dresden*. No. 6.

Palacios, J. (1964). *Dimensional Analysis*, Macmillan, London.

Rayleigh, Lord. (1915). The principle of similitude, *Nature*, **95**, No. 2368, pp. 66–68.

Rouse, H. (1959). *Advanced Mechanics of Fluids*, John Wiley and Sons, New York.

Rozanov, J. P. (1959). *Design of Outlet Works with Low Pressures and High Velocities*, (in Russian), Gosenergoizdat, Moscow.

Sedov, L. I. (1959). *Similarity and Dimensional Methods in Mechanics*, Academic Press, New York, London.

Smetana, J. (1957). *Hydraulics*, (in Czech), ČSAV, Prague.

Vries, M. de (1977). *Scale Models in Hydraulic Engineering*, International Institute for Hydraulic and Environmental Engineering, Delft.

Yalin, M. S. (1971). *Theory of Hydraulic Models*, Macmillan, London.

Yalin, S. (1959). Über die Bedeutung der Theorie der Dimensionen für das wasserbauliche Versuchswesen, *Bautechnik*, **36,** No. **8,** pp. 306–312.

Zegzhda, A. P. (1938). *Theory of Similarity and Method of Computation of Hydraulic Models*, (in Russian), Gosstrojizdat, Moscow.

3 Procedure of Investigation

3.1 Preparatory Work

Preparatory work for hydraulic research consists of a theoretical and a practical part. In the theoretical part the scale, type, and degree of schematization of the model is determined by the analysis of criteria and conditions of similarity, and the content, extent and procedure of research are prepared. The practical part of the preparatory work includes the choice of material for the model, its location, design, construction and link-up with the water supply and circuit of the hydraulic laboratory. Therefore when designing the model it is important to consider its demands on labour, material and space and the water discharge facilities necessary for its operation; other models installed in the laboratory and possibly operating simultaneously must be borne in mind.

If the investigation deals with an actual hydraulic structure, laboratory work must be well ahead of its construction as results concerning the basic concept of the scheme and the design of the main parts of the structure must reach the client in time to be incorporated in the design. Some models, e.g. models of construction stages, should not be dismantled immediately after research is terminated since they can contribute effectively to the solution of hydraulic problems occurring unexpectedly in the course of construction.

The main factor in the design of the model itself is the fulfilment of the criteria of similarity and limiting conditions according to the nature of the problem under consideration, and further the required accuracy of results and economy of research. From the technical point of view the model should be as large as possible to make the results sufficiently accurate. On the other hand economy requires the smallest possible model still satisfying the limiting conditions and ensuring undistorted research results. The model scale therefore depends on the flow features and on the attainable accuracy of measurements on the model. Experience gained from modelling similar hydraulic problems is of great help here.

Before beginning the investigation on the model, prototype data must be carefully studied. All details of the shape and character of surfaces round which the water will flow as well as topographic data for the channel and the adjoining terrain, geological and, of course, hydrological data are essential. The proposed system for operating the hydraulic structure during various construction stages as well as after completion should also be noted. The researcher must be in close contact with the client throughout the investigation.

The stages of preparatory work are roughly as follows:

(a) The client formulates his demands and problems to be solved during investigation (terms of reference).

(b) The researcher, after consultation with the client, proposes the method of solution. On the basis of both existing knowledge in the field of hydrodynamics and experimental experience it is decided whether the solution of the problems requires model research or whether a theoretical analysis and computation will suffice. During this stage it is necessary to consider whether existing survey information is sufficient for the task; the client should be advised about additional field data needed.

(c) The researcher elaborates the method of solution. This contains the analysis of the criteria and conditions of similarity, possibly also the determination of the variables participating in the solution and their grouping into relations describing the problem, and application of methods of dimensional analysis; the manner of processing the experimental results is usually stated here. Apart from this analysis a summary of requirements necessary for the completion of the investigation by the given date and, in the case of basic research, also the results of the literature survey dealing with the problem in hand should be available.

(d) On the basis of the above analysis the number and type of models to be constructed is decided and the degree of schematization for each model determined, i.e. which parts of the actual structure must be reproduced accurately according to geometrical similarity, which may be simplified and which need not be modelled at all. To a great extent the success or failure of the investigation, its cost and laboriousness depend on the design of the models.

(e) When the type of model has been chosen and the limits of similarity considered, the final model scale M_l, and from it the scales of all relevant parameters, are determined.

(f) Finally a decision is taken on the choice of material for the whole model or its separate parts.

3.2 Modelling Technique

3.2.1 Main types of hydraulic models and their placing in the laboratory

Scale models in hydraulics are divided into two main groups, river and coastal engineering models (including tidal models) and models of hydraulic structures. Further combinations of both groups and various models of a special nature exist.

River and estuary models are three-dimensional models of river reaches with or without hydraulic structures. Geometric similarity is not always desirable and river models are frequently built with distorted scales as inclined, narrowed, widened or, most frequently, as vertically distorted models with fixed or movable bed.

(a) Models with *fixed bed* are used mainly when problems of bed-load transport and local scour are not studied or relevant, and when problems of water levels and flow patterns only are investigated.
(b) River models with *movable beds* are used if sediment transport, scour and deposition are involved.

Models of structures are usually geometrically similar to prototype, and are three-dimensional, two-dimensional or combined.

(a) *Three-dimensional* models are used for the study of complicated problems of spatial flow to find the hydraulically and economically most suitable solution for a whole layout or for the individual parts of structures.
(b) *Two-dimensional* models are useful for the investigation of basic flow problems at spillways, outlets, etc., where in all parallel (vertical) planes the flow is either completely or at least approximately identical (two-dimensional problem).
(c) Three-dimensional models *combined* with two-dimensional sections of the main part of the structure are used when problems of spatial flow must be solved and the flow in one plane simultaneously investigated.

At the same time as the choice of type of model and the computation of its scale are made, the problem of placing it most advantageously within the hydraulic laboratory must be solved. The following constraints apply:

(a) Usually only limited space is available in the laboratory and this often influences the choice of the horizontal scale.
(b) The model is placed so as to allow economic construction and operation, and installation of all auxiliary and measuring devices.
(c) Simultaneously the flow circulation must be solved. This means checking at the chosen site whether it is possible to connect the inlet to the model to a sufficiently large laboratory distribution main and to measure the model discharge. Since this may be influenced by the simultaneous operation of other models attached to a common distribution line it is useful to fit a separate inlet to every model or, when using a common

supply, to adapt the operation of the various models so that they do not influence one another. The outlet from the model to the laboratory sump should be as short as possible.

(d) For experiments with sediment the recycling of sediment on the model may have to be ensured.

(e) Possible changes in the construction of the model must be borne in mind in the choice of the model site (and material), as well as access for transport of material, measurements, photographs, etc.

The chosen position of the model (with inlet and outlet) is entered into the laboratory plan and a setting-out procedure is chosen.

Models of rivers or hydraulic structures are placed either in temporary tanks or watertight flumes specially constructed for every model on the laboratory floor or on a raised platform, or in permanent hydraulic flumes with perpendicular side walls. Temporary flumes have the advantage over permanent ones in that their walls may be suitably adapted to the outlines of the modelled river reach to reduce both the material and space needed for the model to a minimum. The walls of a temporary flume may be provided with rails for instrument carriages.

Two-dimensional models are usually built in permanent hydraulic flumes with vertical glass side walls and a horizontal bed of thick steel plate.

3.2.2   Materials and model construction

Accurate and lucid drawings of the model prevent unnecessary delay during time-consuming construction. Care must be taken to prevent deformation or settling of the model and it should be possible to carry out changes easily and quickly. When designing the model it is divided into separate parts and structurally independent units of different materials, guaranteeing accuracy of shape and a surface of the required roughness.

Wood, especially pinewood, cypress, larch, hard wood and watertight plywood, has the advantage that it is easily shaped; its great disadvantages are non-transparency and changes in volume and shape, warping and swelling, which often cannot be fully prevented even by good impregnation with surface coating especially if the model is operated for a long time. It is suitable, therefore, mainly for the production of some less important parts of models where minor deformations are acceptable, for templates (for the shaping of complicated parts of models made of plastics, perspex, glass fibres, etc., and for the construction of river models), for temporary flumes, for the shuttering of concrete parts, etc.

Metals, especially steel and non-ferrous metals, are used as sheets, plates, pipes, angles, bars or casts. Steel is used for the construction of flumes, various pipes, supports, simple model gates, etc. Non-ferrous metals are suitable for more sensitive parts of accurate models and measuring devices, model spillway surfaces, piezometers, etc., where corrosion or protective coating would have harmful effect. The advantages of metals are that they are easily formed, machined, cut, welded or soldered, and that they retain their shape and dimensions. Their non-transparency is a drawback.

Plastics are well suited for pipes and thin-walled parts of all types of models, even those of complicated shape. They can be shaped by various techniques. Models of glass fibre are formed in a cold state by alternately placing a layer of glass fibres and binding material on a previously prepared surface. If transparent walls are required perspex, which can be shaped and pressed when heated, is used. The advantage common to all plastics is their malleability and ease of machining which is similar to that of hard wood. They have the advantage over wood in that they hardly change in volume and shape in water and dampness, nor are they subject to corrosion. Some types are transparent and very smooth.

Complicated details of models requiring great accuracy are sometimes made of *wax* or *paraffin*. This is easily workable, does not deform in water, but is brittle, non-transparent and sensitive to temperature. It is cast in forms and worked after cooling. With suitable additives increasing its brittleness it may be used to simulate the ice cover on rivers or canals and the movement of ice flows.

Concrete is very suitable for the construction of models of some structures and river reaches, as it is firm and after hardening does not change in either volume or shape. For models of structures certain parts can be fabricated separately and then assembled and joined.

In models of rivers and canals a thin layer of concrete placed on a gravel–sand foundation forms the firm bottom and banks. The concrete mixture is shaped with the aid of moulds and templates of wood, metal or plastic. Permanent flumes can also be made of reinforced concrete. A certain disadvantage of concrete and mortar is their relatively great strength so that after hardening additional small changes cannot be made easily. This disadvantage can be partly overcome by using special mixtures which have all the properties of cement mortar but harden slowly.

Fine and slowly setting *plaster* can replace cement for various parts of models. It is more brittle and soft than concrete but can be worked after setting. Its instability in water is a disadvantage, but this can be reduced by the use of various additives, e.g. saltpetre. Hardened plaster does not change either in volume or shape under damp conditions but absorbs water and should, therefore, be coated with paint.

Glass is suitable for the construction of transparent pipes, side walls of hydraulic flumes, inspection manholes and windows, tanks, piezometers tubes, etc. For complicated shapes or easily broken parts it is often replaced by perspex.

Asphalt is used as sealing material mainly for the construction of river channels. *Rubber* is used as packing between pipe flanges and sections of metal flumes and models, for glass side walls in hydraulic flumes, etc. Putty, hemp, and small plastic or rubber hose are also suitable for packing joints in models and flumes. For larger areas sheets of plastic, varnished cloth or various types of coating are used as sealing material.

Bricks, formed bricks and precast concrete are most frequently used for the construction of temporary flumes and for the outside walls of three-dimensional and river models, where gravel and sand are suitable filling materials.

Sand and crushed *coal* briquettes are most frequently used to model movable river beds. Other suitable materials are fragmented hollow bricks or roof tiles, pumice, plastics, treated hardwood, sawdust, etc., depending on the specific weight of the sediment required.

The construction of models is based on detailed drawings the scale of which is chosen according to the complexity of the various parts and requirements for accuracy. For river models not only the general layout but also the channel cross-sections are drawn in the actual scale of the model (i.e. 1:1). Templates cut according to these drawings may be divided into several parts if the sections are long. In special cases, if a larger number of smaller templates would need to be cut, metal wire or plastic bars bent into the required shape on movable pegs may be used instead.

The various parts and sections of the model must be easily positioned and correctly aligned. Adjusting screws can be fixed or metal plates anchored as supports for the screws.

Conventional surveying techniques are used for the setting-out of the model and/or its temporary flume. Models covering an extensive area are usually built directly on the working surface of the laboratory. Narrow, long river models with great differences in height between the inlet and outlet, or requiring accessibility from below for the installation of instrumentation, are often placed on raised platforms. The platform itself is usually made of prefabricated slabs placed on steel beams supported by brick columns. After the erection of the side walls the whole flume is made watertight.

The construction of the model in the flume consists of mounting separate previously manufactured parts or templates and completing the masonry and modelling work. Hollow objects and those made of light materials must either be anchored into the bottom of the flume or sufficiently loaded to prevent floating when the flume has been filled with water.

To ensure similarity the roughness of the model surfaces must be adjusted (smoothed or roughened) to various degrees; they can be plastered or coated with a suitable glue and sprinkled with graded sand of suitable size. Paving can be simulated by forming the concrete with a roller. Vegetation in the flood plains of distorted river models is usually modelled later, as part of the proving tests, using wood, plastic materials, wire mesh, etc.

For river models with a movable bed a fixed bottom is constructed sufficiently below the surface and on it the movable bed is modelled by inserting templates. These are removed from the model after the bed material has been levelled. Sometimes it is more suitable to model the bed using 'negative cross-sections'.

3.2.3 Inlets and outlets of models

The feeding installations of flumes and models in the laboratory normally include a constant head tank, pipes with regulating valves, inlet tanks upstream of the model and sometimes also devices for sediment supply, discharge measuring devices and wave generators.

The inlet tank, which is separated from the model proper by a damping grill or filter, must be of sufficiently large dimensions. Usually various dampers and baffles are used to spread the concentrated flow at the inlet over the entire entry section of the model and/or direct it to simulate the influence of the upstream reach. Baffles are made usually either of wood, perforated sheet metal, bricks or concrete blocks. Filters usually consist of a wire mesh frame filled with gravel, a suitable choice of its grading ensuring the necessary velocity and flow distribution in the inlet section of the model.

The outlet of the model is used for discharge measurement only in exceptional cases as the flow is usually directed from the outlet by a return channel into the supply reservoir (sump) of the laboratory with a minimum of head loss. The model outlet is provided with a device for setting or regulating the downstream water level on the model for various discharges. The regulation of the downstream water level according to the given rating curve is carried out either manually or automatically. Manual control is suitable for separate successive experiments with constant discharge, and automatic control systems for experiments with variable discharge (or water level). A tail gate of simple overflow type, or more complicated venetian blind type gates, or various valves may be used for the downstream control of water levels.

Models with sediment transport and a sediment feeding device at the inlet may have a settling tank or sediment separator at the outlet. Settling tanks are used on mobile-bed models without independent sediment circulation and the sediment is usually removed from the settling tank by hand or conveyor belt. In the bedload separator, provided on models with independent bedload circulation, water is separated from the sediment transported from the model; from the separator sediment falls into a small container from which it can be transported by an ejector and returned, together with the water, through a special pipeline to the model inlet where the excess water is again separated and the sediment passed into the model.

3.3 Procedure During Experiments and their Assessment

In model investigations of hydraulic structures and in three-dimensional flow problems, several alternative solutions for the structure are studied, these having been suggested by the designing engineer or by the researcher on the basis of their experience, and flow patterns, velocities, discharges, scour and other parameters are observed and measured. After an analysis of the results the most suitable alternative is chosen and tested in detail. The results are processed qualitatively, graphically and/or numerically but, in this case, usually not analytically, because they are valid only for the investigated case and cannot be generalized.

A frequent case in applied research is the experimental solution of hydraulic problems whose theoretical solution, based on the physical analysis of the phenomenon, is known and where we are dealing with its application to real conditions. The theoretical equation derived for an ideal fluid and expressing the investigated phenomenon must be adjusted for a real fluid (water) by introducing correcting coefficients investigated by hydraulic research. This group includes, above all, experiments on models of spillways, stilling basins, filling systems of locks, intakes, gates, etc. An analytical expression of experimental results—whenever possible—is particularly valuable here because of its lucidity and unambiguity, especially if several hydraulic parameters participate as independent variables. Within the limits investigated experimentally it permits a general application of experimental results to all similar cases. Dimensional quantities are recalculated for prototype according to the relevant law of similarity used for the construction and operation of the model. The values of non-dimensional parameters and coefficients naturally remain the same for the model and prototype.

The researcher is often faced by a complicated hydrodynamic phenomenon so far theoretically unsolved. Should he be unable to derive a theoretical relationship describing the phenomenon, on the basis of physical analysis, he must at least attempt to determine all the variables which influence it. Using the method of dimensional analysis described in the preceding chapter he then investigates, experimentally on the model, the relationship between the dimensionless arguments of the investigated phenomenon. The experimental result is valid not only for the model but also for the prototype if appropriate similarity laws and their limits have been observed. If there is a larger number of dimensionless arguments, all except two are kept constant during the experiment. One of the two is changed and we then observe how the other changes. The changes of the first argument are attained by the change of any variable participating in the argument. Most frequently we change that quantity which is easily varied and through whose change we achieve the necessary extent of variability of the corresponding argument. We do not usually choose geometric dimensions of the model as a parameter to be changed during experiments, but rather some of the others such as velocity, depth of water, pressure, discharge, roughness of the walls of the model, bedload, size, etc., which can be changed comparatively easily without reconstructing the entire model. Thus on one model the relationship of several dimensionless arguments may often be established. The method of processing experimental data depends on the character of the problem. If we have no analytical basis for the expression at all and do not even know the type of looked for empirical relationship, it is initially possible only to plot experimental data and then look for the most suitable form of expressing the results. Processing of the experimental data with the aid of computers may serve the same purpose. Even if it is possible to express the investigated phenomenon by a simple algebraic relationship, we must bear in mind that the result is exclusively experimental. Therefore the boundary conditions of the conducted experiment are almost as important as the empirical result and extrapolation beyond these limits is uncertain, though often applied.

After completing the experimental work and processing the results, a final report is prepared. This should include the original aims of the study, basic technical data, results of a literature survey, the method of research used, a description of the experimental installations and the experimental procedure and results, as well as the scientific, technical and economical contribution of the conducted research. The final report of an investigation of a proposed hydraulic structure must contain not only the recommendations for a more effective design of the structure and its parts, documented by graphs, photographs and tables, but also an analysis of the possible application of the obtained results to similar cases and the extent of their validity. In well-founded cases, and where it is technically possible, the final report should also recommend a checking of the agreement between prototype and model; for this it is advisable to propose the necessary measuring devices to be installed in the prototype.

References

American Society of Civil Engineers. (1942). *Hydraulic Models–Manual of the Committee on Hydraulic Research of the Hydraulics Division*, ASCE, New York.

Dobrowolski, A., *et al.* (1977). *Physical Modelling of Hydraulic Phenomena*, (in Polish), Prace No. 13, Instytut Meteorologii i Gospodarki Wodnej, Warsaw.

Gabriel, P. and Grund, I. (1962). *The Construction of Models*, (in Slovak), VÚV, Bratislava.

Izbash, S. J. (1938). *Principles of Laboratory Work in Hydromechanics*, (in Russian), Gosenergoizdat, Moscow.

4 Laboratory Installations and Instrumentation

4.1 Laboratory Installations

Hydraulic laboratories work either with a closed-water circuit or with direct supply (without circulation). The former method is used exclusively in covered laboratories, the latter in open-air installations where water is more quickly polluted.

The *closed water circuit* usually consists of an underground supply reservoir, a pumping station delivering water to high-head reservoirs, pipes discharging water from the reservoirs over flowmeters into the flumes and models and, finally, return channels delivering water back to the sump (underground reservoir) which is filled with clean water from the main. If the water in the closed circuit becomes polluted it must be drained or pumped out and replaced.

The overhead tank into which water is pumped must be placed sufficiently high above the models. The tanks are usually fitted with a very long overfall edge to preserve an almost constant water level in them, both during fluctuating water supply from the pumps and during changes in the discharge on the models in the laboratory. It is necessary, of course, for the discharge supplied by the pumps into the tank to be greater than the discharge withdrawn from it for use in the laboratory; excess water spills, unused, over the overfall edge and is conveyed back into the supply reservoir. The head on the very long overfall edge of the flume remains almost constant; even for a variable discharge the water level fluctuation is in the order of millimeters and cannot affect the head above the model or its measuring device (usually several metres) and, thus, does not affect the discharge withdrawn through a constant opening of the regulating valve on the inlet pipe of the model. The overhead tank is usually permanent, built as part of the equipment of a hydraulic laboratory and frequently supplies several models. This solution is economical, but has the disadvantage that flows on separate models working simultaneously, and supplied by a joint distribution pipe, may influence each other. Therefore separate tanks or at least direct supply lines from the tank are sometimes built for every permanent flume or larger model.

56

An open-air laboratory placed near the closed circuit of a covered laboratory may also be linked with it. This solution is economical but difficulties arise in operation because water may be very quickly polluted in the open-air circuit.

Supply installations without circulation are usually set up for models placed in the open air and are used only exceptionally in covered halls. The models are fed either by gravity or by water pumped from rivers, reservoirs, canals, lakes, etc. The scheme and layout of the entire installation are similar to that of the closed water circuit; the difference is that in place of an artificial supply reservoir (sump) there is a natural one from which the water may be pumped into an overhead tank and the water flowing from the model is not returned to the reservoir but discharged downstream.

Models built in the open should be protected against wind, rain and cold. Outdoor models are most frequently protected only against wind (this distorts experimental results) by windbreakers (e.g. canvas stretched between steel poles). Temporary roofing made of scaffolding with a cover placed over it may be used to protect models against rain and cold (effects of solar radiation should be taken into account).

In covered laboratories the construction of models and work on them is greatly facilitated by light bridges or various types of crane. Apart from free surfaces used for temporary models and forming part of every hydraulic laboratory (*see* Fig. 4.2) a variety of permanent equipment for hydraulic research may be installed: fixed and tilting flumes, rigs for investigating cavitation phenomena and for research of flow under high pressure (stand pipes, pressure tanks, etc.), flumes for rating instruments for velocity measurements and tanks for rating flow meters.

Fixed hydraulic flumes have vertical parallel lateral glass walls (size up to 1.0×2.0 m and thickness up to 20 mm) fitted into the reinforced concrete or steel supporting structure of the flume (Fig. 4.1). The horizontal bed of the flume is usually of thick rolled steel sheet metal so that models may easily be anchored or openings drilled for piezometers. The upstream part of the flume is often constructed considerably higher than the rest to permit modelling of the upstream water level of a hydraulic structure. At the end of the flume there is a device for regulating the water level; a wave generator could be provided at either end. A settling tank may be fitted to the outlet. Above the lateral walls of the flume there are rails for the longitudinal movement of measuring devices. Usually two-dimensional models of hydraulic structures are placed in the flume to investigate flow at overfalls, inlets, stilling basins, etc. The glass walls of the flume permit filming or photographing of the flow in planes parallel to the walls of the flume. The dimensions of this type of hydraulic flume are usually: length 6 to 20 m, height 0.5 to 1.0 m (in the raised inlet part up to 2.0 m) and width 0.3 to 1.2 m. The discharge through the flumes does

Fig. 4.1. Fixed steel and concrete flumes (VÚV Prague). [Čábelka and Novák, 1964]

not usually exceed 200 l/s (according to the dimensions of its cross-section).

Flumes are either placed on the floor of the laboratory (Fig. 4.2) or set below its level and covered by removable boards. The former arrangement takes up part of the working surface of the laboratory and decreases free space available for three-dimensional models but provides much easier access and working conditions than the latter, especially if, for most of the year, flumes are partly or fully covered and if three-dimensional models have been constructed above them. Long hydraulic flumes may be constructed also as divisible with the outlet in the centre and feeding from both ends; naturally the whole may also serve as only one flume.

Flumes in which open channel flow and wave phenomena are investigated must be considerably longer than flumes for two-dimensional models of hydraulic structures. Their length is usually more than hundred times the depth of water, i.e. 25 to 100 m. The width of these flumes should be not less than four to five times the depth to exclude the influence of the lateral walls on the flow; usually it is 0.4 to 1.0 m. For research on wave phenomena the flumes are often considerably wider and/or deeper.

These long hydraulic flumes may be erected either on a free surface next to the laboratory where they are usually of a temporary nature, or as a permanent fixture in the covered laboratory hall; here, in exceptional cases they may also be let into the floor. Flumes for research of wave

Fig. 4.2. Main laboratory floor (VÚVH Bratislava). [Čábelka and Novák, 1964]

phenomena are sometimes connected to a wind tunnel for the study of the interaction of air and water flow.

Hydraulic flumes with adjustable slope are used for research on the resistance of channels with various roughnesses, stability of movable beds, sediment transport, etc. Their bottom and walls are mounted on a stiff structure which may be rotated around a horizontal pivot. The longitudinal slope of a tilting flume may be changed, usually up to a slope of 2 to 5%, with the aid of hydraulic or mechanical jacks, cog-wheel segments, suspensions, etc. The width and height of these flumes is most frequently 50 to 60 cm, the length 10 to 40 m. However, due to the structural complexities they are also often smaller. Tilting flumes simplify experimental work by permitting a change in slope which makes the adjustment for the required open channel flow regime possible. The horizontal pivot of the flume may be in the centre of the flume, or more frequently, near the inlet end to simplify its connection to a measuring and inlet tank. The outflow may in this case be through a telescopic pipe.

For investigations of bedload movement it is of advantage if the tilting flume is fitted with an independent circuit with an ejector for transport of the bedload mixed with water from the outlet back to the flume inlet (Fig. 4.3).

Even though adjustable hydraulic flumes are expensive to install, they are essential for any hydraulic laboratory in which open channel flow, bedload movement and river processes are investigated. The costly

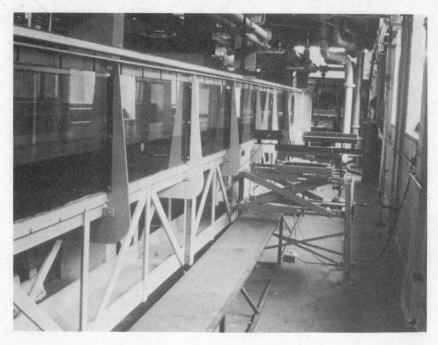

Fig. 4.3. Tilting flume, with laser anemometer (University of Newcastle upon Tyne).

construction of the tilting flume can be avoided by placing another (false) bottom into a fixed flume that may be adjusted to the necessary slope without changing the position of other parts. The sediment bed in long fixed flumes may also be adjusted to the necessary slope with the aid of a mechanical device travelling on the horizontal rails of the flume with a regular vertical shift of an adjustable blade.

For research on aerated water flow and entrainment of air by a high velocity flow with free surface, special adjustable hydraulic flumes are used with a slope of up to 45° (and even more). These flumes, however, are not part of the usual equipment of a hydraulic laboratory.

For research on cavitation phenomena, which usually occur during high-velocity flow round parts of hydraulic structures, special *cavitation tunnels* (Fig. 4.4) are used. These tanks are hermetically sealed, have an independent water circuit and usually need pumps with high discharges. The necessary low pressure is attained both by exhausters reducing air pressure in the space above the water surface and by placing the cavitation tunnel with built-in models at a sufficient height above the downstream water level (Fig. 4.4a).

Another type is an installation in which absolute pressure in fluid may be modelled. Reynolds number should attain a value of 10^6 during work

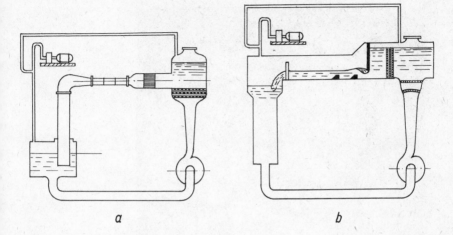

a *b*

Fig. 4.4. Cavitation tunnels.

on this rig. The exhauster regulates the pressure of air above the downstream water level and, when the Froude criterion must be maintained, the same pressure is also produced above the upstream water level. The model of the structure is placed in a hermetically sealed horizontal flume or reservoir which may be provided with an observation window (Fig. 4.4b).

For study of valves, bottom dam outlets, special energy dissipators, outlet and overfall jets, etc., *high-(pressure)-head installations* are constructed with independent water circuits and efficient multi-stage pumps. Such an installation may be a steel tower 10 to 20 m high along the entire height of the laboratory in which a constant water surface may be maintained and water withdrawn at various heads, a tank placed high above the laboratory level, or a pressure tank of sufficiently large dimensions.

Rating flumes (Fig. 4.5) or circular rating tanks are constructed in laboratories for the rating of instruments measuring velocity (current meters, Pitot tubes, etc.). Above the flumes a carriage moves at even, adjustable and measured speeds (time and distance are measured), and the rated unit is fixed to this and submerged in the stationary water of the flume. The carriage usually moves at a velocity of between 5 cm/s and 5 m/s. The flume dimensions must be sufficiently large for the walls not to influence the function of rating device; the cross-section is usually almost square, at least 1.5 m by 1.5 m. The flume must be long enough to leave a sufficient stretch for the rating itself after deducting the starting and braking distance; flumes for current meter rating are often over 100 m long.

Fig. 4.5. Rating flume (VÚV Prague). [Čábelka and Novák, 1964]

The width of the flume permitting, it may be used also to measure the resistance of towed objects, e.g. models of barges, especially for inland navigation. For measurements on models of ocean-going vessels the flume must be wider still.

In the calm water of the circular rating tank the measuring unit attached to a radial arm moves along a circular course.

A further device is the *volumetric rating tank* for the rating of flow meters (notches, venturimeters, orifices, bends, etc.) which are in use on every model. This is basically a large watertight tank, usually underground, with straight perpendicular walls and accurate devices for the measurement of the water level, the relation between the volume and water level in the tank having been established by separate measurements. The level and time of filling the tank are usually registered automatically.

Model research of *ice phenomena* and their effects must be undertaken in special laboratories dealing with the winter regime. Installation and equipment of these laboratories is adapted to the solution of the following special problems:

(a) Research of the thermal regime of rivers, reservoirs, lakes, etc., with and without ice, and methods of modelling temperature and ice phenomena.

(b) Investigations of rivers and reservoirs during frost (formation of ice cover and rime, flow beneath the ice cover, formation and transport of ice, formation of ice barriers, etc.).

(c) Study of measures for the elimination or reduction of difficulties caused by ice during the operation of hydraulic structures under winter conditions (ice pressure acting on structures, passing of ice over weirs, means of breaking up the ice cover and removing ice and rime, etc.).

(d) Study of the structure, physical and mechanical properties of ice of various types; methods of preparation of laboratory ice of differing strength for experimental work in the ice laboratory.

(e) Development and rating of installations and instrumentation used during research in polar regions.

Investigations are usually carried out in covered and insulated concrete circulating flumes of rectangular cross-section and with a sufficiently long, straight working section fitted with observation windows. Water flowing in the flume is cooled by air (temperature $-10°$ to $-20°C$) which is driven by a ventilator into the space between the water level and the ceiling of the flume. Further, special tanks placed in insulated rooms fitted with effective cooling devices for temperatures from $-15°$ to $-25°C$ and smaller cooling cells in which the temperature may be reduced to $-30°$, or even $-60°C$, are also used.

A brief discussion of *tide and wave generators and basins* is included in Section 10.3.

4.2 Measuring Methods and Instrumentation

Instrumentation used almost exclusively to be based on mechanical or optical devices and methods. A qualitative change in the instrumentation of hydraulic laboratories was achieved in the period following the Second World War due to the widespread development and use of electronics and modern measuring methods and techniques; radio-isotopes, transistors, semiconductors, lasers, etc., have accelerated the development of new and more accurate measuring devices, and the use of computers, micro-processors and other data processing techniques has become part of the operation of a large and sophisticated hydraulic laboratory. These developments have only confirmed the need to regard the field of measuring methods, instrumentation and data processing in hydraulic research as an independent scientific discipline where the hydraulics specialist specifies the requirements and cooperates with the electronic and mechanical engineer, the physicist, computer scientist and applied mathematician, all of whom have become important members of the research team.

According to its purpose hydraulic laboratory instrumentation may roughly be divided into devices for the measurement of: water levels (steady or fluctuating) and movable bed levels (during the experiment below water or after termination of the experiment on the dry model), discharge, velocity (and its fluctuations), hydrodynamic pressures (and their fluctuation) and flow of mixtures (sediment transport and suspensions carried by the liquid, air entrained by the flow, etc.). Some of these instruments or their parts are of standard make, but often they are designed and produced by the laboratory.

Despite rapidly developing instrumentation techniques it is not necessary to use sophisticated measuring devices where a simple instrument will do the job.

In the selection of instrumentation the required accuracy, taking into account both systematic and stochastic errors, is decisive; nevertheless the economic viewpoint must also be borne in mind. Thus the correct choice of instrumentation is an inseparable part of the proposed research method. As a reasonably comprehensive account of various measuring techniques and instrumentation would require a separate book and quickly become obsolete, the reader is advised to consult the literature and commercial information available in his particular field of interest. In the following paragraphs only a very brief summary of some of the more basic methods and instruments will therefore be given.

4.3 Measurement of Water Levels and Bed Formation

4.3.1 Measurement of steady water levels

The simplest and most commonly used instrument for the measurement of steady water levels is a point gauge; the required information is read off the scale with an accuracy up to 0.1 mm. For hydraulic flumes gauges are fitted on carriages, permitting longitudinal and transverse motion of the gauge. Indication of the correctly set position of the gauge is achieved by the needle point which may be straight (lowering of the gauge onto the water level to be measured from above) or in the shape of a hook with point directed upwards (gauge approaching the water level from below).

Contact of the point with the water level may be observed by eye or indicated electrically. Sometimes the gauge is fitted with an 'accuracy fork', i.e. two points set at the maximum permitted error in the position of the measured water level, e.g. 0.2 mm. If both points are fitted with an electrical indicator the gauge must be set (or the water level regulated) so that always only one indicator lights up.

When reading the water level in a reservoir where no greater accuracy than 2 mm is required, ordinary water gauges are used.

4.3.2 Measurement of fluctuating water levels

The position of a *slowly fluctuating water level* may be measured in the same way as that of a steady level. However, the gauge must be constantly under observation and so registration devices are most frequently used. Mass produced float gauges with mechanical recording are usually unsuitable for laboratories, which produce their own gauges often with a simple pen recorder attached. For measurements on large models float gauges are used together with transmitters for the concentration of data registration from several dispersed points on the model (or in the laboratory) at one of several recorders.

Slowly fluctuating water levels may also be measured by an apparatus where the vibrating tip of the gauge intermittently in contact with the water surface is automatically adjusted by a servomechanism (e.g. the French 'pointe vibrante' gauge developed by Neyrpic in Grenoble). The Hydraulic Research Station, Wallingford developed a water level transmitter which functions from the changing impedance between an immersed probe and a distant electrode. A sharp-pointed vertical probe is driven by a servo-system so that the tip of the probe is maintained at a depth of about 0.1 mm below the surface. The impedance between the probe and the remote electrode forms one arm of a bridge network which is balanced when the probe tip is at the correct depth. Any change of water level varies the immersion depth of the probe causing an error signal to be produced from the bridge. This signal is amplified and applied to a servo-motor which drives the probe to follow the water surface. The slider of a potentiometer is coupled to the probe and picks off a voltage proportional to the water level. This voltage can be displayed or recorded in digital or analogue form.

To measure *rapidly fluctuating water levels*, instruments with capacitance gauges are often used where the length of the submerged part of the gauge is the measure for the instantaneous position of the water level. The diameter of the gauge should be as small as possible (less than 1 mm).

An instrument consisting of a pair of stainless steel wires may also be used; the electrical conductivity between them is linearly related to their depth of submersion and thus to wave height. Another possibility is a resistance gauge, either with low resistance (usually a wire) or high resistance (non-conductive rod with a thin metal band and resistance of about 50 000 ohms). Oscillographs or special fast recorders are most frequently used as registering devices for the measurement of quickly changing water levels.

The position of the water level may also be ascertained by measuring the hydrostatic pressure (*see* Section 4.6) or photographically by a camera placed either at an angle above the model or at the water level; photographs are taken through the glass wall of the model or flume on which, for better orientation, a coordinate net may often be drawn or a scale fixed. Strongly fluctuating water level positions are best recorded by high-speed film cameras.

Stereophotogrammetry may also be used to record the entire water level surface with local changes (rise and contraction near piers, etc.).

4.3.3 Measurement of bed levels

After the model has been drained the bed level may be measured with a normal point gauge. In three-dimensional models the point gauge is used to find contour lines on the movable bed; simultaneously a white thread is placed on the contour line and the whole is then photographically recorded. Stereophotogrammetric methods may again be used to measure the bed formation on larger models.

The bed levels of larger models may also be measured by laboratory profilographs fitted with the usual devices to ascertain the position of the gauge and with a pantograph tracing the measured section in the required scale. The pick-up is usually a wheel moving on the bed and fixed on a well-balanced arm of the recorder.

Measuring the bed level under water in the course of the experiment is relatively complicated since observation of the instruments is then hindered by light diffraction and the approach of the tip of a gauge to the movable bed during an experiment may also disturb the scour formation. If the bed must be measured during the experiment, thin rods fixed to a normal gauge should be used. A more accurate and sophisticated optical instrument has been developed for measurement of the bed level without contact. It consists of a fork fitted to a normal gauge with both ends carrying a small light source and bent towards each other to form a right angle. The gauge is shifted vertically until the reflection from the light emitted by both sources and observed through a tube reaching close beneath the surface merges into one point on the movable bed. The device is then at a certain constant distance from the bed.

The Hydraulics Research Station Laboratory at Wallingford has developed a bed profile transmitter using a beam of infra-red radiation reflected by the bed. Alternatively a conductivity probe may be used where the bed material is of very low reflectivity. Both instruments maintain a constant distance, about 15 mm, above the bed.

4.4   Measurement and Regulation of Discharge

4.4.1   Measurement of discharge

The most accurate method of discharge measurements is the determination of the liquid *weight* or *volume* delivered over a certain time into specially rated installations. This is rarely used, however, during actual model investigations.

The most common laboratory discharge measurement is by means of various *weirs* built either into fixed or mobile measuring tanks. Most frequently a right angled Thomson triangular (V-notch) weir is used; for larger discharges a rectangular or compound weir is more suitable. For very small discharges a very narrow rectangular (slit) weir or triangular weir with a small angle, or a proportional weir where the ratio between discharge and overfall head is linear, is used. The head above the weir crest is measured with a point gauge, usually situated in a small well connected with the measuring tank. The required tank sizes and the upstream position of the gauge for measuring the head above the crest as well as details of the weir plates together with appropriate discharge coefficients are given in standard specifications. If these are not followed then the tank as a whole (with inlet and baffles, etc.) must be rated before use and the rating checked from time to time. Measuring weirs need a spacious tank and cause loss of head but they are simple, reliable and accurate.

Discharge can be measured by using devices based on the principle of contracting the flow and measuring the resulting pressure differences with a differential manometer. The most common instrumentation of this type is a *venturimeter*, an *orifice* or a *nozzle* fitted into the pipe supplying the model. Venturimeters cause relatively low head loss, but show low sensitivity for relatively small discharges (discharge is directly proportional to the square root of the pressure difference) and must be placed in a long straight pipe (if not rated at the place of use). According to specifications for an orifice a pipe (diameter D) of at least $20D$ length is required upstream and $5D$ downstream of it. The disadvantage of unequal sensitivity for greater ranges of discharges can be eliminated by installing batteries of parallel venturimeters of various diameters. Nozzles and orifices are shorter than venturimeters but cause greater pressure losses. The advantages of both are combined by a shortened venturimeter where the contraction has the shape of a standard nozzle and the downstream expansion is to a smaller pipe diameter than the original one.

In all these devices great attention must be paid to pressure tappings; usually a number of piezometers (or a narrow slit) are connected to an annulus to which the manometer is fitted.

An application of the venturimeter principle for open channel flow is the venturi-flume or the Parshal flume where a hydraulic jump is created by contraction of the rectangular channel. Differences in hydrodynamic pressures on the concave and convex walls of pipe bends (usually 90° bends) are also used to measure discharge. Bend discharge meters, venturimeters, nozzles and orifices—especially where their placing and construction does not agree with the standard specifications—must always be rated and whenever possible under the actual operating conditions.

Watermeters are used only occasionally in a hydraulic laboratory. Small discharges are sometimes measured by rotating discharge meters (*rotameters* with a rotating float in a divergent glass pipe).

Induction discharge meters are based on the principle that during flow of conductive liquids between the poles of a magnet an electromotive force arises, which is directly proportional to the vectorial product of the intensity of the magnetic field and the velocity of movement of the conductor. They are more frequently used for prototype measurements, than on scale models.

Under laboratory conditions discharge may also be determined by the *dilution method*, especially in open channel flow. For a certain time a known and constant quantity of electrolyte (dye, isotopes) is added to the measured flow in one cross-section and conductivity (colour, radiation intensity) recorded in another cross-section sufficiently distant from the dosing section for the measured and dosed liquid to mix completely. The discharge is then assessed on the basis of the mixing law. Equally the salt velocity method may be applied during which the electrolyte is added either once in a slug or periodically. Dilution methods are used only exceptionally in the laboratory and mostly only when other aims are pursued as well.

The methods for measuring local velocities, from which discharge may be established either by integration or by rating the ratio of mean (cross-section) velocity to the velocity at the measured point, are described in Section 4.5.

4.4.2 Regulation of discharge

During laboratory investigation of river processes, flood waves, etc., it may be necessary to change the flow of water on the model with time. Normally metal templates or cams simulating the modelled flood wave and moving at a constant speed given by the time scale are used. At the model inlet there is a measuring tank with a weir and constant inflow. The tank has a second movable weir spilling to waste, which regulates the water level in the tank and thus also the discharge on the model. The movement of the template is transferred to the waste weir by a mechanical gear system or by sensing contacts activating a motor moving the weir.

Another method of discharge regulation works with a constant water level in the measuring tank, which is ensured by fixed weirs spilling to waste. The regulation of the inflow on the model is assured by the movement of the actual discharge weir, which again may be controlled by the movement of a template. In this case it is advisable to choose a proportional weir for the regulation of the discharge. The motor driving the inlet weir can also be remotely controlled electronically by moving a non-transparent film strip (or punched tape) with two rows of perforations between the light source and a photo-cell. Every impulse sets in motion the motor of the weir, which moves by the height of one turn of the spindle. The discharge thus changes in steps of say 1/100 of the regulated range. The impulse from the first row of perforations moves the weir and from the second row changes the direction of motion (up or down). In the case of pipe flow the discharge may be regulated easily by transferring the movement of the template to the movement of a valve, the hydraulic characteristics of which are ascertained by independent measurements.

Both in pipe flow and models with a free water surface servo-control devices with feed-back from a sensor to the control device may be used if appropriate.

4.5   Measurement of Flow Velocity

A frequently used method of measuring local velocities is the determination of velocity from the measured velocity head with the aid of various types of *Pitot tubes*. The magnitude of the relative velocity head is found from the pressure difference at two or more points on the measuring device, which is submerged in the flow. The most commonly used device is the standard type of Prandtl tube (Fig. 4.6a), a Pitot tube shaped so that the drop in pressure caused by an increase in velocity due to flow round the front part of the tube is counterbalanced by the increase in pressure caused by the decrease in velocity in front of the vertical part of the tube; therefore the coefficient of the tube in equation

$$v = c\sqrt{(2gh)},$$

where h is the velocity head, is $c = 1$.

The Prandtl tube measures velocity correctly only when used against the direction of flow with a deviation of $\pm 15°$. Another type of Pitot tube was designed by Brabé (Fig. 4.6b). It also has a coefficient $c = 1$ but measures correctly only for a directional deviation smaller than $\pm 5°$. Apart from these types, spherical and cylindrical probes are used (Figs. 4.6c, 4.6d). These are suitable for greater velocities since with small pressures the small orifices considerably increase the inertia of the micromanometer reading. For larger orifices the active part of the probe is

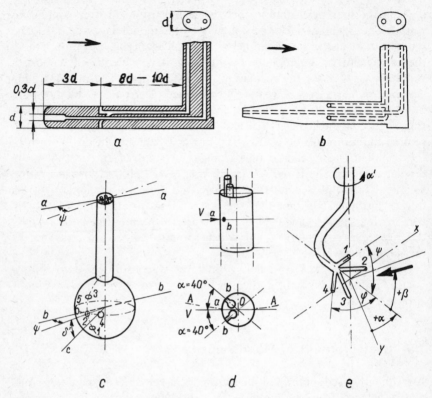

Fig. 4.6.

often too robust for laboratory measurements. The cylindrical probe is directed against the current so that the pressure in both orifices, bb, (Fig. 4.6d) is the same. Then this equals the static pressure and the pressure at point a is the total pressure (i.e. including dynamic pressure). A claw gauge consisting of four or five Pitot tubes turned in various directions, is suitable for measuring the velocity vector, velocity and direction being determined from the pressure differences in the separate tubes (Fig. 4.6e).

Pitot tubes, as well as spherical and cylindrical probes, if differing from thoroughly tested types, must be rated before use and used only within the rated range.

The most widely used velocity measuring device working on a mechanical principle is the *current meter*. For model investigations it is important that the propeller should be as small and as sensitive as possible. These two opposing demands require extremely careful construction, especially of the bearings, and a contactless impulse transmitter. A number of hydraulic laboratories and specialized firms deal with the development of miniature current meters of several millimetres diameter with velocity ranges from 0.03 to 1.00 m/s. The method of registration for most types is based on the principle that during the propeller rotation the distance between a fixed electrode and the rotating propeller blade (or the cogs of a collector) changes. Thus electric resistance increases or decreases and the resulting electrical impulses are recorded on an analogue or digital counter and/or a plotter. The mean local velocity $\bar{u}$ and the instantaneous local velocity u can be measured directly and the turbulence characteristics assessed from the differences

$$u' = u - \bar{u}.$$

A general picture of flow, direction and magnitude of velocity and of turbulence characteristics may be gained by *flow visualization* and the *cinematographic or photographic method.*

The direction of flow is easily determined by cotton threads on a thin wire or by introducing grains of pumice, aluminium powder, etc. into the flow. For two-dimensional flow it is also possible to judge the velocity at various points from the length of the recorded trace and the exposure time. In models of open channel flow small floats carrying a light source may be used; the model must be placed in a darkened room and the path of the floats is recorded on the photographic plate by interrupted exposure (exposure and intervals usually lasting one second). After the experiment the model is lit up and photographed on the same plate.

In the cinematographic method the flow pattern is usually made visible with the aid of an emulsion of vaseline oil dissolved in chlorbenzol and dyed with white oil colour. The mixture forms spherical particles diameter about 1 to 2 mm. From the difference of the coordinates of individual spheres on successive frames, recorded by a high-speed camera, it is possible to calculate the instantaneous velocity and other required parameters. If the flow is recorded in two directions simultaneously (e.g., with the aid of a mirror inclined at 45°), then all velocity components may be recorded. The film record is usually assessed with the use of the corresponding reduction coefficients of lengths and depths and from a time scale determined from the film record of a light source connected to an alternate current of known frequency.

Another type of instrument used for velocity measurement is based on the measurement of *pressure* produced by the flowing liquid on the body submerged in it, e.g., a small disc, placed perpendicular to the direction of flow and fixed to one end of a lever with a mirror on the other. The lever is kept vertical by a spring. The disc and with it the lever and mirror, are deflected by the pressure exerted by the flow. This also deflects the light falling on the mirror, which in turn can be observed and recorded. Accurate rating of the device before use is essential.

A widespread method of measuring flow velocity and turbulence parameters is *hot wire and hot film anemometry*. Probes with electrically heated thin wire or preferably heated metal film supported on a ceramic sub-plate are used on the principle that the rate of heat loss of the sensor, heated to a higher temperature than that of the ambient fluid, is proportional to the velocity of the medium at the point of measurement. This cooling results in a change of resistance of the heated element, which becomes an indirect measure of the velocity. For a constant current anemometer the change in resistance causes a change in voltage which is measured and recorded. In a constant temperature anemometer a feedback circuit keeps the temperature constant and the fluctuating current gives rise to fluctuating voltage, which is again the output. The instrument may be provided with a linearizer which modifies the amplified output from the anemometer so that it is proportional to velocity. The linearized voltage is then recorded on an analogue recorder or sampled at set intervals and stored in digital form on tape.

Termistors can be used to measure very small velocities (several mm/s). Their disadvantages are difficult compensation of temperature influences and great time constant (as against a hot wire probe).

Recently instrumentation using a *laser* beam has been developed for local velocity and turbulence measurements. The technique is based on the fact that the crossing of two coherent light beams causes an interference pattern, which is displaced by the movement of scattered particles suspended in the fluid flow. The Laser-Doppler anemometer (LDA) consists of a light source (laser), beam splitter and focussing lens (transmission optics), light collecting optics, photo-detector and signal processor.

4.6 Measurement of Hydrodynamic Pressure

Hydrodynamic pressure is most frequently measured by simple glass or perspex tube manometers connected to the piezometric opening by rubber or plastic tubing. The manometers are usually placed next to each other on a panel with a grid where the position of the piezometer is shown so that the value of the pressure head on the model at that position can be read straight off. The accuracy of measurement (reading of meniscus) is increased by drawing a line on the panel behind the axis of the glass tube manometer. The tube diameter should be at least 10 to 15 mm to reduce the influence of surface tension; for a diameter 10 mm the capillary elevation of water in the tube is still about 3 mm. The details of the actual piezometric opening are very important. Its axis must be perpendicular to the surface where the pressure is being measured. The orifice diameter must be relatively small, 1 to 1.5 mm, its edge must not be too rounded and there must be no projection or obstacle to flow. Figure 4.7 shows errors in piezometric orifices, (a) increasing or (b) decreasing

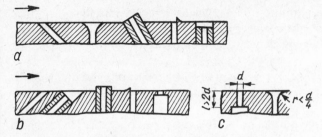

Fig. 4.7. [After Rouse, H. (Ed.) (1950).]

the pressure readings; (c) shows the correct shape and suitable execution of the orifice. The surface round the opening must be smooth up to a distance of at least 50 times the diameter of the piezometer orifice.

Apart from the most frequent simple tube manometers various fluid manometers, micromanometers and differential manometers with water, mercury, alcohol, etc., are used. These are either commercially produced or constructed in the laboratory workshops.

Membrane or other mechanical manometers or manographs are more suited for field work. Under laboratory conditions they are rarely used and then only for measuring relatively high pressures where the fluid manometer is less suitable.

Devices for measuring pressure transients and pressure fluctuations are important both for investigations involving negative pressures, especially close to cavitation phenomena, and for the study of pressure fluctuations caused by strongly turbulent flow acting on hydraulic structures. Most transducers of this type are based on the action of the pressure on an elastic membrane which must be without plastic deformation and without, or with a small hysteresis only. Deformation of the membrane is most frequently transformed to changes in electrical resistance, capacitance or induction. Changes in electric magnitudes are then measured by electronic instruments and recorded, e.g. on an oscillograph. Tensometers can also be used as pressure transducers.

4.7 Measurement of Two-phase Flow

The measurement of the hydraulic characteristics of mixtures of *solids and liquids* is important in particular during research on hydraulic transport of solids through pipelines and during the operation of such systems. The passage of the mixture is measured by one of the methods for measuring the discharge of the carrying liquid, most frequently by volumetric or weight measurement in tanks. Orifices, nozzles or venturimeters are also used. In homogeneous suspensions of fine particles greater throttling may be permitted in the measuring section than for thick mixtures or mixtures with coarser particles. Bend meters have been found suitable as also have electromagnetic meters, which do not influence the flow of the mixture.

The mean velocity of flow is ascertained by measuring the discharge or by the salt velocity method. The chemical dilution method or radio-isotopes may also be used.

The important measurement of the mixture concentration is again carried out by volumetric or weight measurement (at the delivery end of the pipe), or during continuous measurement or when determining the local values of concentration by monitoring and recording the passage of waves or radiation through the mixture. The distribution of the concentration at various points of the flow can be determined by a special probe.

The velocity of various particles in the flow of the mixture may be measured by the cinematographic method or with the aid of radio-isotopes.

During work with a mixture of sediment and water on river models with movable bed various types of sediment dosing equipment are used. They are mostly based on the use of conveyors, screws or vibrators, taking either dry or wet material from a container with an adjustable opening.

The granulometric curve, the geometric characteristics and specific weight of bedload and suspended sediment are usually determined before as well as after the experiment.

When working with a mixture of *air and liquid* two problems are of paramount interest, i.e. the quantity of air passing through the measuring cross-section and the size of the air bubbles. The quantity of air drawn into the water flow for example by an aeration pipe can easily be measured by standard means, e.g. by an orifice placed in the aeration pipe. To measure the quantity of air entrained by the liquid in a conduit radiation may be used in the same way as for a mixture of solids and liquid. The measurement is based on the fact that gamma radiation is absorbed in the same way whether it passes through a mixture of two fluids (water–air) or two independent layers of the same fluids. A radiation source (e.g., isotope cobalt Co 60) is attached to one side of the conduit and a Geiger counter is fixed to the opposite side. If this meter is rated by measuring the absorption of various layers of liquid at rest (or flowing without aeration) then it is possible to measure directly the quantity of air entrained in the form of bubbles by the flow of liquid through the full cross-section or also by a flow at a certain known depth.

The size of the air bubbles and their velocity and direction is again measured best by cinematographic or photographic methods.

The quantity of air contained in a certain vertical of aerated water flow with free surface may also be ascertained by measuring the hydrostatic pressure acting on the bed of the channel and comparing the specific weight of the mixture with the specific weight of liquid alone. Finally the quantity of air entrained by the flow of liquid of known discharge without air may be ascertained by measuring the discharge of the mixture which can be determined from the depth of the aerated flow and the mean velocity found by integration from point measurements.

References

Akademija Nauk SSSR. (1961). *New Methods of Measurement and Instrumentation for Hydraulic Research*, (in Russian), Izdatelstvo ANSSR, Moscow.

Bradley, J. N. (1946). *Hydraulic Laboratory Manual*, Hydraulic laboratory report No. 193, Bureau of Reclamation, Denver, Colorado.

British Standards Institution. (1964). *Methods for the Measurement of Fluid Flow in Pipes*, BS1042, BSI, London.

British Standards Institution. (1964–1974). *Methods of Measurement of Liquid Flow in Open Channels*, BS3680, BSI, London.

Broda, E. and Schönfeld, T. (1956). *Die technischen Anwendungen der Radioaktivität*, Verlag Technik, Berlin.

Čábelka, J. and Novak, P. (1964). *Hydraulic Research 1—Research on Models*, (in Czech), SNTL, Prague.

Durrani, T. S. and Greated, C. A. (1976). *Laser Systems in Flow Measurement*, Plenum Publ. Co., New York.

Durst, F., Melling, A. and Whitelaw, J. H. (1976). *Principles and Practice of Laser-Doppler Anemometry*, Academic Press, London.

Greated, C. (1970), Measurement of Turbulence Statistics with a Laser Velocimeter, *J. Phys. E: Scient. Instr.*, **3**, pp. 158–160.

Hinze, J. O. (1959). *Turbulence, An Introduction to its Mechanism and Theory*, McGraw-Hill, New York.

Hydraulics Research Station. *Instrumentation and Control Notes*, HRS, Wallingford.

Jones, E. B. (1953). *Instrument Technology*, Butterworths, London.

Ling, S. L. and Hubbard, P. G. (1956). The hot-film anemometer: a new device for fluid mechanics research, *J. Aero Sci.*, **23**, No. 9, pp. 890–891.

Mathieson, R. and Stebbings, J. (1964). Design of modern hydraulics laboratory for teaching and research, *Proc. ICE*, **29**, 657–676.

Preston, J. H. (1954). The determination of turbulent skin friction by means of Pitot tubes, *J. Roy. Aero. Soc.*, **58**, pp. 109–121.

Resch, F. J. (1970). Hot film turbulence measurement in water flow, *Proc. ASCE, J. Hydraul. Div.*, **96**, No. HY3, pp. 787–800.

Rouse, H. (Ed.) (1950). *Engineering Hydraulics*, John Wiley, New York.

5 Models of Pressure Systems

5.1 Steady Flow in Pipes

5.1.1 Basic principles and equations

A more detailed analysis of various equations and approaches is beyond the scope of this book, which is mainly concerned with models and similarity. It is, however, necessary to state some of the basic principles and results in order to appreciate their implications for hydraulic models of pressure systems as well as for similarity of open channel flow (*see* Chapter 6).

The pressure loss due to friction $\Delta p = \gamma h_f$ in pipe flow will depend on the specific mass ρ, the coefficient of viscosity μ, and the mean (cross-sectional) velocity v of the liquid, and on the diameter D, length l and effective roughness k of the pipe. By dimensional analysis

$$h_f = \frac{lv^2}{Dg} \, \phi\!\left(\frac{vD}{\nu}, \frac{k}{D}\right) \tag{5.1}$$

If we compare Equation (5.1) with the well-known equation for friction loss in pipes

$$h_f = \frac{\lambda l v^2}{2gD} \tag{5.2}$$

which may also be written as

$$h_f = \frac{4\tau_0 l}{\rho g D} \tag{5.3}$$

(where τ_0 is the shear stress at the wall), the equation for resistance coefficient λ will be

$$\lambda = \phi\!\left(\frac{vD}{\nu}, \frac{k}{D}\right) = \phi\!\left(Re, \frac{k}{D}\right) \tag{5.4}$$

If we introduce into Equation (5.2) the hydraulic radius $R = D/4$ instead of the diameter of the pipe D, then

$$h_f = \frac{\lambda l v^2}{8gR} = \frac{\lambda_R l v^2}{2gR} \tag{5.2'}$$

From Equations (5.2), (5.2') and (5.3) we obtain the relation between the coefficients λ and λ_R and between λ and τ_0

$$\lambda = 4\lambda_{R'} \tag{5.5}$$

$$\tau_0 = \frac{\lambda}{8} \rho v^2 = \rho v_*^2 \tag{5.6}$$

where v_* is the shear (friction) velocity.

It is known from hydraulics that the slope of the energy line in laminar flow in a pipe is

$$\frac{h_f}{l} = \frac{32 \nu v}{gD^2} \tag{5.7}$$

Comparison of Equations (5.2) and (5.7) shows that for laminar flow losses do not depend on the wall roughness and

$$\lambda = \frac{64\nu}{vD} = \frac{64}{Re} \tag{5.8}$$

The laminar regime is maintained for flow through a pipe up to the critical value $Re_{cr} = 2300$. Below this limit flow at a sufficient distance from the inlet into the pipe is always laminar. In favourable circumstances (perfect flow, absolutely quiet water in the inlet reservoir) laminar flow may also be achieved for $Re > Re_{cr}$. Quite exceptionally laminar flow has been obtained up to $Re = 150\,000$.

For values of the Reynolds number above the critical limit Re_{cr} the flow passes through the transitional zone into the region of turbulent flow where energy losses are much greater than for laminar flow and where there are three possible regimes: smooth turbulent flow, transition from 'smooth' to 'rough', and rough turbulent flow (see Fig. 5.1). The exponent of mean cross-sectional velocity in the head loss equation changes from 1 (see Equation (5.7)) up to 2 for fully developed rough turbulent flow. Therefore Reynolds number disappears from Equation (5.4) and the resistance coefficient is only a function of the relative roughness k/D. The Reynolds number for which rough turbulent flow begins, i.e. for which the friction loss is proportional to the square of mean velocity, is denoted as Re_{sq}. For $Re \geqslant Re_{sq}$ the resistance coefficient λ is therefore independent of the Reynolds number.

When drawing up the general equation for friction loss h_f (5.1) the effective roughness size k of the pipe wall was used. It is evident that the roughness coefficient will be influenced not only by the magnitude of wall protuberances, but also by their shape, homogeneity and concentration. For homogeneous roughness formed by regularly spaced sand grains of equal size glued to the inside wall of smooth bronze pipes Equation (5.4) was solved experimentally by Nikuradse. He used relative roughness values $30 < D/k < 1014$. The resultant graph illustrating the relation between the resistance coefficient λ, Reynolds Number $Re = vD/v$ and the relative roughness value r/k, (where r is the radius of the pipe and k the size of the sand grains forming roughness) is shown in Fig. 5.1. The above mentioned various regions are clearly indicated on the graph:

(a) for $Re < Re_{cr}$ Poiseuille's straight line expressed by Equation (5.8) for λ in the case of laminar flow is valid.
(b) for $Re > Re_{sq}$ the coefficient λ in rough pipes is independent of the Reynolds number and is only a function of the relative roughness k/r. It may be seen from Fig. 5.1 that the value of Re_{sq}, is variable and depends again on the relative roughness. The smaller the relative roughness k/r the greater Re_{sq}.
(c) for the zone $Re_{cr} < Re < Re_{sq}$ the coefficient λ is a function both of the Reynolds number and of relative roughness.

Zones (a) and (b) are an example of an automodelling region where $La = $ constant and $Eu = $ constant (*see* Sub-section 2.4.2).

Prandtl introduced the concept of the *boundary layer* which may be defined as a region within the flowing liquid, at the surface of a body

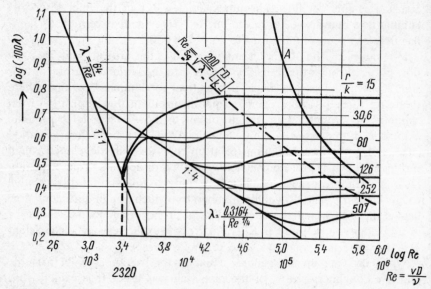

Fig. 5.1.

placed in the path of the flow, where the influence of viscosity is noticeable.

The *laminar boundary layer* is a layer of liquid where, in the vicinity of fixed walls, laminar flow occurs even though the rest of the flow is turbulent. The thickness of a developing laminar boundary layer for a finite plate in a fluid stream (before the layer becomes generally turbulent) is given by

$$\frac{\delta}{x} = \frac{5}{\sqrt{(Re_x)}} \tag{5.9}$$

where x is the distance from the upstream end and $Re_x = Ux/\nu$, where U is the mean velocity at infinity.

When increasing the Reynolds number (e.g. in Equation (5.9) for $Re_x > 10^5 - 10^6$) the flow even in the boundary layer becomes turbulent resulting in a *turbulent boundary layer*, its thickness is given by

$$\frac{\delta}{x} = \frac{0.37}{Re_x^{1/5}} \tag{5.9'}$$

The thickness of the fully developed boundary layer may be defined in various ways. One of the definitions will be found in Fig. 5.2, where the thickness is given by the distance from the wall of the intersection of the tangent to the curve of the velocity distribution graph at its beginning (at the wall) with the asymptote to this curve (at infinity). Other definitions (e.g. thickness δ is defined by the distance from the wall at which the velocity attains 99 per cent of the mean velocity at infinity) give comparable values for δ.

Due to the fact that close to the wall velocity fluctuations must tend towards zero, in the case of smooth walls even the turbulent boundary layer contains a very thin layer, a *laminar sub-layer*, where flow is laminar (Fig. 5.2).

In the laminar sublayer with thickness δ' the velocity distribution is parabolic; for a small distance from the wall this may be replaced by a linear distribution (curve 'a' and straight line 'b' in Fig. 5.2). In the turbulent boundary layer a power law is valid

$$u = y^{1/m} \tag{5.10}$$

where m is a constant.

The validity of Equation (5.10) has been proved experimentally for $m = 7$ up to values of $Re = 20 \times 10^6$. Using Prandtl's concept of mixing length l, assuming that near a fixed wall l is directly proportional to the distance y from the wall, and using the value 0.4 for the coefficient of proportionality κ (the 'universal constant') the logarithmic velocity dis-

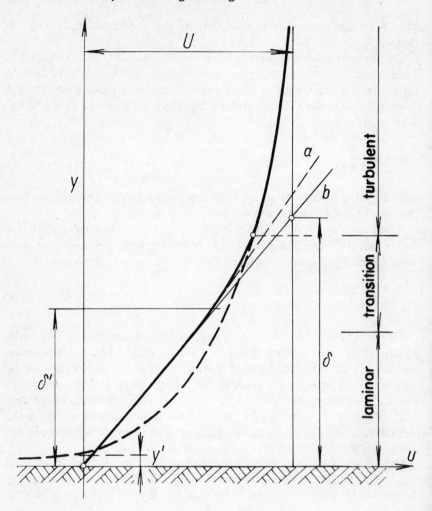

Fig. 5.2.

tribution valid for fully turbulent flow is obtained:

$$\frac{\bar{u}}{\sqrt{(\tau_0/\rho)}} = 5.75 \log \frac{y}{y'} \tag{5.11}$$

where y' is the distance from the wall for $\bar{u} = 0$ (Fig. 5.2).

When applying the above principles to pipe-flow, on the basis of Nikuradse's (1932) experimental results for smooth pipes, we can put

$$\delta' = \frac{11.6\nu}{\sqrt{(\tau_0/\rho)}} \tag{5.12}$$

and

$$y' = \frac{\delta'}{107} = \frac{0.108\nu}{\sqrt{(\tau_0/\rho)}} \tag{5.13}$$

For rough walls a laminar layer cannot be assumed if the magnitude of the roughness elements is of the same order as the previously determined thickness δ'. Nikuradse's (1933) experiments show that for $k > 10\delta'$

$$y' = \frac{k}{30} \tag{5.14}$$

Substituting for y' into Equation (5.11) and integrating across the whole pipe cross-section we obtain for smooth pipes

$$\frac{v}{\sqrt{(\tau_0/\rho)}} = 5.75 \log \frac{r\sqrt{(\tau_0/\rho)}}{\nu} + 1.75 \tag{5.15}$$

and for rough pipes

$$\frac{v}{\sqrt{(\tau_0/\rho)}} = 5.75 \log \frac{r}{k} + 4.75 \tag{5.16}$$

If we now introduce the friction coefficient λ from Equation (5.6) and carry out a small correction in the coefficients according to experimental results we obtain the Karman–Prandtl equations for the friction coefficient for turbulent flow in smooth pipes ($Re = vD/\nu$):

$$\frac{1}{\sqrt{\lambda}} = 2 \log Re \sqrt{\lambda} - 0.8 \tag{5.17}$$

or

$$\frac{1}{\sqrt{\lambda}} = 2 \log \frac{Re\sqrt{\lambda}}{2.51} \tag{5.17'}$$

and for rough pipes

$$\frac{1}{\sqrt{\lambda}} = 2 \log \frac{r}{k} + 1.74 \tag{5.18}$$

or

$$\frac{1}{\sqrt{\lambda}} = 2 \log \frac{3.71D}{k} \tag{5.18'}$$

We also obtain a single equation for the relative velocity distribution in rough and smooth pipes

$$\frac{\bar{u} - v}{\sqrt{(\tau_0/\rho)}} = 5.75 \log \frac{y}{r} + 3.75 \tag{5.19}$$

or

$$\frac{\bar{u} - v}{v\sqrt{\lambda}} = 2 \log \frac{y}{r} + 1.32 \tag{5.19'}$$

From these equations it is simple to calculate the distance from the pipe wall of the point where the velocity $\bar{u}$ equals the mean cross-sectional velocity $v : y_v = 0.22r$.

For maximum velocity u_{max} in the axis of the pipe from Equation (5.19') for $y = r$ we obtain:

$$\frac{\bar{u}_{max}}{v} = 1 + 1.32\sqrt{\lambda} \tag{5.20}$$

From Equations (5.6) and (5.12) we obtain the relationship.

$$\frac{\delta'}{r} = \frac{11.6v}{rv\sqrt{(\lambda/8)}} = \frac{65.6v}{vD\sqrt{\lambda}} = \frac{65.6}{Re\sqrt{\lambda}} \tag{5.21}$$

By substituting Equation (5.21) into (5.17) we arrive at the conclusion that in smooth pipes λ depends only on the relative thickness of the laminar sublayer δ'/r and from Equation (5.18) we see that in rough pipes λ depends only on the relative roughness k/r.

From these results it follows that every pipe of a certain roughness will behave like a smooth pipe for low Re and for high Re like a rough pipe. Between the two cases there must be a transitional zone in which loss due to friction is caused both by the viscosity of the liquid and by the roughness of the pipe. As long as the inequalities of the pipe wall are submerged in the laminar sub-layer they do not influence the magnitude of the losses at all. However, as soon as the thickness of the laminar sub-layer decreases to such an extent that, as a result of the protruding parts on the wall of the pipe, it becomes unstable, the resistance of flow will increase.

If Nikuradse's results are illustrated so that we plot $1/\sqrt{\lambda} - 2 \log r/k$ against k/δ', which, considering that

$$\frac{\delta'}{r} \sim \frac{1}{Re\sqrt{\lambda}}$$

Equation (5.21) may be replaced by $Re\sqrt{\lambda}/(r/k)$, we obtain simultaneously the graphical expression of the transitional zone and of Equations (5.17) and (5.18) (Fig. 5.3).

It may be seen from Fig. 5.3 that the transition from the smooth to the rough pipe occurs at about $\delta' = 4k$ and finishes at $\delta' = k/6$.

By substituting for δ' we obtain the limiting value Re_{sq} from Equation (5.21)

$$Re_{sq} = \frac{6.65, 6r}{k\sqrt{\lambda}} = \frac{394r}{k\sqrt{\lambda}} \simeq 400 \frac{r}{k\sqrt{\lambda}} \tag{5.22}$$

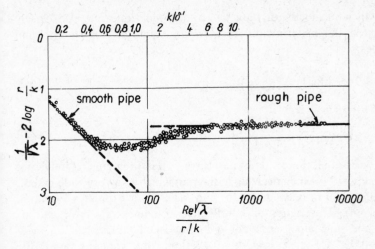

Fig. 5.3.

where λ is defined by Equation (5.2) and $Re = vD/\nu$.†

Equation (5.22) can also be written as

$$Re_R \geqslant 100 \frac{R}{k\sqrt{\lambda_R}} \tag{5.22'}$$

or

$$Re_k^* = \frac{v_* k}{\nu} \geqslant 70 \tag{5.22''}$$

The above considerations referred to a uniform roughness of pipe walls as used by Nikuradse. In reality, however, the roughness of the wall of every pipe is caused by protuberations of various sizes, shapes and density. Thus it is not possible to characterize the roughness of a pipe manufactured from a certain material by a single dimension; we may, however, choose an equivalent roughness k corresponding to a uniform grain size and causing in a pipe of given diameter the same value of coefficient λ as an actual heterogeneous roughness. On this basis the results of the experimental studies of many researchers may be assessed. The experimental results of Colebrook and White (1937, 1939) with the use of heterogeneous sand roughness led to a single semi-empirical

† In the application of Equations (5.1) to (5.22) particular attention must be paid to the interpretation of Re and λ. It is essential to differentiate between λ and λ_R (Equation (5.5)), and to take care in the definition of the Reynolds number, where the dimension of length is sometimes diameter D, elsewhere the radius r or the hydraulic radius R. This is why we frequently state the definition of Re to avoid errors which unfortunately sometimes occur in literature. In the above exposition always $Re = vD/\nu$, unless a special index, e.g. Re_x, has been used.

relation which included not only the transitional zone but also closely approximated the experimental results and equations for smooth and rough pipes:

$$\frac{1}{\sqrt{\lambda}} = 1.74 - 2\log\left(\frac{k}{r} + \frac{18.7}{Re\sqrt{\lambda}}\right) \tag{5.23}$$

or

$$\frac{1}{\sqrt{\lambda}} = -2\log\left(\frac{2.51}{Re\sqrt{\lambda}} + \frac{k}{3.71D}\right) \tag{5.23'}$$

On the basis of all these studies and further measurements on industrial pipes, Moody (1944) then drew up a diagram which to a very wide extent, presents the relation between λ, Re and k/D, i.e. it expresses Equation (5.4) (Fig. 5.4). The values of k (effective roughness size) for various materials and new pipes are quoted in published tables (e.g. for steel $k = 0.005-0.05$, for cast iron $k = 0.12-0.60$, for concrete $k = 0.30-3.0$ mm). For one year's operation of metal and concrete pipes an increase in the value of λ by 0.0005 to 0.0001 should be allowed for.

The Karman–Prandtl and the Colebrook–White equations, of course, represent only one type of an expression for the friction coefficient, which, however, is the most suitable one for the needs of hydraulic research.

Some hydraulic engineers have proposed a simplification of the coefficients in these equations, which would not influence the results of the computations (e.g., Thijsse, 1949), or they have replaced the logarithmic relationship by an exponential one, again without noticeable deviations from the actual course of the function (e.g., Bretting, 1948).

Apart from the mentioned equations there exist a whole number of older (and more recent) empirical and semi-empirical formulae for the mean cross-sectional velocity for flow through a pipe and for the roughness coefficient, which are valid for the zone of fully developed, turbulent flow. Details of these equations with the respective tables of coefficients are to be found in almost any textbook of hydraulics. Since some of these formulae are also used for the computation of models the following at least ought to be mentioned:

Chézy formula

$$v = C\sqrt{(RS)} \tag{5.24}$$

where for pipe flow $S = h_f/l$ is the slope of the piezometric line (hydraulic gradient), here equal to the slope of the energy line;

Manning formula

$$v = \frac{1}{n}R^{2/3}S^{1/2} \tag{5.25}$$

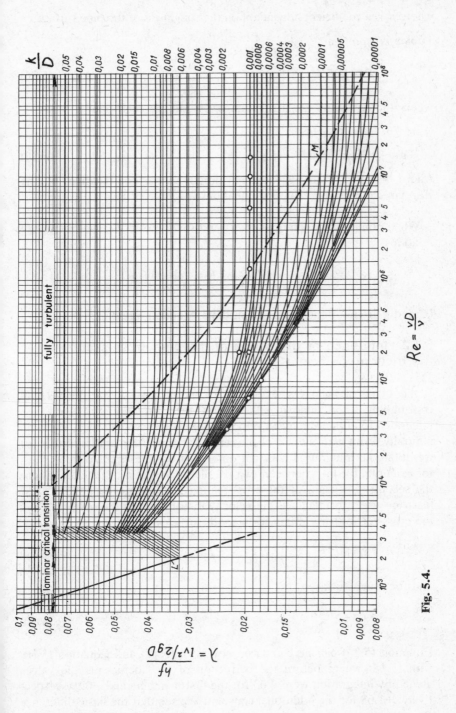

Fig. 5.4.

where n is a coefficient dependent on the roughness of the pipe surface;

Pavlovskij formula

$$v = \frac{1}{n} R^y \sqrt{(RS)} \tag{5.26}$$

where the exponent y is a function of R and the coefficient n;

Agroskin formula (1954)

$$v = 17.72(k' + \log R)\sqrt{(RS)} \tag{5.27}$$

where $k' = 1/(17.72n)$ is derived already as a combination of the Karman–Prandtl and Manning equations ($17.72 = 2\sqrt{(8g)}$).

When comparing Equations (5.2') and (5.24) to (5.27) we obtain the relations

$$C = \frac{1}{n} R^{1/6} = \frac{1}{n} R^y = \frac{1}{n} + 17.72 \log R = \sqrt{\left(\frac{8g}{\lambda}\right)} = \sqrt{\left(\frac{2g}{\lambda_R}\right)} \tag{5.28}$$

(C and n are not dimensionless constants, λ and λ_R are dimensionless).

5.1.2 Influence of the shape of the pipe cross-section on the friction coefficient

If the shape of the cross-section of a conduit is such that the velocity distribution is the same in all its parts, then Equation (5.11) may be integrated to obtain the mean velocity in the given cross-section whereby, naturally (even with the use of the same Karman's 'universal constant' κ) we obtain an integration constant different from the circular pipe. Thus, for example, for flow between two parallel planes at a distance a (where the second dimension of the cross-section is theoretically infinite or at least too great to influence the velocity distribution in the major part of the cross-section) we obtain for smooth surfaces

$$\frac{1}{\sqrt{\lambda}} = 2.03 \log\left(\frac{2av}{\nu} \sqrt{\lambda}\right) - 0.47 \tag{5.29}$$

and for rough surfaces

$$\frac{1}{\sqrt{\lambda}} = 2.03 \log \frac{a/2}{k} + 2.11 \tag{5.30}$$

Equation (5.29) can be compared now with (5.17) and Equation (5.30) with (5.18) where before the correction of the coefficients the values gained by integration were 2.03 for the first members and -0.91, respectively, $+1.68$ for the additional constant. We see that the basic difference lies in the value of the additional integration constant which reflects the change in the shape of the cross-section.

If the pipe cross-section has a shape such that the velocity distribution varies at every section (i.e. the walls meet at various angles, e.g. in a rectangular, or triangular cross-section) the tangential stress at the wall cannot be constant and the integration of Equation (5.11) will provide only a qualitative result. At the same time, it may be assumed that the mean tangential stress at the wall $\overline{\tau_0}$ will again be given by Equation (5.6) (whereby λ is determined from Equation (5.2') with the use of the hydraulic radius R). Generally, the differences in the integration constants for a very wide (or very high) pipe cross-section as compared with the circular shape as shown above, may be regarded as extremes. The more the ratio of the width to height of the cross-section approaches one, the more the value of these constants will approach those in Equations (5.17) and (5.18) for circular pipes, and the greater will be the justification of using the graphs in Fig. (5.1), or Fig. (5.4), for the determination of λ.

If we introduce in Equations (5.17) and (5.18) instead of D and r the hydraulic radius $R = D/4 = r/2$ and further, if we put in Equations (5.29) and (5.30) for a large second dimension $R = a/2$ we find that λ for a cross-section other than circular is always larger than for the circular one. This increase in the friction coefficient and resultant energy losses, is caused primarily by secondary currents whose streamlines are in a plane perpendicular to the axis of the pipe. The resultant is a spiral flow leading to increased mixing of particles from the zones of higher and lower velocities, and to an increase in turbulence and thus also in the friction coefficient of the pipe. If we were again to plot the function Equation (5.4) we would obtain a graph parallel to Nikuradse's but increasingly shifted into the zone of higher values for λ as the extent to which the cross-section differs from a circular one increases.

The change in the cross-section also influences the magnitude of the critical Reynolds number Re_{cr}. If a is the height and b the width of the cross-section of the conduit, $Re_{cr} = vR/\nu$ changes from 525 for $b/a = 1$ to 730 for $b/a = 5$ (Allen, 1947) (for a circular cross-section $Re_{cr} = 580$).

Thus the Karman–Prandtl equations may generally be rewritten as

$$\frac{1}{\sqrt{\lambda}} = A \log Re_R \sqrt{\lambda} + B \tag{5.31}$$

for a smooth pipe and

$$\frac{1}{\sqrt{\lambda}} = A \log \frac{R}{k} + B' \tag{5.32}$$

for a rough pipe, where $Re_R = Rv/\nu$ and A, B, B' are constants; B and B'

express the influence of the shape of the pipe cross-section and $A = 4$ for $\kappa = 0.4$.

More recent research indicates that for shapes differing from circular the 'universal constant' κ is smaller than 0.4. Even for large circular pipes a smaller value has been suggested, e.g. Shevelev (1953) proposed the equation

$$\kappa = \frac{0.337}{D^{0.08}} \tag{5.33}$$

where D is in metres. However, this does not affect the above stated conclusions or the form of Equations (5.31) and (5.32).

It is evident from Equations (5.6), (5.11), (5.15), (5.16), (5.29) and (5.30) that we could also write for smooth pipes

$$v = \frac{v_*}{\kappa} \ln \frac{aR}{\delta'} \tag{5.15'}$$

and similarly for rough pipes

$$v = \frac{v_*}{\kappa} \ln \frac{bR}{k} \tag{5.16'}$$

where a and b are constants depending on the conduit shape. Thus for a circular pipe $a = 46.6$ and $b = 14.3$, and for a wide rectangular conduit $a = 38.4$ and $b = 11.0$.

5.1.3 Local losses in pipelines

In pipe flow, apart from head losses due to friction, local losses caused by sudden or gradual changes in the cross section and direction of flow also occur. All these 'local losses' h_e may be expressed by the following type of equation:

$$h_e = \xi \frac{v^2}{2g}$$

where ξ is a coefficient depending on the type of loss, its geometry, wall roughness and the conditions of flow (Reynolds number and velocity distribution at entry).

In more common cases (e.g. change of direction of the pipe by a standard bend, change in the pipe diameter, orifice, etc.), the relationship between the coefficient ξ, the flow Reynolds number and the geometric parameters of the change have been thoroughly investigated and values of ξ tabulated (Kolář, 1966; Miller, 1978). Otherwise, however, the whole function and the values of coefficient ξ are not yet well known.

From the preceding text it is evident that the coefficient ξ is independent of the Reynolds number only after achieving a certain limiting value Re_{sq} as was the case for the friction coefficient λ. For this function of the coefficient ξ few data exist in the literature. However, considering that every change in direction and cross-section necessarily causes secondary currents and increased turbulence upstream of the section under consideration, as well as far beyond it, it may be safely assumed that the value Re_{sq} will in most cases be lower for relatively smooth pipes, and for relatively rough pipes will, at most, be equal to the value given by Equation (5.22). Figure 5.5 gives an idea of the dependence of the coefficient ξ on Reynolds number for certain types of local losses (the velocity and Re refer to the downstream condition). It can be seen that the values of Re_{sq} are appreciably lower than those associated generally with flow in pipes (*see* Fig. 5.4).

For the case of head losses in diffusers the geometry is again of paramount importance (Miller, 1978, Daily and Harleman, 1966). The design of a conical diffuser for minimum energy dissipation requires that the expansion angle be small enough to avoid unnecessary losses due to excessive length. The optimum angle is about 3° to 4° depending on the velocity distribution at the entrance to the diffuser.

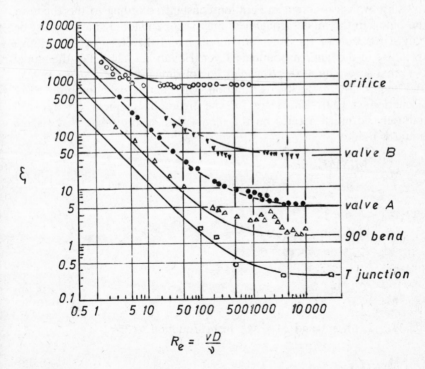

Fig. 5.5.

Local losses may be substantially influenced (increased or decreased) by the upstream pipe configuration unless the distance between the fittings or appliances causing the loss is sufficiently large (more than about $40D$).

5.1.4 Similarity for laminar flow

On the basis of the analysis in Sub-section 5.1.1 we can draw the conclusion that if we want to obtain the same friction losses on the model as in prototype we must ensure the identity of Reynolds numbers ($Re = idem$). Velocity distribution is naturally parabolic for every laminar flow and Equation (5.8) is valid for λ.

5.1.5 Similarity for smooth turbulent flow

The fact that the prototype pipe is hydraulically smooth ($\delta' > 4k$) is checked by calculation from Equation (5.21) or from the graph in Fig. 5.4. For λ in prototype and on the model, Equation (5.17) is valid (possibly with a different integration constant according to the shape of the pipe). In the model, roughness may also be ignored since λ must be only a function of the Reynolds number and therefore of the relative thickness of the laminar boundary layer (Equation (5.21)). For the model operated according to the *Reynolds law* of similarity ($Re = idem$) $\lambda_p = \lambda_m$ and the relative velocity distribution will be the same in both cases (Equation (5.19′)). The slope of the hydraulic gradient $S = h_f/l$ will naturally be much greater on the model than in prototype if the same liquid is used as

$$M_{hf} = \frac{M_\lambda M_l M_v^2}{M_D} \tag{5.34}$$

and for

$$M_v = \frac{M_v}{M_D} ; \qquad \left(\frac{M_v M_D}{M_v} = 1\right)$$

$$\frac{M_{hf}}{M_l} = \frac{M_\lambda M_v^2}{M_D^3} \tag{5.35}$$

for $M_v = 1$, $M_\lambda = 1$ and $M_l = M_D$ from Equation (5.35)

$$M_{hf} = \frac{1}{M_D^2} \tag{5.35′}$$

If, on the other hand, we want to obtain the same slope of the hydraulic gradient on the model as in the prototype, we get, for $Re < 10^5$ after substitution into equation (5.34), for M_λ from the Blasius equation $\lambda = 0.3164/Re^{0.25}$ (for $Re_p \neq Re_m$), for $M_\nu = 1$ and for $M_{hf}/M_l = 1$

$$M_v = M_D^{5/7}$$
$$M_\lambda = M_D^{-3/7} \tag{5.36}$$

This means, of course, that the velocity distribution on the model differs from the prototype. For the model operated according to the *Froude law* of similarity ($Fr = idem$) $M_v = M_D^{1/2}$; because the Reynolds number on the model will be $M_d^{3/2}$ times smaller than in the prototype $\lambda_m > \lambda_p$, and thus the slope of the hydraulic gradient on the model will also be bigger than in the prototype ($M_s < 1$). Thus, in this case it is impossible by any method to attain similarity simultaneously in the relative velocity distribution ($M_\lambda = 1$) and in head loss due to friction ($M_{hf} = M_l$). The only way open to fulfil these conditions would be a 'model' with a length scale $M_D = 1$.

5.1.6   Similarity for transition flow

If the prototype pipeline is in the transitional zone ($\frac{1}{6} < \delta'/k > 4$), to a certain extent the same conclusions as in the previous case are valid because the coefficient λ is a function of the Reynolds number and the relative roughness. If the prototype pipe is in the transitional zone, the model must also be in the transitional or smooth zone. But here the value of coefficient λ may at least be already partly influenced by the adjustment of relative roughness (5.23) so that with the preservation of the Froude law of similarity ($Fr = idem$, $Re \neq idem$) the value of the Reynolds number on the model should be such that for a relatively smoother model pipe the same, or nearly the same, value λ as in prototype would be achieved. Hence in this case, at the cost of neglecting the relative roughness similarity, it is possible to achieve similarity both for velocity distribution and friction losses ($M_\lambda = 1$, $M_v = \sqrt{M_D}$ and therefore from Equation (5.34) $M_{hf} = M_l$). The model scale must be chosen in such a way as to fulfil at least approximately the condition from Equation (5.23):

$$\frac{k_p}{r_p} + \frac{18.7}{Re_p\sqrt{\lambda_p}} = \frac{k_m}{r_m} + \frac{18.7}{Re_m\sqrt{\lambda_m}} \tag{5.37}$$

This condition can naturally be fulfilled for one discharge only; for a change in discharge on the same model, i.e. for a change of Re, $\lambda_p \neq \lambda_m$ will again be valid. This will be explained further below. As before, here also the condition $Re_m > Re_{cr}$ is valid.

5.1.7 Similarity for rough turbulent flow

If the prototype pipe is hydraulically rough ($k > 6\delta'$), which is a frequent case since in prototype Re is often large, the coefficient λ is independent of the Reynolds number (5.18) and is only a function of relative roughness.

To attain mechanical similarity in the model, i.e. the same velocity distribution as in prototype ($M_\lambda^x = 1$) and the similarity of friction losses ($M_{hf} = M_l$) with complete geometric similarity, i.e. with the same relative roughness on the model as in prototype ($M_k = M_D = M_l$) we must ensure that the model scale is such that with the preservation of the Froude law of similarity λ on the model is also independent of the Reynolds number. This is only the case if the minimum value of the Reynolds number on the model is greater than (or at the most equal to) Re_{sq} (5.22). For the same liquid on the model as in prototype ($M_\nu = 1$) and for $M_\upsilon = M_D^{1/2}$ (Froude law) the following relation will be valid for the scale of the model:

$$\frac{Re_p}{Re_m} = \frac{M_\upsilon M_D}{M_\nu} = M_D^{3/2} \geqslant \frac{Re_p}{Re_{sq}} \geqslant \frac{Re_p k_m \sqrt{\lambda}}{400 r_m} \geqslant \frac{Re_p k_p \sqrt{\lambda}}{200 D_p} \tag{5.38}$$

(since $r_m/k_m = r_p/k_p = D_p/2k_p$).

Sometimes, however, the condition expressed by Equation (5.38) cannot be fulfilled and then the model gets into the transition zone or even becomes hydraulically smooth. For example in the case of dams one scale model is often used to simulate the spillway, the bottom outlet and the stilling basin, with the outlet represented by a smooth brass or perspex pipe; in such cases the model pipe is 'smooth' even if the prototype pipe is 'rough'. The model is operated according to the Froude law of similarity with regard to the decisive part played by inertia forces. By using a smooth pipe on the model the condition of geometric similarity for the roughness is violated ($M_k \neq M_D$); nevertheless satisfactory results may be obtained by the following procedure.

Let us consider that using the same liquid as in prototype we want to simulate on a model friction losses and flow through a prototype pipe with relative roughness of $k_p/D_p = 0.001$ and $Re_p = 10^7$. From Fig. 5.4 it will be seen that $\lambda = 0.0197$ (alternatively Re_p and λ may be given and we determine k_p/D_p from Fig. 5.4). This case is illustrated in Fig. 5.6 by point 1. If we fulfil Equation (5.38), i.e. for $Re_m \geqslant Re_{sq}$, the model situation is illustrated on Fig. 5.6 by point 2 (or any point between 2 and 1). For the model in the transitional zone for the same relative roughness (0.001) we shall get, e.g. to point 3, (if $Re_m = 2 \times 10^5$) with $\lambda_m = 0.0212 \neq \lambda_p$. If we want to preserve the condition $\lambda_p = \lambda_m$ we must, for $Re = 2 \times 10^5$, choose $k_m/D_m = 0.0007$, i.e. point 4 (Fig. 5.6). If we want to achieve $M_\lambda = 1$ for a smooth pipe, the model scale is determined by the fact that for the modelled discharge calculated according to Froude law, Re_m must be on

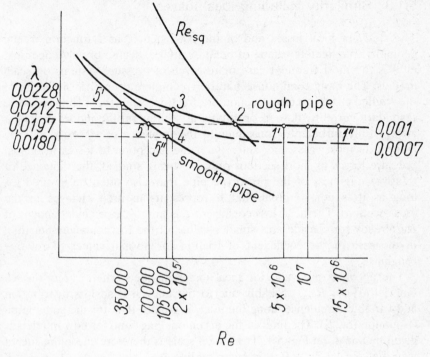

Fig. 5.6.

the point of intersection of the horizontal line for the given prototype relative roughness and the curve of the smooth pipe law (Equation (5.27) — point 5 on Fig. 5.6). For the case under consideration the model scale is given by $Re_m = 70\,000$:

$$\frac{Re_p}{Re_m} = M_v M_D = M_D^{3/2} = \frac{10^7}{7 \times 10^4}$$

hence the model scale is $M_D = 27.5$.

Thus we can satisfy the condition $M_\lambda = 1$ for one discharge only since λ changes with discharge (Reynolds number) on the model but not in prototype. In this case the model scale is usually chosen so that the condition $M_\lambda = 1$ is valid for the mean or maximum discharge; for the other cases we can compute λ_m on the model and when scaling the model results into prototype we apply the appropriate correction numerically. If in the above example Re_p is within the limits 5×10^6–15×10^6 (points 1′ and 1″ on Fig. 5.6), for $M_D = 27.5$ Re_m will be between 35 000 and 105 000 (points 5′ and 5″ on Fig. 5.6) and λ_m will vary within the limits 0.0228 to 0.0180.

5.1.8 Similarity including local losses

The study of local losses and of the coefficient ζ as a function of the geometric parameters (shape of bend or intake, degree of valve opening, etc.) is the most frequent case of research of pressure systems on scale models. The basic condition is naturally complete geometric similarity of the studied change in cross-section or direction. Since these changes cause secondary currents, flow in prototype as well as on the model is almost always fully turbulent. Consequently the influence of viscosity may be ignored in most cases and, since (with the exception of losses in bends) pressure losses in short sections only are being studied, the influence of relative roughness of the prototype pipe may also often be ignored (as long as it is not so great that it represents in itself changes in the cross-section). The head loss coefficient ζ is in most cases independent of Re already for considerably smaller values of the Reynolds number than in the case of the coefficient of friction for normal values of relative roughness.

The above is not valid for local losses at inlets where, according to Gabriel (1964) Re_{sq}, probably due to the uneven head loss distribution and variable turbulence along the inlet, is greater than for the actual pipe (Equation (5.22)). The limit of the automodelling zone for flow in inlets is given by line A on Fig. 5.1. The model scale is therefore chosen in such a way that $Re_m > Re'_{sq}$ (Re'_{sq} is given by line A).

In the case of models of longer pipes with local losses (e.g. a long bottom outlet with inlet, change in direction, valve, change in cross-section at the outlet) both friction losses and local losses must be correctly reproduced on the model. If the model scale can be chosen so as to give the identity $\lambda_p = \lambda_m$ (see Sub-section 5.1.7), with the use of the Froude law, then, for geometric similarity of changes in direction or section, similarity of the entire system is attained. It must be pointed out here that even though it is desirable to have a correct representation of relative roughness (in size, shape and concentration) on the model, small deviations in friction losses for higher values of Re ($Re > 10^6$) cannot substantially influence the validity of results obtained from scale models. For greater changes in the friction coefficient the adjustment of friction losses in extrapolating model results into prototype may be carried out by computation. However, it is still better to reduce the relative roughness on the model (see Sub-section 5.1.7) or to shorten the pipe length on the model so that $h_{fp} = h_{fm}$.

Finally, if only the total head losses in the whole system (including local losses) are to be illustrated and if for operational or economic reasons not all the changes in direction and cross-section are modelled, the effect of local losses may be simulated by a friction loss in an equivalent length of the straight pipe. This procedure is chosen, e.g., for the modelling of losses in the conduit when investigating a whole supply line with a surge tank.

5.2   Unsteady Flow in Pipes

5.2.1   Subject and aims of research and similarity conditions

Changes in the flow in pressure pipes caused, for example, by changes in discharge at a hydroelectric power station or by fast manipulation of gates and valves or a pump shut-down in a supply system, produce waterhammer, i.e. quick changes (increase or decrease) of pressure in the pipeline (pressure waves). These pressure changes, particularly the maximum increase or decrease in pressure at various points of the pipe, have to be taken into account when designing the pipe line and considering anti-waterhammer devices. In simple cases (e.g. single line) waterhammer can be calculated relatively easily from theoretically derived and experimentally verified equations. Computation is more complicated and time-consuming for combined and branching pipes since here it is necessary to take into account the reflection and transmission of the pressure waves. The solution in such cases may be obtained either by a mathematical method or more suitably, by the graphical method of Schnyder–Bergeron. The former method is time-consuming, not very lucid and open to errors in calculation. The latter is somewhat quicker and clearer, but its application in complicated cases requires considerable experience.

In recent years digital computers have been used increasingly when dealing with problems of waterhammer as—when applied in the method of characteristics—they eliminate the main disadvantages of the preceding methods. Solutions thus obtained are quick, allow for investigation of different alternative designs and the results have a predetermined accuracy. The main problems lie in setting up a general algorithm permitting the solution of extensive and complicated pressure systems and in the determination of the pressure wave velocity under presence of dissolved and/or dispersed air in the fluid.

The verification of computation methods and results by direct measurements on constructed pressure conduits, as well as a further, more detailed study of the waterhammer on them often meets with insurmountable difficulties, in particular in the case of large and important hydraulic structures where it is also difficult to interrupt operation even for the short period required for the experiments. Further, many problems involving pressure surges in two-phase flow and flow separation have defied theoretical treatment so far and cannot be experimentally investigated in prototype. Thus scale models are also being used for experimental studies of complicated waterhammer phenomena.

To establish conditions of similarity for models of unsteady flow in pipes we set out from the basic differential equations taking into account elasticity and friction. These are: The dynamic equation

$$\frac{\partial H}{\partial l} + \frac{v}{g}\frac{\partial v}{\partial l} + \frac{1}{g}\frac{\partial v}{\partial t} + S_f = 0 \tag{5.39}$$

or

$$\frac{\partial H}{\partial l} + \frac{1}{g}\left(\frac{v}{a}+1\right)\frac{\partial v}{\partial t} + S_f = 0 \tag{5.39'}$$

and the continuity equation

$$\frac{\partial v}{\partial l} + \frac{g}{a^2}\cdot\frac{\partial H}{\partial t} = 0 \tag{5.40}$$

or

$$\frac{\partial v}{\partial t} + \frac{g}{a}\cdot\frac{\partial H}{\partial t}\left(1+\frac{v}{a}\right) = 0 \tag{5.40'}$$

Apart from the already known quantities these equations also contain the velocity of the pressure wave a given by the relationship:

$$a = \sqrt{\left(\frac{K/\rho}{1+\dfrac{D}{e}\dfrac{K}{E}}\right)} = \frac{a_o}{\sqrt{\left(1+\dfrac{D}{e}\dfrac{K}{E}\right)}} \tag{5.41}$$

where D is the diameter of the pipe, e is the thickness of its wall, E is Young's modulus of elasticity of the pipe material, K is bulk modulus of the liquid and a_o—the velocity of sound (pressure wave) in the liquid (for water at normal temperature $a_o = 1425$ m/s).

By introducing the scales of the various parameters into the above equations and by comparing the individual members (*see* Sub-section 2.4.2) we obtain the following four similarity criteria:

the pipe criterion (Allievi's characteristic)

$$\frac{av}{gH} = idem, \tag{5.42}$$

the criterion of closing (opening) the gate, or alternatively Strouhal's criterion related to a

$$\frac{aT_p}{l} = \frac{at}{l} = idem = \frac{1}{Sh} \tag{5.43}$$

the friction criterion

$$\frac{S_f}{S} = idem,$$ (5.44)

and the general regime criterion, i.e. the Froude number related to velocity of flow v and of the pressure wave a in the pipe

$$\frac{v}{\sqrt{(gH)}} = idem = Fr_v$$ (5.45)

$$\frac{a}{\sqrt{(gH)}} = idem = Fr_a$$

In these relationships T_p is the time of closing (opening) the gate at the end of the pipe, l is the length, S is the slope of the hydraulic gradient and

$$S_f = \frac{v^2}{C^2 R} = \frac{4v^2}{C^2 D}$$

Both regime criteria (Froude numbers) in Equation (5.45) after dividing result in

$$\frac{v}{a} = idem = Ma \qquad \text{(Mach number)}.$$ (5.46)

If we start out from the classical equations for waterhammer, assuming an ideal fluid without friction and without taking into consideration the ratio v/a, it suffices to fulfil only the first two conditions of similarity (5.42) and (5.43) for modelling the waterhammer.

The equation for unsteady flow in a pipe expressed in terms of the relative pressure head change H/H_0, in this case is

$$\frac{H}{H_0} = \phi\left(\frac{av}{gH}, \frac{at}{l}\right) = \phi\left(\frac{av}{gH}, \frac{aT_p}{l}\right)$$ (5.47)

where H_0 is the initial (hydrostatic) pressure head.

For $M_t = 1$ (all characteristic constants of time are the same on the model as in prototype) according to the above criteria of similarity, Equations (5.42) and (5.43), the inequality of scales of all geometric characteristics of the model $M_l \neq M_H \neq M_D \neq M_e$ as well as the equality of the relationships $M_a M_v = M_H$ and $M_a = M_l$ is valid. The distortion of the length scale in relation to pressure will be

$$\beta_H = \frac{M_l}{M_H} = \frac{1}{M_v} < 1$$

The condition $M_a > 1$ means that to preserve similarity the velocity of the pressure wave on the model should be only a fraction of the prototype velocity. Such a reduction may be achieved either by suitably increasing the elasticity (decreasing the thickness) of the pipe walls on the model (a requirement difficult to comply with in practice) or, more easily, by inserting a rubber hose filled with compressed air into the rigid conduit made of metal or some other material. The theoretical and experimental studies have proved that the pressure wave velocity a in the conduit with inserted rubber hose decreases at the same ratio as that of the air volume in the hose to the water volume in the pipe, and further that the velocity of the pressure wave is the same both in the hose and in the pipe. A reduction in the velocity a on the model of the pipe may therefore be brought about over a very wide range.

When modelling the waterhammer according to the complete similarity criteria, Equations (5.42) to (5.45), the lengths l of the model must be β times distorted according to the relation $M_H = M_D = M_l/\beta$ and the conditions $M_a = M_v = M_H^{1/2} > 1$ preserved. Also in this case it is possible to ensure a reduction of the pressure wave velocity a on the model and the regulation of its values within wide limits.

5.2.2 Modelling technique in waterhammer research

Pressure changes in the modelled pressure system caused by the waterhammer are of very high frequency and a sufficiently sensitive pressure gauge without inertia must be used for their measurement. To record pressure changes oscilloscopes with a camera or ultra-violet recorders are normally used.

Simultaneously with the design of the model the method of control of boundary conditions on it must be elaborated. The characteristics of the valve placed at the end of the pipeline and causing the waterhammer must be determined. To permit a change in the time of closure a spring-loaded quick-action valve with adjustable damping is suitable.

Figure 5.7 shows in schematic form a simple model used for waterhammer experiments (Kingdon, 1954). The upper end of the experimental pipe (13) is attached to a pressure reservoir (12) with constant water level into which water may be pumped from the downstream reservoir (17). A spring-loaded quick-action valve (drawn to a larger scale) is fitted to the lower pipeline end; beyond the valve the pipeline is connected with the downstream reservoir or with the delivery pump (18). By manipulation with the various valves it is possible to achieve steady flow in the pipe in either direction; this permits the testing of both positive and negative waterhammer.

The quick-action valve is kept open by a catch (15) that can be quickly released by an electro-magnet. The speed and time of closing the quick-action valve is regulated by means of a hydraulic damper (14). The

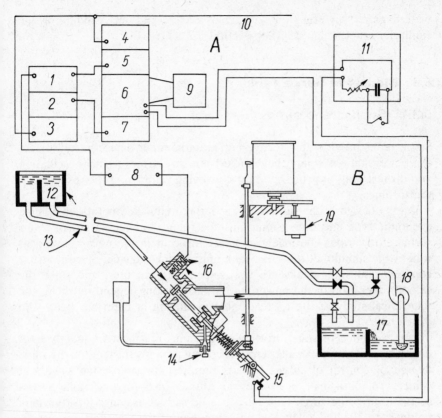

Fig. 5.7. Modelling of waterhammer. [After Kingdon, 1954]

movement of the valve is recorded on paper on a drum driven by a motor (19). By releasing the catch (15) the entire recording device A of the model is put into operation. It consists of the following parts: 1. primary amplifier, 2. chronometer, 3. power supply, 4. high voltage source, 5. amplifier, 6. screen, 7. cathode tube, 8. oscillograph, 9. camera, 10. source of alternating current supply, 11. control panel. The pressure transducer (16) fitted closely to the quick-action valve is part of circuit (A) in which changes in pressure cause changes in oscillation frequency. After amplifying these changes are observed on the screen of the cathode oscillograph, or photographed by camera (9) on paper with a time base.

This model was used for experiments with both a simple pipeline (Fig. 5.7) and a branching line on which one of the branches was closed.

Measurements carried out either with the time of closing $T_p \leqslant 2l/a$ (fast closure) or with a much longer time of closing (slow closure) showed good agreement with the theoretically or graphically determined values of pressure changes. Experiments have thus proved the feasibility of waterhammer investigations on scale models and the validity of the similarity criteria stated in Sub-section 5.2.1.

5.3 Models of Surge Tanks

5.3.1 Subject and aims of research

Surge tanks provide an effective anti-waterhammer device at hydroelectric power stations where they convert pressure surges to mass oscillation and protect long pressure conduits conveying water from the reservoir to the turbines.

During design of the surge tank the structurally and operationally most economic type and dimensions must be found and the surges in water surface for various contingencies likely to occur in the power station as well as the stability of the surge tank must be investigated. Since pressure conduits and surge tanks are very expensive structures, and since the smooth operation of the power station installations depend on them, the theoretical study of the unsteady flow occurring in them has been well developed.

For economic reasons throttled surge tanks are most frequently used nowadays, as a much smaller cross-sectional area is sufficient for the same degree of control of surges than is required for simple tanks without orifices (diaphragms) or nozzles at entry. Also for the same cross-sectional area the surge tank need not be as high (savings in surge tank volume are 30–40%). The hydraulic function of the throttled surge tanks is, however, somewhat more complicated than for a tank without a diaphragm, as, apart from the water surface oscillations, pressures and surge tank stability, the shape, size and functioning of the orifice must also be determined.

The analytical integration of the basic differential equations of unsteady flow in a pressure conduit/surge tank system is possible only in simple cases. For a complicated system it is more difficult and time consuming and, therefore, is replaced by the graphical integration and finite-difference methods. However, even these methods are very laborious for a complicated system consisting of several conduits or surge tanks. These difficulties are overcome with the use of digital and, in particular, analogue computers wherever it is possible to formulate the problem fully mathematically. Where this is not possible it is advantageous and sometimes necessary to resort to scale model studies.

Models enable us not only to check or complement computations but also to study and compare a large number of alternatives with ease. The comparison of water level oscillations in model and prototype surge tanks with the results of theoretical solutions have shown very good agreement if the friction coefficients and head losses at orifices at tank entry assumed in the theoretical and experimental solution correspond to reality. In computation friction losses and losses in the diaphragm are treated as directly proportional to the square of the velocity of flow. This is practically always the case for the friction loss (in fully developed turbulent flow in a pressure conduit). On the other hand for head losses at the orifice this is often so only if the whole discharge passes through it, e.g., if the turbines are suddenly completely closed. When the turbines are opened and part of the discharge flows from the conduit and part from the surge tank, the loss is not proportional to the square of the velocity and the actual water level oscillations in the surge tank may not agree with the computed ones. It is also difficult to express exactly in the computation the complicated changes in the discharge caused by the automatic turbine regulators, in particular during water level oscillations in the surge tank.

The laws of similarity for a simple tank were first formulated by Durand (1921) and later elaborated by a number of researchers (Haindl, 1956).

A scale model of a long pressure conduit with the same scale for frictional losses and length would be difficult and costly to build. Distorted models of surge tanks are therefore widely used.

5.3.2 Similarity criteria for surge tank oscillations

The basic equations of unsteady flow in a pressure conduit and surge tank with diaphragm, are:

the dynamic equation

$$\frac{l}{g} \cdot \frac{\mathrm{d}v}{\mathrm{d}t} + z \pm cv^n \pm c'v'^p = 0 \tag{5.48}$$

and the continuity equation

$$vA = v'A' + Q \tag{5.49}$$

where

$$v' = \frac{\mathrm{d}z}{\mathrm{d}t} \tag{5.50}$$

In these equations l is the length of the conduit, Q the discharge through the power station, A and A' are the cross-sections of the conduit and of the surge tank with diameters D and D' and mean velocities v and v', z is the height of water level in the surge tank relative to the water level in the reservoir, c and c' are coefficients of losses in the conduit and in the tank diaphragm and n and p are the exponents of the velocity terms.

From Equations (5.48) to (5.50) the following conditions of similarity are obtained (5.51) to (5.53) (*see also* Sub-section 2.4.2):

$$\frac{M_l M_v}{M_t} = M_z = M_c M_v^n = M_{c'} M_{v'}^p \tag{5.51}$$

$$M_v M_D^2 = M_{v'} M_{D'}^2 = M_Q \tag{5.52}$$

$$M_{v'} = \frac{M_z}{M_t} \tag{5.53}$$

We have thus six equations with ten variables and are therefore able to express six variables as the function of the other four. It is most advantageous to choose as independent geometric parameters of the model variables M_D, $M_{D'}$, $M_{c'}$, and M_z:

$$\left. \begin{array}{ll} M_l = M_z^{2(1-1/p)} \, M_c^{2/p} \, M_{D'}^{-2} \, M_D^2 & M_Q = M_z^{1/p} \, M_{c'}^{-1/p} \, M_{D'}^2 \\[2mm] M_v = M_z^{1/p} \, M_{c'}^{-1/p} \, M_{D'}^2 \, M_D^{-2} & M_t = M_z^{(1-1/p)} \, M_{c'}^{1/p} \\[2mm] M_{v'} = M_z^{1/p} \, M_{c'}^{-1/p} & M_c = M_z^{(1-n/p)} \, M_{c'}^{n/p} \, M_{D'}^{-2n} \, M_D^{2n} \end{array} \right\} \tag{5.54}$$

The choice of the basic scales of the model is limited on the one hand by constraints imposed by the best use and the most economic construction of the model (accuracy of measurement of the water level changes in the surge tank, suitable time scale, acceptable dimensions of the model of the surge tank, the pipe dimensions available for the model of the pressure conduit, the capacity of the laboratory pumps, etc.), and on the other hand by constraints arising from two conditions:

(1) Head losses in the conduit on the model must not exceed the value corresponding to prototype.
(2) Head losses in the model conduit, similarly as in prototype, are determined by the square law of resistance. The conduit on the model must therefore behave like a hydraulically rough pipe during most of the time that unsteady flow takes place.

In Equation (5.54) n may therefore be considered as (2). This applies also to p ($p = 2$) particularly in the case of a sudden complete closure of the turbine. To illustrate correctly on the model the loss in the junction of the conduit and the surge tank and the loss in the diaphragm at the tank entry, the coefficient of local losses c' should have the same value on the model as in prototype ($M_{c'} = 1$). This means that for all parts of the junction of the conduit with the surge tank that may influence the total head loss in the diaphragm the same scales must be used, i.e. $M_{D_1} = M_{D'} = M$ diaphragm (D_1 is the diameter of the conduit at its junction with the tank; on the model the diameter D_1 usually differs from diameter D of the actual conduit upstream of its junction with the tank). Thus for the entire junction geometric similarity is valid.

After introducing the above mentioned values into Equation (5.54):

$$
\left.\begin{aligned}
M_l &= M_z M_D^{-2} M_D^2 & M_Q &= M_z^{1/2} M_{D'}^2 \\
M_v &= M_z^{1/2} M_D^2 \cdot M_D^{-2} & M_t &= M_z^{1/2} \\
M_{v'} &= M_z^{1/2} & M_c &= M_{D'}^{-4} M_D^4
\end{aligned}\right\}
\tag{5.55}
$$

It is evident from Equation (5.55) that condition

$$
c_m = c_p M_{D'}^4 \cdot M_D^{-4}
\tag{5.56}
$$

must be fulfilled with the aid of a suitable choice of pipe material or by a modification of the model pipe wall roughness. If pipes with very smooth walls (glass, perspex, etc.), i.e. where the coefficient of friction losses depends on Reynolds number, are used for the model conduit the concentration of pressure losses and validity of the square law of resistance may be attained by introducing a valve or orifice into the line. The adjustment of the appropriate roughness throughout the length of the pipe is usually difficult to achieve. It is advisable therefore to fulfil the condition of Equation (5.56) whilst using commercially manufactured pipes of a certain roughness for the model conduit. Then

$$
\frac{1}{2g}\left(1 + \lambda_m \frac{l_m}{D_m}\right) = c_p M_{D'}^4 \cdot M_D^{-4}
\tag{5.56'}
$$

If l_m and D_m are expressed as the function of the prototype parameters, then

$$
\frac{1}{2g}\left(1 + \lambda_m \frac{l_p}{D_p} \cdot \frac{M_{D'}^2}{M_z M_D}\right) = c_p M_D^{-4} M_{D'}^4
\tag{5.56''}
$$

Equations (5.55) and (5.56″) are sufficient for the determination of the geometric and hydraulic characteristics of the model.

By expressing the ratio M_z/M_D from Equation (5.56″) we obtain

$$
\frac{M_z}{M_{D'}} = \frac{\lambda_m l_p}{D_p} \cdot \frac{M_{D'} M_D^{-1}}{\xi_p M_{D'}^4 \cdot M_D^{-4} - 1}
\tag{5.57}
$$

where

$$
\xi_p = 2g c_p = \left(1 + \lambda_p \frac{l_p}{D_p}\right)
\tag{5.58}
$$

As ξ_p must always be bigger than one

$$
0 < \frac{1}{\sqrt[4]{(\xi_p)}} < 1
$$

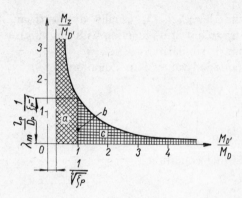

Fig. 5.8.

For the modelled system the values $l_p D_p \xi_p$ are given and the roughness coefficient λ_m of the pipe used for the model conduit is also known. Thus, for further analysis there remains the function

$$\frac{M_z}{M_{D'}} = \phi\left(\frac{M_{D'}}{M_D}\right) \tag{5.59}$$

Analysis shows that the value

$$\xi_p\left(\frac{M_{D'}}{M_D}\right)^4 - 1$$

can neither be smaller than zero nor equal to it, because this would lead to negative values of the scales $M_{D'}$ or M_z, or to zero values of the hydraulic parameters on the model, Q_m, v_m, v'_m and l_m, which is not possible. Therefore the inequality

$$\frac{M_{D'}}{M_D} > \frac{1}{\sqrt[4]{(\xi_p)}} \qquad \text{or} \qquad \frac{M_z}{M_{D'}} > 0$$

is valid, which is practicable. On the graph (Fig. 5.8) of Equation (5.59) three zones, a, b, c, may be distinguished.

Zone a:

$$\frac{1}{\sqrt[4]{(\xi_p)}} < \frac{M_{D'}}{M_D} < 1$$

The scale of the model tank is smaller than the scale of the model conduit. It follows from this that

$$\frac{M_z}{M_{D'}} > \lambda_m \frac{l_p}{D_p} \frac{1}{\xi_p - 1}$$

If surge tanks with overflow or of the differential type are modelled for similarity of the discharges flowing over the overflow, it is necessary to fulfil an additional condition:

$$M_Q = M_z^{5/2}$$

from which $M_z/M_{D'} = 1$

For a given value of the roughness coefficient λ_m of the pipe to be used for the model conduit this condition can only be fulfilled for

$$\lambda_m < \frac{D_p}{l_p}(\xi_p - 1)$$

Then it is possible to model only for one value of the ratio $M_{D'}/M_D$.

Zone b:

$$M_{D'}/M_D = 1$$

The conduit scale is the same as the tank scale. Therefore

$$\frac{M_z}{M_{D'}} = \lambda_m \frac{l_p}{D_p} \frac{1}{\xi_p - 1}$$

In the special case where for a tank with an overflow the condition $M_z/M_{D'} = 1$ must be simultaneously fulfilled, we obtain the following relations from Equation (5.55):

$$
\begin{aligned}
M_Q &= M_z^{5/2} & M_l &= M_z \\
M_v &= M_z^{1/2} & M_t &= M_z^{1/2} \\
M_{v'} &= M_z^{1/2} & M_c &= 1
\end{aligned}
\tag{5.60}
$$

This is really the Froude criterion of similarity, from which

$$\lambda_m = \frac{D_p}{l_p}(\xi_p - 1) = \lambda_p$$

Modelling according to the Froude criterion of similarity is thus a special case of modelling according to Durand. Since the Froude law demands the same value of the roughness coefficient in the conduit both in the model and in the prototype and also contains geometric similarity (a costly and expensive undistorted model) it is only rarely used in the modelling of pressure conduits with surge tanks.

Zone c:

$$M_{D'}/M_D > 1$$

The conduit scale is smaller than the surge tank scale. Therefore

$$\frac{M_z}{M_{D'}} < \lambda_m \frac{l_p}{D_p} \frac{1}{\xi_p - 1}$$

The condition $M_z/M_{D'} = 1$ (tank with overflow) can only be fulfilled when

$$\lambda_m > \frac{D_p}{l_p} (\xi_p - 1)$$

In this case again only one solution exists for the given value of the relation $M_{D'}/M_D$.

The above analysis permits the following main conclusions to be drawn:

(1) Function (5.59) (Fig. 5.8) is valid for the values

$$\frac{M_z}{M_{D'}} > 0 \quad \text{and} \quad \frac{M_{D'}}{M_D} > \frac{1}{\sqrt[4]{(\xi_p)}}$$

(2) For a given value of the friction coefficient λ_m, only one solution exists for $M_{D'}/M_D$ which also fulfils the condition that $M_z/M_{D'} = 1$ (surge tanks with overflow).

(3) Modelling according to the Froude law ($M_{D'}/M_D = M_z/M_D = 1$) is rarely used and only if the friction coefficient of the pipe (conduit) fulfils the condition $\lambda_m = \lambda_p$.

The following practical points should be borne in mind when choosing the model scale:

(a) The whole model of the conduit/surge system should be designed so that it can be used, before investigating unsteady flow, for the determination of the hydraulic characteristics of the junction of the conduit and the surge tank.

(b) The joining of the pipe used for modelling the conduit to the model of the junction of the conduit and surge tank (reduced at the same scale as the surge tank), must be carried out at a small angle (about 4°) to prevent distortions during the water level oscillations. According to experience the value of $M_{D'}/M_D$ should lie within the limits of 0.75 to 1.50, if possible.

(c) The junction of the pressure conduit and surge tank is modelled without distortion (geometric similarity).

(d) When in the calculation of the model scales the value of the friction coefficient λ_m is unknown (pipes of various roughness are available) for the model conduit the function (5.59) may be given a more general form

$$\frac{M_z}{M_{D'}} \frac{1}{\lambda_m} = f\left(\frac{M_{D'}}{M_D}\right)$$

The plot of this relationship may considerably simplify and accelerate the computation of different alternative model dimensions.

(e) For surge tanks with overflow (length of crest b) extending over the whole tank circumference ($\pi D'$) it is necessary for similarity to observe the condition $M_z/M_{D'} = 1$. If, however, $b < \pi D'$ (partial overflow) then the choice of scales is only constrained by

$$\frac{M_z}{M_D} \geqslant \frac{b}{\pi D'}$$

If this is not observed the model exhibits greater overfall heads h than correspond to prototype according to the height scale M_z, i.e. $M_z h_m > h_p$; this, in turn, causes a greater suppression of oscillations of pressures in the conduit and of water levels in the surge tank than corresponds to prototype. It is then necessary to decide whether this increased value of h_m can substantially influence the oscillations and whether the spillway crest in the surge tank has to be altered (lengthened) accordingly.

5.3.3 Stability of surge tanks

When studying surge tanks it is also necessary to take into consideration the function of the automatic turbine regulators. If the turbine discharge increases (decreases) as the result of an increased (decreased) loading, fluctuations of the water level occur in the surge tank. If the regulator preserves a constant turbine output during such a change in flow, it will react to the water level fluctuations in the tank in such a way that the turbine blades open with a drop and close with a rise in the water level, so that for a variable head the discharge always corresponds to a stable output given by the relation

$$N = k'QH = \text{const.} \tag{5.61}$$

Through this function of the regulator the water level fluctuations in the surge tank are increased.

If the oscillations are gradually dampened the surge tank is stable; if not, or if they increase still further, the tank is unstable and the power station cannot operate properly. Thus the stability of the surge tank should also be tested on the model.

For this purpose the function of the automatic turbine regulator must be reproduced on the model. For example, in the hydraulic laboratory of VÚV Prague, Czechoslovakia, (see Fig. 5.9), a specially adapted valve (1) was used; its spindle (2) was pulled by means of a pulley (3) suspended from a lever (4) which was moved by a template (5) fixed to the trolley (6) moving along horizontal rails (7). The trolley carried a graph corresponding to a stable output (8) and was moved in such a way that the water level in the glass tube (9) connected with the surge tank (10) always coincided with the graph of constant power. The water level fluctuations

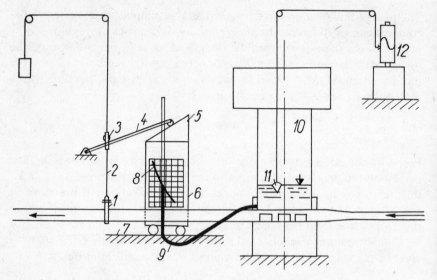

Fig. 5.9. Modelling of surge tank oscillations. [Čábelka and Novák, 1964]

in the tank were registered with the aid of a float (11) and limnigraph (12). The template of the regulator was constructed so that a linear movement of the trolley caused a linear change in flow. For the investigation of the stability of surge tanks it is also possible to illustrate in a similar manner on a model other conditions of automatic turbine regulation as they occur during the operation of hydroelectric power stations.

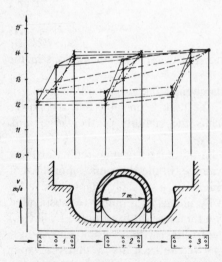

Fig. 5.10. Surge tank inlet. [Wisner and Bratosin, 1960]

The example quoted referred to model tests of an important surge tank and hydroelectric development in Roumania (Wisner and Bratosin, 1960). According to the original design the surge tank was to be linked to the conduit by a short connecting tunnel with diaphragm. Investigations on the model, scale 1:28, proved this solution unsuitable since for a sudden closure of turbines a large vertical water jet occurred in the surge tank accompanied by a great increase in pressure in the conduit. Following laboratory tests the design was substantially altered by extending the conduit through the lower part of the tank so that above its suitably formed bottom there was a semi-cylindrical concrete guide wall (formed by the horse-shoe shaped section of the extended conduit) with three lateral throttling orifices on either side (*see* Figs. 5.9 and 5.10). Figure 5.10 also shows the uniform velocity distribution in the side orifices for a turbine stoppage.

5.4 Models of By-pass Valves and Pressurized Closed Conduit Energy Dissipators

5.4.1 Turbine by-pass valves

In hydroelectric power stations with Francis turbines, conduit pressures caused by a sudden shut-down may be considerably reduced by using synchronized by-pass valves to release water from the spiral casing. Simultaneously with the fast closure of the turbine guide-vanes the regulator opens the valve through which the discharge flows from the conduit directly into the downstream pool without a waterhammer occurring. The valve then closes very slowly so that the pressure in the conduit increases only very slightly.

Water flows from the by-pass valve in a high-velocity concentrated jet whose energy must usually be dissipated immediately downstream of the point of discharge. The conduit of the by-pass valve is usually short but curved so that all conditions for the occurrence of cavitation with all its unfavourable consequences exist (vibration, cavitation corrosion, noise, etc.). Since a hydraulically effective and economical design of the valve and its stilling basin cannot be achieved by computation, model research has to be carried out.

The Froude law of similarity is used. Pressure conduits are modelled at a different scale to achieve similarity of pressure heads at the inlet to the by-pass valve. As far as the valve air-vent design and modelling are concerned the conclusions stated in Sub-section 7.3.2 and 7.4.2 are also valid here.

5.4.2   Closed conduit energy dissipators

The dissipation of the energy of a high-velocity jet can be achieved by using energy dissipators working under pressure. Model investigations of these were carried out, e.g. by Chanishvili (1951), for the Sevan cascade in the USSR. On a model scale 1:20 he investigated the energy dissipation at the outflow from two pressure conduits with a discharge of 70 m³/s flowing under a head of 70 m into a free surface outlet tunnel at the end of which the original design proposed a horizontal stilling basin. Model studies showed that not even a 120 m long and 10 m deep stilling basin fitted with baffles was sufficient in this case, which led to the experimental investigation of another method of energy dissipation in a vertical co-vered shaft, which the pressure conduit with a valve at its end enters centrally and vertically from above. Energy dissipation is achieved by the strongly turbulent supercritical flow from the valve penetrating the mass of water in the vertical shaft, which is hewn out of the rock with a circular cross-section of diameter 9.0 m and depth 15.6 m. The most suitable position for the outlet from the shaft is just below the ceiling, because then no free water surface occurs in the shaft even at reduced discharges and the inflowing stream of water is more effectively slowed down by the water rising from the bottom to the outlet.

An even distribution of the rising flow over the whole shaft area was achieved by a horizontal perforated baffle placed between the valve 'and the outlet of the shaft. A hollow jet or Howell–Bunger valve is more suitable for the pressure pipe than a needle valve with its concentrated outflow.

On the same principle a shaft energy dissipator was designed for a flow of 0.6 m³/s and head 250 m at the hydroelectric power station at Fláje, Czechoslovakia (Kutiš, 1959). During model tests at a scale of 1:5, special attention was paid to pressures acting on the bottom of the shaft (they should be evenly distributed) and on its side (dynamic pressures should not substantially exceed hydrostatic pressure), to the valve air vent and to the de-aeration of the shaft at its outflow. Figure 5.11 shows the model and Fig. 5.12 shows the details and principal dimensions of the shaft energy dissipator.

A horizontal energy dissipator operating under pressure and using a cone dispersion valve with a ring hydraulic jump may also be used (*see* Sub-section 5.4.3). The energy dissipated in this case can be of the order 400 kW for 1 m³ whereas in the original design of the vertical shaft dissipator as proposed by Chanishvili this amounts to only 40 kW for 1 m³; for a free water surface stilling basin the corresponding values are only 10–20 kW for 1 m³ depending on the detailed design.

Fig. 5.11. Pressurized energy dissipator. [Kutiš, 1959]

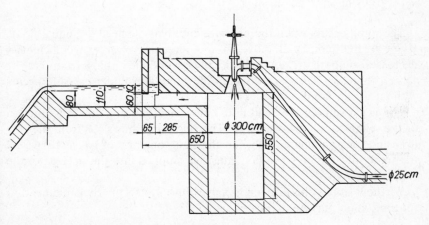

Fig. 5.12. Pressurized energy dissipator. [Kutiš, 1959]

5.4.3 Ring hydraulic jump

The ring hydraulic jump is a form of two-phase flow under pressure where the liquid flows in ring formation along the walls of the pipe with a nucleus filled with a gaseous component. The jump drives gas from the nucleus of the ring flow into the pressure discharge beyond it and in the turbulent vortices both mix perfectly into a homogeneous dispersion.

According to Haindl (1969) the dynamic head, θ, of the ring jump may be expressed from the momentum principle as

$$\theta = \frac{4\alpha_1\phi Q^2}{g\pi^2 D^2 C_c R(D-R)} - \frac{16\alpha_2 Q^2}{g\pi^2 D^4}(1+\beta\varepsilon) - K \tag{5.62}$$

where, apart from symbols evident from Fig. 5.13,

$\beta = \dfrac{Qa}{Q}$ relative discharge of gaseous and liquid components

$\varepsilon = \dfrac{h_b - K}{h_b + h}$

h_b = barometric pressure head

Q_a = gas discharge at a pressure $(h_b - K)\gamma$

h = pressure head downstream of the hydraulic jump

K = negative pressure head in the nucleus of the ring flow

$\phi = \dfrac{v_1}{v_0}$ coefficient of velocity

C_c = coefficient of contraction

$\alpha_{1,2}$ = Boussinesque coefficients.

The jump occurs when the pressure and dynamic head are equal $h = \theta$. If $h < \theta$, the jump will move in the direction of flow (coefficient ϕ decreases) till both are equal. If directly beyond the outflow from the ring space (where $\phi \simeq 1$) $h > \theta$, a direct outflow into flow under pressure occurs without a ring jump.

The negative pressure head in the nucleus of the ring flow is a function of the relative gas (air) discharge. The ring jump draws gas from the ring flow and for attaining equilibrium the same quantity of gas as drawn by the jump into the pressure flow must be supplied into the nucleus of the ring flow.

For flow from cone dispersion valves into a pipe the dynamic head of the ring jump may be expressed as

$$\theta = \frac{16\alpha_1\phi\zeta Q^2}{g\pi^2 D^2 d^2\sqrt{2}\cdot m(2-\zeta m)} - \frac{16\alpha_2 Q^2}{g\pi^2 D^4}(1+\beta\varepsilon) - K \tag{5.63}$$

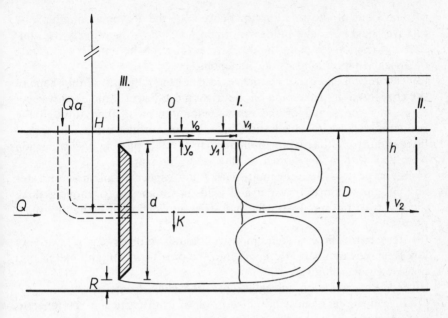

Fig. 5.13. Ring hydraulic jump [After Haindl, 1969]

where $m = x/d$ is the relative opening of the valve and $\zeta = d/d'$ the ratio of the diameters of the body and the sleeve of the valve.

The practical application of the ring jump is extensive. It includes dissipation of excess energy at the outflow from valves, simultaneous dissipation of energy and aeration (or adding gas to the liquid or mixing of dosing chemicals, e.g., at the outlets into reservoirs and water treatment plants) and purely technological processes of mixing liquids and gases (water treatment, chemical and biological engineering, etc.).

5.5 Main Trends in Research of Pressure Systems

The main research areas are:

(1) Basic research aiming at a better understanding of Karman's 'universal constant' κ; study of the velocity distribution, size and properties of boundary layers at rough surfaces; detailed analysis of the transitional zone between 'smooth' and 'rough' surfaces; study of the influence of shape, density and location of roughness elements on velocity distribution and the friction coefficient in pipe flow.

(2) Investigations of the head loss coefficient ξ in the equation for local pressure losses for various cases of changes in cross-section and direction

of pipes and of the relationship between ξ, the Reynolds number and relative roughness; the influence of secondary flow on velocity distribution and friction losses in the downstream part of the pipe. Investigation of losses at pipe branches and junctions.

(3) Theoretical and experimental research of the influence of the shape of the cross-section of the pipe on the friction coefficient. Studies of ways of expressing the shape of the cross-section otherwise than through the hydraulic radius R, which sometimes causes certain anomalies (e.g. a discontinuity in the depth–discharge curve of a pipe in the transition from flow with a free surface to flow under pressure).

(4) Study of two-phase (or multi-phase) flow especially mixtures of water and air, and mixtures of water and solids in suspension (or moving along the invert of the pipe) with the industrial application in hydraulic transport.

(5) Research of flow of some industrial liquids in pipes (e.g. oil), at very low Reynolds numbers. Research into the pipe flow of liquid metals and non-Newtonian fluids.

(6) Study of cavitation and flow separation phenomena.

(7) Investigations of unsteady flow in pipes, with particular reference to waterhammer in a complicated network and to anti-waterhammer devices. Unsteady flow of two-phase systems and non-Newtonian fluids.

(8) Study of the technology and economics of hydraulic transport in pipes.

The results of most of these studies are also directly relevant to design and modelling of pressure systems as they enhance our knowledge of similarity criteria and improve the prediction of prototype behaviour.

References

Agroskin, I. I., Dmitrijev, G. T. and Pikalov, F. I. (1954). *Hydraulics*, (in Russian), Gosenergoizdat, Moscow.

Allen, J. (1947). *Scale Models in Hydraulic Engineering*, Longmans, Green and Co., London.

Bain, A. G. and Bonnington, S. T. (1970). *The Hydraulic Transport of Solids by Pipeline*, Pergamon Press, Oxford.

Batchelor, G. K. (1967). *An Introduction to Fluid Dynamics*, Cambridge University Press, Cambridge.

Bradley, J. N. and Thompson, L. R. (1951). *Friction Factors for Large Conduits Flowing Full*, Engineering monographs No. 7, Bureau of Reclamation, Denver.

Bretting, A. E. (1948). A set of practical hydraulic formulae based on recent experimental research; comparison with older formulae, *Proc. 2nd General Meeting, IAHR, Stockholm*, pp. 399–415.

British Hydromechanics Research Association. (1970, 1972, 1974, 1976, 1978).

Proc. Int. Confs on Hydrotransport 1–5, BHRA Fluid Engineering, Cranfield, UK.

British Hydromechanics Research Association (1973, 1977). *Proceedings of the First and Second International Conferences on Pressure Surges*, BHRA Fluid Engineering, Cranfield, UK.

Čábelka, J. and Novák, P. (1964). *Hydraulic Research 1–Research on Models*, (in Czech), SNTL, Prague.

Chanishvili, A. G. (1951). Pressure energy dissipators at high-head power stations, (in Russian), *Gidrotechnicheskoje strojitelstvo*, No. 4, pp. 24–28.

Colebrook, C. F. (1939). Turbulent flow in pipes with particular reference to the transition region between the smooth and rough pipe laws, *J. ICE*, pp. 133–156.

Colebrook, C. F. and White, C. M. (1937). Experiments with fluid friction in roughened pipes, *Proc. Roy Soc. (London)*, *Series A*, **161,** No. 906, pp. 367–381.

Creasey, J. D. and Sanderson, P. R. (1977). Surge in water and sewage pipelines: WRC TR51, August.

Daily, J. W. and Harleman, D. R. F. (1966). Fluid Dynamics, Addison-Wesley Publ. Co., Reading, Massachusetts

Durand, W. (1921). Application of the law of kinematic similitude to the surge tank problem, *Mech. Engng*, **43.**

Fox, J. A. (1977). *Hydraulic Analysis of Unsteady Flow in Pipe Networks*, Macmillan Press, London.

Gabriel, P. (1964). *Design of Inlets into Power Station Penstocks*, (in Slovak), Buletin VÚV, Bratislava.

Haindl, K. (1956). Mechanical similarity of surge tank models, (in Czech). *Vodní hospodářství*, No. 9, pp. 241–242.

Haindl, K. (1969). Zone lengths of air emulsion in water downstream of the ring jump in pipes, *Proc. 13th Congress IAHR, Kyoto*, **2**, pp. 9–19.

Haindl, K. (1970). Possibilities of fixed dispersion cone valves and needle valves for mechanical energy dissipation, *Symposium on Hydraulic Machinery and Equipment*, IAHR, Stockholm, pp. 643–649.

Idelchik, I. E. (1954). *Hydraulic Friction Losses*, (in Russian), Gosenergoizdat, Moscow.

Jaegger, C. (1977). *Fluid Transients in Hydro-electric Engineering Practice*, Blackie, Glasgow and London.

Jegiazarov, I. V. (1958). Modèles réduits de grands réseaux avec usines hydroélectriques, et influence du coup de bélier, *La houille blanche*, No. 4, pp. 454–458.

Karman, T. von. (1930). Mechanische Ähnlichkeit und Turbulenz, Verhandlungen des 3, *Internat. Kongresses für technische Mechanik, Part I, Stockholm*, pp. 85–93.

Kingdon, D. W. (1954). Model technique for the solution of waterhammer problems, *Water Power*, No. 6, pp. 226–229.

Knapp, R. T., Daily, J. W. and Hammitt, F. G. (1970). *Cavitation*, McGraw-Hill, New York.

Kolář, V. (Editor) (1966). *Hydraulics*, (in Czech), SNTL, Prague.

Kutiš, L. (1959). Pressure energy dissipator at a high head power station, (in Czech), *Konference o hydrotechnickém vyzkumnictví*, VVUH — VUT, Brno.

Marchi, E. (1961). Il moto uniforme delle correnti liquide nei condotte chiusi e aperti, *L'Energia Elettrica*, **38**, No. 4., pp. 289–301.

Martin, C. S. (1973). Status of fluid transients in Western Europe and the UK. *Trans. ASME Journal of Fluid Engineering*, June, pp. 303–318.

Miller, P. S. (1978). *Internal Flow Systems*, BHRA Fluid Engineering, Cranfield, UK.

Moody, L. F. (1944). Friction factors for pipe flow. *Trans. ASME*, **66**, pp. 671–684.

Mostkov, M. A. (1954). *Hydraulics Handbook*, (in Russian), Gos izd. lit. po stroitelstvu i architekture, Moscow.

Nikuradse, J. (1932). *Gesetzmässigkeiten der turbulenten Strömung in glatten Rohren*, Forschungsheft des Ver. dtsch. Ing, No. 356.

Nikuradse, J. (1933). *Strömungsgesetze in rauhen Rohren*, Forschungsheft des Ver. dtsch. Ing., No. 361.

Novak, P. and Nalluri, C. (1978). Sewer design for no sediment deposition. *Proc. ICE Part 2*, **65**, pp. 669–674.

Novak, P. (1977). *Waterhammer and Surge Tanks*, 2nd Edn., International Institute for Hydraulic and Environmental Engineering, Delft.

Pearsall, I. S. (1965). The velocity of waterhammer waves. *Symposium on Surges in Pipelines*, pp. 12–20, IMechE.

Prandtl, L. (1952). *Essentials of Fluid Mechanics*, Blackie, London (translation of *Führer durch die Strömungslehre*, Vieweg and Sohn, Brunswick, 1949).

Prandtl, L. and Tietjens, O. (1931). *Hydro- und Aeromechanik*, Springer-Verlag, Berlin.

Rouse, H. (Editor) (1950). *Engineering Hydraulics*, John Wiley and Sons, New York.

Rouse, H. (1959). *Advanced Mechanics of Fluids*, John Wiley and Sons, New York.

Schlichting, H. (1968). *Boundary Layer Theory*, 6th Edn, McGraw-Hill, New York.

Shevelev, F. A. (1953). *Investigations of Turbulent Flow in Pipes*, (in Russian), Gosizdat po Stroit i Arch. Moscow.

Thijsse, J. TH. (1949). Formulae for the friction head loss along conduit walls under turbulent flow, *Proc. 3rd General Meeting IAHR*, Grenoble.

Valembois, J. (1973). *Manuel d'Hydraulique Général*, Eyrolles, Paris.

Wisner, P. and Bratosin, D. (1960). Study of surge tanks with a diaphragm, (in Roumanian), *Hidrotehnica*, No. 1, pp. 9–12.

Wylie, E. B. and Streeter, V. L. (1978). *Fluid Transients*, McGraw-Hill, New York.

Zandi, I. (1971). *Advances in Solid-Liquid Flow in Pipes and its Application*, Pergamon Press, Oxford.

Zegzhda, A. P. (1957). *Friction Losses in Pipes and Open Channels*, (in Russian), Gosstrojizdat, Moscow.

6 Models of Rivers and Open Channels

6.1 General

Model studies of rivers and open channels deal with all types of flow, i.e. steady uniform, non-uniform and unsteady flow (flood waves) and with all types of sediment movement.

River structures, which form a major part of the subject of river models, may be divided into the following four main groups:

(a) River training structures designed to improve natural conditions by creating favourable geometric and kinematic conditions.

(b) Bank revetment and river training works advantageous to navigation but not contributing towards creating an optimum shape of the channel.

(c) Bridge piers, cofferdams, some types of intakes, etc. that is, structures not creating directly substantial changes in water and/or bed levels, but causing secondary currents and uneven velocity distribution and hence generating local scour or deposition.

(d) River control structures having a major effect on river levels and sediment transport.

In river studies we are interested primarily in the influence of the structure or several types of structures on the river and its flow regime and we are not dealing with the reverse problem, i.e. the influence of the hydraulic regime of the river and the flow on the structure (e.g. investigations of hydrodynamic pressures, discharge coefficients, etc.). The basic aim of research in this case is to solve problems of open channel flow experimentally and to evolve a tool enabling us to forecast the changes occurring in nature during the construction or after the completion of the proposed structures.

If the basic hydrological and hydraulic data are known, two procedures may be chosen: either computation or laboratory experiments. The two may, of course, be combined. The complexity of hydrological and hydraulic phenomena of river flow and of morphology, the transience of flow, problems of turbulence and the relative lack of understanding of the entire mechanism of erosion and sediment transport, all make a mathematical procedure possible only after a number of simplifying assumptions have been introduced; the solution will naturally be only approximate and the results will often require checking and testing by laboratory investigations (and later by field measurements). Indeed, experimental model studies may be the only possible method of solution for some more complicated cases.

The cost of model studies must also be borne in mind, however, as this is often high due to the large dimensions of river models. Since the space covered by river models is considerable and since due to the criteria of similarity the depth scale M_h in particular cannot be increased excessively, different scales are often used for depth and length ($M_h \neq M_l$) or the models are distorted in other respects. This means that in such models basic geometric similarity is often dispensed with and similarity of water levels and, in the case of models with movable bed, similarity of bedload movement is of primary importance. A model where the criterion of geometric similarity has not been fully observed is a distorted model. Apart from a difference in vertical and horizontal scale, there may be a distortion of the longitudinal slope (by tilting the model about its lower end in such a way that the longitudinal slope is greater or smaller than in prototype), or different scales for length, width and height, or a distortion of the sediment size, etc.

After a concise analysis, Section 6.2 presents a set of seven equations for the computation of a river model with movable bed and five equations determining the limiting conditions. Section 6.3 discusses in greater detail some problems connected with roughness and sediment transport in rivers and their models.

6.2 Basic Equations for Open Channel Flow and Similarity of River Models

6.2.1 Similarity of water levels

Let us consider an element of nonuniform flow between the sections A and B (distance Δl) (Fig. 6.1). From Bernoulli's equation

$$z_1 + h_1 + \frac{v_1^2}{2g} = z_2 + h_2 + \frac{v_2^2}{2g} + \frac{\lambda_R \, \Delta l \bar{v}^2}{2g\bar{R}} + \xi \frac{\bar{v}^2}{2g} \tag{6.1}$$

where the expression $\xi(\bar{v}^2/2g)$ includes all the losses between the two sections with the exception of friction losses ($\bar{v} = (v_1 + v_2)/2$). It is assumed that for nonuniform flow the velocity distribution in a certain cross-section is the same as for uniform flow (for the same area of cross-section and same discharge).

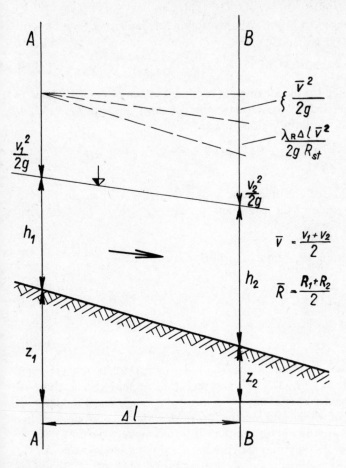

Fig. 6.1.

If we write now for $(z_2 - z_1)$ the change in energy ΔE_z, for $(h_2 - h_1)\Delta E_h$ etc., we obtain

$$\Delta E_z + \Delta E_h + \Delta E_v + \Delta E_f + \Delta E_\xi = 0 \tag{6.2}$$

where ΔE_v refers to the change in kinetic energy, ΔE_f the loss of energy through friction and ΔE_ξ the loss of energy due to the change in cross-section and direction between sections A and B. If Equation (6.2) is regarded as valid for the model and scales are introduced, for example $M_h = h_p/h_m$, the following equation is valid for prototype:

$$M_z \Delta E_z + M_h \Delta E_h + M_v^2 \Delta E_v + M_\lambda M_v^2 M_l M_R^{-1} \Delta E_f$$
$$+ M_\xi M_v^2 \Delta E_\xi = 0 \tag{6.3}$$

(a) From Equations (6.2) and (6.3) we obtain for similarity of *nonuniform flow*

$$M_z = M_h = M_v^2 = M_\lambda M_v^2 M_l M_R^{-1} = M_\xi M_v^2 \tag{6.4}$$

From the equation for the mean cross-sectional velocity $v = Q/A$ where Q is the discharge and A the cross-section of flow, and for $M_A = M_b M_h$ (where M_b is the scale of widths) it follows that

$$M_v = \frac{M_Q}{M_A} = \frac{M_Q}{M_b M_h} \tag{6.5}$$

Further the scale of the hydraulic radius $M_R (R = A/P)$ is generally a function of the scale of the width and depth

$$M_R = \Phi(M_b, M_h) \tag{6.6}$$

After substituting Equation (6.5) into (6.4) we obtain

$$M_z = M_h \tag{6.7}$$
$$M_Q = M_h^{3/2} M_b \tag{6.8}$$
$$M_R = M_l M_\lambda \tag{6.9}$$
$$M_\xi = 1 \tag{6.10}$$

We thus have five Equations (6.6) to (6.10) for eight variables $(M_z, M_h, M_b, M_l, M_Q, M_\lambda, M_R, M_\xi)$ and therefore we may choose three of them. In the most common case of a vertically exaggerated model with identical scales of widths and lengths $(M_b = M_l \neq M_h)$ we may choose only two parameters and finally for the non-distorted model where $M_l = M_b = M_h = M_R$, one scale only may be chosen, usually the model scale M_l.

Equation (6.8) is the previously stated Froude law of similarity, as $M_Q = M_v M_b M_h = M_h^{3/2} M_b$ and thus $M_v = M_h^{1/2}$. This is also the first basic equation in the system of equations for the computation of models of open channels.

$$M_Q = M_h^{3/2} M_b \tag{I}$$

For an undistorted model $M_h = M_b = M_l$, and this results again in the Froude law (in the originally mentioned form) for the discharge scale

$$M_Q = M_l^{5/2} \tag{I'}$$

From Equation (6.10) it is evident that for similarity the aggregate coefficient of losses caused by changes in cross section and direction must be identical on the model and in prototype $(\sum \xi_p = \sum \xi_m)$.

From Equation (6.7) a further important conclusion may be drawn, i.e. that the scale of heights above datum must be identical with the scale of depth. Therefore, the scale of longitudinal slopes is given by the ratio of the scales for height and length and the model thus must not be tilted about its end

$$M_{S_0} = \frac{M_z}{M_l} = \frac{M_h}{M_l} = M_{S_e} \qquad \text{(II)}$$

Considering that M_R in a model of a wide channel with little distortion is roughly equal to M_h, from Equation 6.9 we obtain

$$M_\lambda = \frac{M_R}{M_l} = \frac{M_R M_h}{M_l M_h} = M_{S_e} \frac{M_R}{M_h} \simeq M_{S_e} \qquad \text{(III)}$$

For a non-distorted model we obtain

$$M_S = M_\lambda = 1 \qquad (6.11)$$

(b) For *uniform flow*

$$\Delta E_h = \Delta E_v = \Delta E_\xi = 0 \qquad (6.12)$$

Thus it follows from Equations (6.2) and (6.3) that

$$M_z = M_\lambda M_v^2 M_l M_R^{-1}$$

and after substitution for M_v

$$M_\lambda = \frac{M_z M_h^2 M_b^2 M_R}{M_l M_Q^2} = M_S \frac{M_R M_h^2 M_b^2}{M_Q^2} \qquad (6.13)(\text{III}')$$

Preserving the Froude law of similarity after substituting from Equation (6.8) we obtain from Equation (6.13)

$$M_\lambda = \frac{M_z M_R}{M_l M_h} = M_S \frac{M_R}{M_h} \qquad (\text{III}'')$$

We thus have two Equations (6.6) and (III') for seven variables (M_z, M_h, M_b, M_l, M_Q, M_λ, M_R) and may choose five parameters. For the most common case of $M_b = M_l$ we may choose four scales (for example $M_l = M_b$, M_h, M_λ, M_Q). Observing the Froude law of similarity a further Equation (6.8) has to be included and then only three scales may be chosen, i.e. one more than for nonuniform flow. This means that here, for example, the model may have another longitudinal slope than the one given by the ratio of the height and length scales (Equation (6.13)) and that whilst preserving the similarity of water levels the model may be 'tilted'. Equally, from Equation (6.13) the necessity of choosing the discharge scale M_Q according to the Froude law of similarity does not generally arise, and we may—if it is found necessary during calculation or model proving tests—change it somewhat as compared with the Froude law. This problem will be discussed further in the following paragraphs.

For the undistorted model $M_l = M_h = M_b = M_z = M_R$ and from Equation (6.13) it follows that

$$M_l^5 = M_\lambda M_Q^2$$

after substituting for $M_Q = M_l^{5/2}$ we obtain

$$M_\lambda = 1$$

(*see* Equation (6.11)).

Equation (6.11) thus shows that to attain similarity of water levels for both uniform and nonuniform flow in the case of an undistorted model the coefficient of friction losses on the model and in prototype must be identical, i.e. $\lambda_m = \lambda_p$.

Let us recall here some equations for the mean cross-sectional velocity in open channels:

Chézy's equation

$$v = C\sqrt{(RS)} = C\sqrt{\left(R\frac{h_f}{l}\right)} \qquad (5.24)\,(6.14)$$

Manning's (Gauckler's) equation

$$v = \frac{1}{n} R^{2/3} S^{1/2} \qquad (5.25)\,(6.15)$$

Strickler's equation

$$v = K' R^{2/3} S^{1/2} = \frac{c}{\sqrt[6]{d}} R^{2/3} S^{1/2} \qquad (6.16)$$

and the normal equation for frictional loss

$$h_\lambda = \frac{\lambda_R l v^2}{2gR} = \frac{\lambda l v^2}{8gR} \qquad (5.2)\,(6.17)$$

From Equations 6.14 to 6.17 we obtain the equation expressing the relation between all coefficients:

$$C = \sqrt{\left(\frac{8g}{\lambda}\right)} = \sqrt{\left(\frac{2g}{\lambda_R}\right)} = \frac{R^{1/6}}{n} = K' R^{1/6} = \frac{cR^{1/6}}{d^{1/6}} \qquad (5.28)\,(6.18)$$

and further

$$\left.\begin{array}{l} \lambda = 4\lambda_R \\[2mm] n = \dfrac{1}{K'} = \dfrac{d^{1/6}}{c} \end{array}\right\} \qquad (5.5)\,(6.19)$$

From Equation (6.11) it thus follows that for an undistorted model the relationships between the coefficient of friction on the model and in prototype must be given by

$$
\left.
\begin{aligned}
&C_m = C_p \qquad \lambda_m = \lambda_p \qquad \lambda_{Rm} = \lambda_{Rp} \\[1em]
&\text{but} \\[1em]
&n_m = \frac{n_p}{M_l^{1/6}} \qquad K'_m = K'_p M_l^{1/6}
\end{aligned}
\right\}
\tag{6.20}
$$

The friction coefficient λ may be further expressed with the aid of the Prandtl–Karman equation for fully developed turbulent flow

$$
\frac{1}{\sqrt{\lambda}} = A \log \frac{h}{k} + B' \tag{6.21}
$$

or alternatively

$$
\frac{1}{\sqrt{\lambda}} = A \log \frac{R}{k} + B' \tag{5.32} \tag{6.21'}
$$

where k is the height of the roughness of the bed and sides of a channel or the equivalent roughness magnitude. (For a sediment bed we introduce the equivalent diameter size of the sediment mixture d into Equation (6.21) instead of k.)

Generally it may be said from Equations (6.18) to (6.21) that the scale of the roughness coefficients M_λ will be a function of the scale of depth M_h (or the scale of the hydraulic radius M_R) and the roughness scale M_k (or M_d). This function can be expressed only if we know the corresponding constants

$$
\left.
\begin{aligned}
&M_{\lambda_R} = \Phi(M_h, M_k) \\[1em]
&\text{or} \\[1em]
&M_{\lambda_R} = \Phi(M_R, M_k)
\end{aligned}
\right\}
\tag{IV}
$$

Further equations expressing the limiting conditions must be added to the basic criteria for the similarity of the water levels (Equations (I) to (IV)).

Considering that the Reynolds number on the model for the above derived laws of similarity will be much smaller than in prototype ($Re_p = Re_m M_l M_h^{1/2}$ at the same temperature, and thus also the same viscosity on the model as in prototype), i.e. $M_{Re} \neq 1$, the discharge on the model (and in prototype) must be such that the friction coefficient is independent of the Reynolds number. This is the case when $Re > Re_{sq}$, where Re_{sq} is the Reynolds number characterizing the beginning of the region where resistance is proportional to the square of velocity.

Thus the first limiting condition for the model is

$$
Re_m \geqslant Re_{sq} \tag{a}
$$

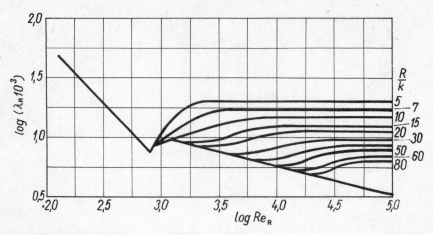

Fig. 6.2. [After Zegzhda, 1938]

For prototype this condition is practically always fulfilled. The value of Re_{sq} may be ascertained roughly either from the relationship between λ_R and Re_R, which has been experimentally established for open channels, e.g. by Zegzhda (by a method similar to that of Nikuradse for pipes) (Fig. 6.2), or by calculation. The exact value of Re_{sq} for a given depth and roughness can be found only by direct measurements in a flume with variable slope, but it is often sufficient when computing model scales to determine Re_{sq} from Zegzhda's (1938) graph or by calculation from Zegzhda's equation, $(Re = vR/\nu)$

$$Re_{sq} = \frac{126R}{k\sqrt{\lambda}} = \frac{63R}{k\sqrt{\lambda_R}} \tag{6.22}$$

(*see* Equation (5.22′) for pipes). Alternatively the fulfilment of this limiting condition can be tested by the use of the criterion that for the quadratic region of resistance the laminar boundary layer δ' must be smaller than about one sixth of the equivalent roughness size. Nikuradse's equation is used to calculate δ'

$$\delta' = \frac{11.6\nu}{\sqrt{(\tau_0/\rho)}} = \frac{11.6\nu}{\sqrt{(gRS)}} = \frac{11.6\nu}{v\sqrt{(\lambda/8)}} \tag{5.12} (6.23)$$

thus

$$k \geqslant 6\frac{11.6\nu}{v\sqrt{(\lambda/8)}} \tag{6.24}$$

for $\nu = 1.31 \times 10^{-6}$ m^2/s and with the use of Equation (6.18)

$$k \geqslant 2.9 \times 10^{-5}\frac{C}{v}\,(m) \tag{6.24′}$$

In Equations (6.22) and (6.24) the equivalent diameter d of the bed load mixture can be used instead of the k values for a movable bed.

The second limiting condition states that the relative roughness k/R should not be so great as to disturb the flow pattern too much. According to experience this limiting value is about $R/k = 5$, even if in exceptional cases good results have been obtained for greater roughness. Thus

$$\frac{R}{k} \geqslant 5 \qquad \qquad \text{(b)}$$

To attain similarity the same flow regime must be preserved on the model as in prototype, i.e. turbulent and not laminar, and further, mostly subcritical and not supercritical. When preserving the derived criteria of similarity and limiting conditions, however, these additional conditions are preserved automatically.

When observing condition (a) the Reynolds number on the model is always greater than the critical number Re_{cr} denoting the transition from laminar to turbulent flow:

$$Re_m \geqslant Re_{kv} > Re_{cr} \qquad \qquad \text{(a')}$$

If, however, the model is designed for a certain discharge Q for which the model $Re_m \geqslant Re_{sq}$ is preserved, during approximate studies on the same model with a discharge smaller than Q ('approximate' because here the limiting condition (a) may not be preserved) the Reynolds number on the model must at least not be smaller than the critical, i.e. in this case at least always $Re'_m > Re_{cr}$. For the transition of subcritical flow into supercritical it holds good that the Froude number is equal to one, i.e. $Fr = v/\sqrt{(gh)} = 1$. But if in prototype there is subcritical flow, then on the model also

$$v < \sqrt{(gh)} \qquad \qquad \text{(6.25)}$$

or

$$S < \frac{gh}{C^2 R} \qquad \qquad \text{(6.26)}$$

Observing the Froude law of similarity, where $M_v = \sqrt{H_h}$, condition (6.25) or (6.26) is automatically complied with. It has only to be checked on a model with uniform flow in which a slight distortion of discharge may be used (*see* Equation (III')). This is why these additional conditions are not included in the general system of criteria of similarity.

Let us return once more to Equations (III), (III') and (III''). All of them include the scale of the hydraulic radius M_R; it is advisable to clarify further the relationship between this scale and the scales of depths and widths (i.e. Equation (6.6); Fig. 6.3).

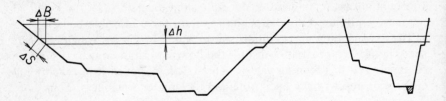

Fig. 6.3.

In a general cross-section $M_A = M_h M_b$. For the wetted perimeter we can write

$$P_p = \sum \Delta P_p = \sum \sqrt{(\Delta B_p^2 + \Delta h_p^2)} = \sum \sqrt{(M_b^2 \Delta B_m^2 + M_h^2 \Delta h_m^2)}$$

further

$$P_m = \sum \Delta P_m = \sum \sqrt{(\Delta B_m^2 + \Delta h_m^2)}$$

Therefore,

$$M_R = \frac{R_p}{R_m} = \frac{A_p/P_p}{A_m/A_m} = \frac{M_b M_h \sum \sqrt{(\Delta B_m^2 + \Delta h_m^2)}}{\sum \sqrt{(M_b^2 \Delta B_m^2 + M_h^2 \Delta h_m^2)}}$$

$$= M_h \frac{\sum \sqrt{(\Delta B_m^2 + \Delta h_m^2)}}{\sum \sqrt{(\Delta B_m^2 + (M_h^2/M_b^2)\Delta h_m^2)}} \tag{6.27}$$

In a distorted model $M_h < M_b$ and thus in Equation (6.27) the numerator is always greater than the denominator. Therefore for a distorted model

$$M_b > M_R > M_h \tag{6.28}$$

(for the undistorted model $M_b = M_h = M_R$). Since the wetted perimeter changes with the depth, it may be seen from Equation (6.27) that M_R is not only a function of M_h and M_b, but also of the depth h, in other words M_R changes with depth and therefore, strictly speaking, similarity is possible only for one depth.

The relationship between M_R, M_b, M_n and depth may also be expressed as follows (Watkins and Brebner, 1954):

$$R = K_R h^c b^{1-c} \tag{6.29}$$

where K_R and c are the constants obtained from a plot of $\log R$ against $\log h$ (for the model as well as the prototype) and b is a certain dimension of width in the considered cross-section (e.g., width of bottom). It then follows that

$$M_R = M_h^{c_m} M_b^{1-c_m} M_{K_R} \left(\frac{h_p}{b_p}\right)^{c_p - c_m} \tag{6.30}$$

If instead of the exponent c an exponent c' is used in Equation (6.29), c' being equal to $1 - c$, then similarly an alternative relation is obtained

$$M_R = M_b^{c'_m} M_h^{1-c'_m} M_{K_R} \left(\frac{b_p}{h_p}\right)^{c'_p - c'_m} \qquad (6.30')$$

or generally

$$M_R = \Phi \left[M_h, \left(\frac{M_b}{M_h}\right), h \right] \qquad (6.30'') \ (V)$$

(extended Equation (6.6)). For $K_{R_m} = K_{R_p}$ and $c_p = c_m$ we obtain from Equation (6.30)

$$M_R = M_b \left(\frac{M_h}{M_b}\right)^c \qquad (6.6) \ (6.30'')$$

for $c = 1$, $M_R = M_h$

From Equation (6.30) it also follows that for models with a distorted vertical scale similarity is possible only for one depth h or for a constant ratio h/b. In wide channels, however, h/b will change only within small limits and approximate similarity may therefore be assumed to be valid; otherwise it is necessary to compute the model scales for a mean depth (and thus the mean value h/b) from the range of depths and take into account the scale effect introduced in the case of other depths.

The considerations have so far assumed constant scales throughout the model, an assumption that is almost always fulfilled. In very special cases a variable scale of depth $\Delta M_h \neq 0$ may be used. Then, with the aid of a similar, though somewhat more complicated mathematical procedure we obtain, after several simplifications, a general equation:

$$\frac{\Delta M_h}{M_{h1}} = \frac{M_z \Delta E_z + M_h \Delta E_h + \dfrac{M_Q^2}{M_b^2 M_{h1}^2} \left[\Delta E_v + \dfrac{M_l}{M_b} \left(\dfrac{M_b}{M_{h1}}\right)^c M_\lambda \Delta E_f + M_\xi \Delta E_\xi \right]}{-M_{h1} h_2 + \dfrac{M_Q^2}{M_b^2 M_{h1}^2} \left[2v_2 + \dfrac{2+c}{2} \left(\dfrac{M_b}{M_{h1}}\right)^c \dfrac{M_l}{M_b} M_\lambda \Delta E_f + M_\xi \Delta E_\xi \right]}$$

$$(6.31)$$

For $\Delta M_h = 0$ we obtain Equation (6.3) from Equation (6.31) (after substituting equation (6.5) and (6.30'')).

The above analysis of conditions of similarity is sufficient for the design and calculation of fixed-bed models under steady flow conditions.

Approximate similarity of water levels and mean velocities can be achieved in the case of distorted models of rivers and open channels with nonuniform flow and experience shows that with sufficient care the results of model research should be more accurate than those obtained by calculation with the use of simplifying assumptions.

If the flow is *unsteady*, additional criteria have to be considered. We can write the two basic differential equations (continuity and St Venant's equations)

$$\frac{\partial A}{\partial t} + \frac{\partial Q}{\partial l} = 0 \tag{6.32}$$

$$S_0 - \frac{\partial h}{\partial l} - \frac{1}{g}\frac{\partial v}{\partial t} - \frac{v}{g}\frac{\partial v}{\partial l} = \frac{v^2 \lambda_R}{2gR} = S_f \tag{6.33}$$

Applying the same principle of analysis as in Sub-section 2.4.2, i.e. rewriting these equations for the model and prototype, we would again obtain Equations (6.7), (6.8) and (6.9) (or conditions (I), (II) and (III)) derived for nonuniform flow and also the condition

$$\frac{M_l}{M_v M_t} = 1 \tag{2.32} \tag{6.34}$$

This is the condition of identity of the Strouhal number for model and prototype (*see* Sub-section 2.4.2). Indeed, for steady flow $\partial A/\partial t = \partial v/\partial t = 0$ and Equation (6.33) leads only to another method of deriving criteria (I) to (III) for steady nonuniform flow. Writing

$$-S_0 + \frac{\partial h}{\partial l} + \frac{v}{g}\frac{\partial v}{\partial l} = S_e \text{ (energy slope)}$$

and

$$\frac{\partial v}{g\,\partial t} = S_a \text{ (acceleration slope)}$$

we could also write Equation (6.33) as

$$S_e + S_a + S_f = 0 \tag{6.35}$$

Conditions (I) to (III) derived for nonuniform flow ($S_a = 0$) and Equation (2.32) again follow directly. It is perhaps useful to note at this stage that we used the notation M_{S_e} for M_h/M_l (or the scale of the ratio $\Delta h/\Delta l$) in Equations (II) and (III) although strictly speaking it applies to

$$\frac{M\,|\Delta(z + h + (v^2/2g)|}{M(\Delta l)}$$

(*see also* Fig. 6.1); however, as condition (I) implies $M_v = M_h^{1/2}$ and, further, for steady nonuniform and unsteady flow $M_z = M_h$, it is possible in these two cases to use the notation M_{S_e} for M_h/M_l.

Strouhal's criterion, together with the Froude law ($M_v = M_h^{1/2}$), establishes the time scale as

$$M_t = \frac{M_l}{M_v} = \frac{M_l}{\sqrt{M_h}} \tag{6.36}$$

As this time scale must be uniform throughout the model for water movement in all directions for the vertical velocity w (e.g. rate of rise of water level) we derive the scale

$$M_w = \frac{M_h}{M_t} = \frac{M_h^{3/2}}{M_l} \tag{6.37}$$

and for the transverse velocity u (here u, v, w denote the velocities in the direction of the axes y, x, z)

$$M_u = \frac{M_b}{M_t} = \frac{M_b M_h^{1/2}}{M_l} \tag{6.38}$$

In simpler cases where we are concerned with unsteady flow in one direction only, e.g. in straight long hydroelectric power or navigation canals, it is possible to accept distorted models where $M_b \neq M_l \neq M_h$ and even models where M_l varies in certain sections. However, if we are concerned with more complicated cases of unsteady flow in the whole x–y plane, with wave interference and with refraction problems, then clearly to satisfy the condition of $M_u = M_v$ only one constant length scale M_l (i.e. $M_b = M_l$) is necessary. Furthermore if we want to model the region of the formation of the wave front, the length of which will be a function of steady flow depth and the Froude number, then it is necessary to use an undistorted model with $M_h = M_b = M_l$.

For the velocity of a surge (c) the following equation is valid for a general cross-section:

$$c = \sqrt{\left(g\left(\frac{A + \Delta A}{\Delta A} y + \frac{A + \Delta A}{A} \bar{y} \right) \right)} \pm v \tag{6.39}$$

where A is the area of flow, v is the mean velocity in front of the wave and y, ΔA and $\bar{y}$ are the height, sectional area of the wave front and the depth of its centre of gravity.

For a rectangular channel we obtain from Equation (6.39) the expression

$$c = \sqrt{\left(gh\left[1 + \frac{3}{2}\frac{y}{h} + \frac{1}{2}\left(\frac{y}{h}\right)^2 \right]\right)} \pm v \tag{6.40}$$

According to Allen (1947) it is possible to use Equation (6.40) for distorted river models and for a general cross-section to substitute the greatest depth of the section for h putting $v = 0$; for a trapezoidal section we may use a substitute depth h_n

$$h_n \simeq \frac{bh + \frac{1}{2}sh^2}{b + sh}$$

(where s is the slope of the sides); and for a triangular section to substitute the mean depth of the section for h.

From the above analysis and Equation (6.40) it may be seen that in agreement with the Froude law the scale of velocity of a surge as well as of long flood waves is $M_v = M_h^{1/2}$.

In comparison with prototype the model may have a considerably greater longitudinal slope and distorted roughness. It is therefore advisable to consider the influence of these circumstances on the movement of surges and steep waves. A certain answer is given to this problem by Keulegan (Rouse, 1950) who states that the velocity distribution in the cross-section has an appreciable influence only if the Froude number of the flow is considerably greater than one (i.e. in supercritical flow). He further states that the influence of roughness and longitudinal slope of the channel is small on the whole, if the values usual in the hydraulics of open channels are not exceeded. As the same flow regime must be used on the model as in prototype, i.e. usually subcritical flow, exceeding the critical longitudinal slope in the model must be avoided, and it can thus be assumed that even a considerable longitudinal slope on the model will not substantially influence the modelled unsteady flow. The same holds good for greater roughness of the channel, though possibly to a smaller extent.

This is why with care, and whilst observing the criteria of similarity for steady nonuniform flow and the Strouhal law, it is also possible to model unsteady flow on models of rivers and open channels successfully.

6.2.2 Similarity of the beginning of sediment motion

When analysing the conditions of similarity of incipient sediment motion some further parameters connected with sediment transport must be added to the variables used so far, in particular their specific mass ρ_s and grain size d. It is also necessary at least to mention the bed form and the position of individual grains on the bed, the shape of the various grains and their size distribution and the intensity of turbulence of the flow.

To arrive at a condition for similarity of the beginning of sediment motion we can use the well known Shields (1936) diagram for the case of incipient motion of uniform grains on a flat bed (Fig. 6.4). The diagram shows the relationship between the 'grain Froude number'

$$Fr_*^2 = \frac{v_*^2}{gd(s_s - 1)}$$

and the shear Reynolds number $Re_* = dv_*/\nu$, where d is the grain diameter, v_* the shear velocity ($v_* = \sqrt{(gSR)} = \sqrt{(\tau_0/p)} = v\sqrt{(\lambda/8)}$; Equation (5.6)) and s_s is the specific gravity of the sediment.

It is evident from Fig. 6.4 that for values $Re_* > 400$ the value Fr_*^2 becomes independent of the Reynolds number and viscosity and that for $Re_* < 3.5$ the influence of the Reynolds number is predominant (with a transition region between these two values of Re_*). A further discussion

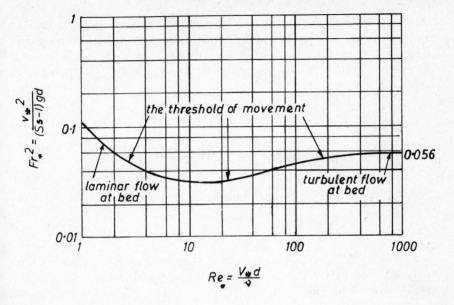

Fig. 6.4. [After Shields, 1936]

of the design implications of the Shields diagram is included in Subsection 6.3.2.

For the region where the condition of incipient motion is expressed by $Fr_*^2 = \text{const.}$ the condition of similarity may be simply derived from equating the value of $\dfrac{SR}{d(s_s - 1)}$ on model and prototype.

$$M_S M_R = M_d M_{(S_s - 1)} \tag{6.41}$$

Noting that $g\rho(s_s - 1) = \gamma_s'$, i.e. the specific weight of sediment under water for the same fluid on model and prototype ($M_\gamma = 1$) and further for $M_R \simeq M_h$ (*see* Equation (V)) Equation (6.41) may be expressed as

$$M_{\gamma_s'} = \frac{M_h M_{S_e}}{M_d} \tag{VI}$$

In Equation (VI), which is another basic equation introducing a new variable $M_{\gamma_s'}$, M_d is not a new unknown, because for the sediment bed the scale of roughness size or of equivalent roughness is replaced by that of the decisive (equivalent, i.e. giving the same energy loss) diameter of the bedload mixture d_s. S_e is used instead of S for reasons shown in further analysis.

Equation (VI) may also be derived from other equations expressing incipient bedload movement, e.g. from the theoretically better founded equation of Kalinske (1947), which equates the instantaneous maximum tangential stress on the bed τ and the resistance of the individual sediment grains τ_d for the beginning of bedload motion:

$$\tau = (Kr + 1)^2 \gamma h S_e \tag{6.42}$$

where

$$K = \frac{u_{max} - \bar{u}}{\sigma}, \qquad r = \frac{\sigma}{\bar{u}}, \qquad \sigma = \sqrt{\left(\frac{\sum (u - \bar{u})^2}{n}\right)}$$

(r is the relative intensity of turbulence, which is a form of the Karman number Ka),

$$\tau_d = \psi p \gamma_s' d \tan \phi \tag{6.43}$$

where ψ is the shape coefficient, p is the share of the surface of the sediment bed exposed to flow, and ϕ the angle of repose of sediment under water. Therefore

$$(Kr + 1)^2 \gamma h S_e = \psi p \gamma_s' d \tan \phi \tag{6.44}$$

From Equation (6.45) for $M_\gamma = 1$ we obtain

$$M_{Kr+1}^2 M_h M_{S_e} = M_\psi M_p M_{\gamma_s'} M_d M_{\tan \phi} \tag{6.45}$$

If a mixture with similar granulometrical curve and grains of the same shape as in prototype is used for the sediment on the model then

$$M_\psi = M_{\tan \phi} = M_p = 1 \tag{6.46}$$

Since experiments have shown that the intensity of turbulence in a prototype river channel and in the model or in a laboratory flume do not differ too greatly, it also holds good that

$$M_{Kr+1} = 1 \tag{6.47}$$

Thus from Equation (6.46) we again obtain the previously derived basic Equation (VI).

A further limiting condition must be fulfilled for the validity of the above equations, i.e. it must be ensured that the forces acting on the sediment grain on the bed in the prototype and on the model are caused mainly by its frontal resistance and the influence of the forces of viscosity and of the tangential stress are negligible. This condition is fulfilled, according to the experimental results and the previously discussed Shields diagram, if

$$Re_* = \frac{d \sqrt{(gSR)}}{\nu} > 3.5 \tag{c}$$

For complete absence of viscous effects $Re_* > 400$, but in modelling of open channel flow it may sometimes be necessary to use the lower limit. The limiting condition (c) is important in particular for the smallest grains in the mixture and the smallest discharge on the model still causing sediment movement.

6.2.3 Similarity of sediment transport

According to the mechanism of transport two modes may be distinguished: bedload transport (by rolling, sliding or saltation) and suspended load transport. Although a clear distinction between the two modes is not possible it is generally accepted that the value $v_*/w \simeq 2$, where w is the particle fall velocity, clearly signifies the beginning of suspended load. According to the origin of the transported material we distinguish bed material transport, i.e. material originating in the river channel which can be suspended or bedload, and wash load, i.e. material originating in overland flow which is transported only in suspension (generally $d < 50 \ \mu$m).

Let us deal now separately with similarity of bedload and suspended sediment transport.

For similarity of the quantity of transported *bedload* the ratio between the transport in prototype and on the model must be constant for all observed discharges. Meyer–Peter's (1948) semi-empirical equation is often used for bedload transport:

$$\gamma \frac{Q_s}{Q} \left(\frac{K_b'}{K'}\right)^{3/2} hS = A_1 \gamma_s' d_p + B_1 \left(\frac{\gamma}{g}\right)^{1/3} g_s'^{2/3} \tag{6.48}$$

In Equation (6.48), which is valid for uniform flow, S is the longitudinal slope of the bed ($= S_0$ and S_e), Q_s refers to the part of the entire discharge Q acting on bedload movement (i.e. the part of the discharge acting on the river bed), K_b' and K_s' are Strickler's coefficients referring to the total roughness of the bed (including its configuration) and the roughness corresponding to the sediment size only, γ_s' is the specific weight of bedload and g_s' its mean specific discharge weighed below water, A_1 and B_1 are constants, d_p is the mean diameter of the bedload mixture where $d_p = \sum d \Delta p/100$ (usually $d_p = d_{50\%}$ to $d_{60\%}$) and h is the depth of water.

Rewriting Equation (6.48) for the model and prototype, introducing the corresponding scales and assuming that ratios Q_s/Q and K_b'/K_s' are the same on the model as in the prototype, we obtain apart from relation (VI) (for $g_s' = 0$) a further equation:

$$M_h M_s = M_{g_s'}^{2/3} \tag{6.49}$$

In Equation (6.49) it is assumed that the constant B_1 in Equation (6.41) is the same for the model and prototype $(M_{B_1} = 1)$. Equation (6.49) may then be rewritten

$$M_{g_s'} = M_h^{3/2} M_{S_e}^{3/2} \qquad \text{(VII)}$$

$M_{g_s'}$ may also be derived from another equation for bedload movement. Let us again choose the theoretically well founded equation of Kalinske for bedload movement:

$$\frac{g_s'}{\bar{u}_D d \gamma_s'} = \frac{2p}{3} \frac{\bar{u}_d}{\bar{u}_D} \qquad (6.50)$$

where $\bar{u}_D$ is the mean point velocity near the bed and $\bar{u}_d$ the mean velocity of the moving bedload grains. The ratio $\bar{u}_d/\bar{u}_D$, which is a function of the ratio of the critical and mean shear stress $\tau_d/\bar{\tau}$ and the relative intensity of turbulence r, must be the same on the model and in prototype for attaining similarity of the bedload discharge, i.e. $M_{\bar{u}_d/\bar{u}_D} = 1$. This condition is fulfilled if both on the model and in prototype the intensity of turbulence $M_r = 1$ (*see also* Sub-section 6.2.2 and Equation (6.47)) and the ratio $\tau_d/\bar{\tau}$ are the same.

As $\bar{\tau} = \gamma S_e R \simeq \gamma S_e h$ (in wide channels) condition

$$M_{\tau_d/\bar{\tau}} = 1 \quad \text{i.e.} \quad \frac{\tau_{d_p}}{\tau_{d_m}} = \frac{\bar{\tau}_p}{\bar{\tau}_m}$$

leads to Equation (6.45) and to the already derived condition (VI). It is, therefore, possible to write for $M_p = 1$ from Equation (6.50)

$$M_{g_s'} = M_{\bar{u}_D} M_d M_{\gamma_s'} \qquad (6.51)$$

Since

$$\bar{u}_D = \text{const.} \sqrt{\frac{\bar{\tau}}{\rho}} = \text{const.} \sqrt{(gS_e R)} \simeq \text{const.} \sqrt{(gS_e h)}$$

it follows that

$$M_{\bar{u}_D} = M_{S_e}^{1/2} M_h^{1/2} \qquad (6.52)$$

If we substitute Equation (6.52) and expression (VI) into Equation (6.51) we obtain

$$M_{g_s'} = M_{S_e}^{1/2} M_h^{1/2} M_{S_e} M_h = M_h^{3/2} M_{S_e}^{3/2}. \qquad \text{(VII)}$$

Again both equations—Meyer-Peter's and Kalinske's—lead to the same equation for the scale of bedload discharge.

Similarly other equations for the law of bedload movement might be used (for example Einstein's) and we could derive an identical result for $M_{g_s'}$ from them, (possibly with a small deviation).

Equation (VII) is stated as a basic condition of similarity, even though it follows from the preceding analysis that for the similarity of increase in bedload transport, fundamentally the condition of similarity of the beginning of bedload movement (Equation (VI)) and the condition of identity of turbulence intensity on the model and in prototype suffice (the left sides of Equations (6.41) and (6.49) are identical), as in some special cases $M_{g_s'}$ may be included in the basic system of variables. Equation (VII) will mostly be used, not, however, as the basis in the system of equations for determining scales on the model but for the conversion of the bedload discharge from the model into prototype and vice versa. The similarity of bedload discharge also requires that not even the smallest grain of the mixture in the model should move in suspension, unless this is the case in prototype. This condition may be expressed by stating that the velocity of fall of the smallest grains in the water w, i.e. the sedimentation velocity or hydraulic granularity, must be greater than the maximum shear velocity on the model:

$$w_{min} > \sqrt{(gSR_{max})} \tag{d}$$

Equation (d) expresses a further limiting condition. The settling velocity w may be expressed from

$$w = W \sqrt{\left(dg\frac{\rho_s - \rho}{\rho}\right)} \tag{6.53}$$

where

$$W = \sqrt{\left(\frac{2}{3} + \frac{36\mu^2}{gd^3\rho(\rho_s - \rho)}\right)} - \sqrt{\left(\frac{36\mu^2}{gd^3\rho(\rho_s - \rho)}\right)}$$

If local scour is to be studied on a model of a river channel with movable bed it must not be forgotten that, in the case of distorted models, the extent of the scour may be enlarged by the fact that its slope cannot exceed the natural stable slope of bed material under water. Since the slope of the scour on the model is M_l/M_z times greater than in prototype, the following further limiting empirical condition is introduced for these models:

$$\frac{M_l}{M_z} \quad \text{and} \quad \frac{M_b}{M_z} < 5 \tag{e}$$

The introduction of sedimentation velocity w and condition (d) enables us, at this stage to discuss some aspects of similarity of the *suspended sediment* transport. Based on the theory of turbulence outlined in Subsection 5.1.2, the logarithmic velocity distribution law, and the basic differential equation for suspended sediment transport under steady flow conditions in a wide channel

$$wC' = \frac{\varepsilon_y}{\rho} \frac{\partial C'}{\partial y} \tag{6.54}$$

where C' is the concentration of sediment and (ε_y/ρ) the momentum transfer coefficient in the vertical direction y, for example the following equation can be derived for the concentration at any height y above the bed if the concentration C_a' at one point at a distance a above the bed is known:

$$\frac{C'}{C_a'} = \left[\frac{h-y}{y} \frac{a}{h-a} \right]^z \tag{6.55}$$

where

$$z = \frac{w}{\kappa \sqrt{(\tau_0/\rho)}}$$

For similarity of the suspended sediment concentration obviously:

$$M_z = 1 \tag{6.56}$$

(This condition is sometimes denoted as the Rouse criterion.) Thus

$$M_w = M_{S_e}^{1/2} M_h^{1/2} \qquad \text{(for } \kappa_p = \kappa_m)$$

Substituting for M_w from Equation (6.53) we obtain for constant W and suspended grain diameter d'

$$M_{d'} M_{\gamma_s'} = M_{S_e} M_h \tag{6.41'}$$

which is identical with condition (VI) for incipient sediment motion. Thus the previously derived conditions of similarity for bedload transport are also broadly sufficient and valid for suspended sediment transport (assuming that W in Equation (6.53) is constant, i.e. d is large enough for $W \simeq \sqrt{(2/3)}$).

It must be pointed out, however, that for similarity of sedimentation velocity with a time scale of sedimentation equal to the time scale of water flow

$$M_t = \frac{M_l}{M_v} = \frac{M_l}{M_h^{1/2}}$$

we would get

$$M_w = \frac{M_h}{M_t} = \frac{M_h^{3/2}}{M_l}$$

(see Equation (6.37)). As $M_{S_e} = M_h/M_l$ (see Equation (II)) the equation $M_w = M_{S_e}^{1/2} M_h^{1/2}$ results in $M_w = M_h/M_l^{1/2}$. Both equations for M_w can be reconciled only for $M_h = M_l$, i.e. an undistorted model.

Some of these points will be further qualified and discussed in Sub-section 6.3.2 and Chapters 9 and 10.

6.2.4 Summary of similarity conditions and determination of model scales

In the preceding analysis the conditions of similarity for attaining correct data from model research on rivers and open channels have been determined. These apply to observations of water levels in uniform, nonuniform and unsteady flow, sediment transport and incipient bedload motion, and thus also to observations of the morphological changes in the channel. Ten variables have been used:

M_l, M_b, M_z – scales of length, width and height (above datum); $(M_z/M_l = M_{S_0}$ is the scale of the longitudinal slope of the model bed);
M_R, M_h, M_Q – scales of hydraulic radius, depth and water discharge;
$M_\lambda, M_k(M_d)$ – friction coefficients and scale of decisive roughness size (or decisive diameter of bedload mixture);
$M_{\gamma_s'}, M_{g_s'}$ – scales of specific weight of bedload and specific discharge of bedload (both in weight when submerged).

For these ten variables seven equations have been derived:

$$M_Q = M_h^{3/2} M_b \tag{I}$$

$$M_{S_0} = \frac{M_z}{M_l} = \frac{M_h}{M_l} = M_{S_e} \tag{II}$$

$$M_\lambda = \frac{M_R}{M_l} = M_{S_e} \frac{M_R}{M_h} (\approx M_{S_e}) \tag{III}$$

$$M_\lambda = \Phi(M_h, M_k) \tag{IV}$$

$$M_R = \Phi\left[M_h, \left(\frac{M_h}{M_b}\right), h \right] \tag{V}$$

$$M_{\gamma_s'} = \frac{M_h M_{S_e}}{M_d} \tag{VI}$$

$$M_{g_s'} = M_h^{3/2} M_{S_e}^{3/2} \tag{VII}$$

In Equation (IV) M_R may be used instead of M_h and M_d instead of M_k, e.g., in Equation (6.18) or (6.21) (with the corresponding coefficients). More simply, Zegzhda's graph may be used (Fig. 6.2).

Equation (V) must be derived separately for every case considered, using graphical analysis or by computation. For shallow or wide channels $M_R = M_h$ approximately, which reduces the number of variables and the number of equations by one.

Equations (I) to (V) are valid for the similarity of water levels in models with nonuniform or (together with the Strouhal law) unsteady flow and are sufficient for the solution of river models with fixed bed. For uniform flow Equation (II) is unnecessary and Equation (III), whilst preserving condition (I), is altered to

$$M_\lambda = \frac{M_z M_R}{M_l M_h} = M_S \frac{M_R}{M_h} \tag{III''}$$

and when Equation (I) (the Froude law) is ignored, to

$$M_\lambda = \frac{M_R M_z M_h^2 M_b^2}{M_l M_Q^2} = M_S \frac{M_R M_h^2 M_b^2}{M_Q^2} \tag{III'}$$

Equations (VI) and (VIII) must be added for models with movable bed. Equation (I) cannot be ignored for nonuniform flow or for a model of a river with structures. It may be neglected, however, for models on which only river training problems are to be solved. Thus there are seven equations for ten unknowns; from this follow three degrees of freedom for nonuniform flow. For uniform flow there are only six equations and therefore four unknowns may be chosen. Ignoring the Froude law (Equation (I)) we have five equations and can choose five unknowns. This case, however, is exceptional and its application requires considerable experience and skill.

When using Equations (I) to (VII) the following limiting conditions on the model should also be fulfilled:

$$Re_m \geqslant Re_{sq} \tag{a}$$

$$\frac{R}{k} \geqslant 5 \tag{b}$$

$$Re_* = \frac{d\sqrt{(gSR)}}{v} \geqslant 3.5 \text{ (or preferably } Re_* > 400; \text{ see previous}$$
$$\text{discussion)}$$
$$\tag{c}$$

$$w_{min} \geqslant \sqrt{(gSR_{max})} \tag{d}$$

$$\frac{M_l}{M_z} \text{ and } \frac{M_b}{M_z} \leqslant 5 \tag{e}$$

Conditions (a) and (b) refer to the similarity of the water levels, conditions (c) and (d) to the similarity of bedload transport and the beginning of its movement, and condition (e) to models with a movable bed where the extent of local scour is under observation. These limiting conditions may be exceeded in special cases, but the experimental procedure and especially the interpretation of results in the case of such models require particular care and experience.

Re_{sq} in equation (a) can be determined either from the graph on Fig. 6.2 (or even from Moody's diagram, *see* Chapter 5) or from Equation (6.22). Alternatively the fulfilment of the limiting condition (a) is ascertained by comparing the magnitude of the decisive roughness, k, (alternatively d), and the thickness of the laminar boundary layer, δ', according to Equation (6.24). w_{min} in Equation (d) is found from Equation (6.53).

Equation (6.10) also shows that the coefficient of energy losses ξ at a change of channel cross-section or direction must be the same in prototype and on the model. Since in distorted models ($M_b < M_l$ or $M_h < M_l$) the coefficient of energy loss for a change in cross-section is usually greater on the model than in prototype, this difference must be compensated for by a reduction in the losses due to change of direction or due to the roughness of the channel.

Finally it is necessary to point out again that in the derivation of the above system of equations the following assumptions have been made:

(a) the influence of the roughness of channel walls has not been taken into account;
(b) relative intensity of turbulence is the same on the model and in prototype: $M_r = 1$, Equation (6.47);
(c) the shapes of the grain distribution curve for sediment in prototype and on the model are identical;
(d) the shapes of the sediment grains on the model and in prototype are identical.

It is now possible to determine all the basic scales for model studies. The scales of model dimension M_l, M_b, M_z of the hydraulic radius, depth and discharge M_R, M_h, M_Q, of the friction coefficient, and the bed roughness size (decisive sediment diameters) $M_\lambda M_k (M_d)$, of the specific weight and of the specific discharge of bed load $M_{\gamma_s'}$, $M_{g_s'}$ are obtained by solving Equations (I) to (VII) and choosing three scales. From these ten scales the others are then determined as follows:

scale of cross-sectional areas

$$M_A = M_h M_b$$

scale of volumes

$$M_V = M_h M_b M_l$$

scale of velocities

$$M_v = M_Q / M_A = \frac{M_h^{3/2} M_b}{M_b M_h} = \sqrt{M_h}$$

scale of the Reynolds numbers

$$M_{Re} = \frac{M_v M_h}{M_v} = M_h^{3/2}$$

for $M_v = 1$ (for the same temperature of water on the model as in prototype);
scale of the Froude numbers

$$M_{Fr} = \frac{M_v}{\sqrt{(M_g M_h)}} = 1$$

scale of longitudinal bed slope

$$M_{S_0} = \frac{M_z}{M_l}$$

scale of longitudinal slope of energy line

$$M_{S_e} = \frac{M_h}{M_l}$$

scale of total discharge of bedload in weight under water

$$M_{G_s'} = M_{g_s'} M_b$$

scale of time for water flow

$$M_t = \frac{M_l}{M_v} = \frac{M_l}{M_h^{1/2}} \tag{6.36}$$

The scale of time for bedload movement is determined in such a way that the corresponding bed load volumes are transported in prototype and on the model in corresponding time intervals.

The scale of total bed load discharge in volume (for unit of time):

$$M_{Q_s} = \frac{M_{G_s'}}{M_{\gamma_{vol}'}} = \frac{M_{g_s'} M_b}{M_{\gamma_{vol}'}}$$

where $M_{\gamma'}$ is the scale of the sediment weight per unit bulk volume when submerged: this is defined as the ratio of the buoyant weight of a sediment column in water to the volume of this column. The scale of time for bedload movement is, therefore

$$M_{t_s} = \frac{M_V}{M_{Q_s}} = \frac{M_h M_b M_l M_{\gamma_{vol}'}}{M_{g_s'} M_b} = \frac{M_h M_l M_{\gamma_{vol}'}}{M_{g_s'}} \tag{6.57}$$

After substitution for $M_{g_s'}$ from Equation (VII) we obtain

$$M_{t_s} = \frac{M_h M_l M_{\gamma_{vol}'}}{M_h^{3/2} M_{S_e}^{3/2}} = \frac{M_l M_{\gamma_{vol}'}}{M_h^{1/2} M_{S_e}^{3/2}} \tag{6.57'}$$

Finally, substituting for $M_{S_e} = M_h/M_l$ (Equation (II)) we get

$$M_{t_s} = \frac{M_l^{5/2} M_{\gamma'_{col}}}{M_h^2} \tag{6.57''}$$

It is interesting to note the implications of Equations (6.36) and (6.57) for the scale of time of water and bedload movement.

(a) For $M_{\gamma'_{col}} = M_{\gamma_s'}$

$$M_{t_s} = \frac{M_l^{5/2}}{M_h^2} M_{\gamma_s'} = \frac{M_l^{5/2}}{M_h^2} \frac{M_h M_S}{M_d} = \frac{M_l^{3/2}}{M_d}$$

and

$$\frac{M_{t_s}}{M_t} = \frac{M_l^{3/2} M_h^{1/2}}{M_d M_l} = \frac{M_l^{1/2} M_h^{1/2}}{M_d}$$

(b) For $M_t = M_{t_s}$,

$$M_{\gamma'_{col}} = \frac{M_h^2}{M_l^{5/2}} \frac{M_l}{M_h^{1/2}} = M_S^{3/2} \ (<1 \text{ for } M_h < M_l)$$

(c) For $M_t = M_{t_s}$ and $M_{\gamma'_{col}} = M_{\gamma_s'}$

$$M_S^{3/2} = \frac{M_h M_S}{M_d}$$

Thus

$$M_d = M_h^{1/2} M_l^{1/2} \ (>M_h \text{ for } M_h < M_l)$$

(d) For $M_d = M_{\gamma_s'} = M_{\gamma'_{col}} = 1; M_l = M_b$

$$M_h^2 = M_l; \qquad M_t = M_h^{3/2}; \qquad M_{t_s} = M_l^{3/2} = M_h^3 = M_t^2$$

$$\frac{M_{t_s}}{M_t} = M_h^{3/2}$$

Substituting from Equation (I) for $M_h^{3/2} M_l = M_Q$ we get:

$$M_h = M_Q^{0.286} \tag{6.58a}$$

$$M_b = (M_l) = M_Q^{0.572} \tag{6.58b}$$

$$M_s = \frac{M_h}{M_l} = M_Q^{-0.286} \tag{6.58c}$$

Even though approximate mechanical similarity only is applied on models of rivers and open channels, as is generally the case in hydraulic research, and even though, in the case of distorted models, due to their size, geometric similarity also must often be neglected, amazingly good and accurate results may be obtained if the conditions of similarity are preserved and the correct procedure is applied.

Some authors (e.g. Altunin and Orlov (1949) and Velikanov (1946)) have even developed a theory on the necessity of distorted models of rivers, regarded as a natural flow of small dimensions, which must have the same relationship between width and depth as a natural stream. Thus Altunin used the relationship between width b and depth h of a prototype channel:

$$b^m = Kh$$

where m changes from 1.0 for mountain currents to 0.5 for lowland rivers and K is a constant of 8 to 12. When preserving the same equation for the model and for the identical value of K we obtain

$$M_b = M_h^{1/m}$$

This means that for upland streams we would obtain an undistorted model ($m = 1$) and for the lowland rivers we would get a large model distortion $M_b = M_h^2$. For the average scales of depths used, ranging from 20 to 100, this results in such a distortion (narrowing) of the model, that it cannot normally be used.

6.3 Further Considerations of Friction Losses and Sediment Transport

6.3.1 Friction coefficients in open channel flow

In this Sub-section the analysis presented in Chapters 5 and 6 is supplemented by some further remarks insofar as they are necessary as a guideline to the problems of roughness and head losses in, and to the modelling of open channels.

Let us return to Equations (5.43) and (5.44) for the roughness coefficient, derived with the use of Karman's universal constant $\kappa = 0.4$ for a discharge between two parallel plates at a distance a (infinitely wide cross-section). If height h is introduced instead of $a/2$ in an open wide channel then we obtain equation

$$\frac{1}{\sqrt{\lambda}} = 2.03 \log \left(\frac{hv}{\nu} \sqrt{\lambda} \right) - 0.47 \tag{6.59}$$

for a smooth channel and

$$\frac{1}{\sqrt{\lambda}} = 2.03 \log \frac{h}{k} + 2.11 \tag{6.60}$$

for a rough channel. As in a pipe (Equation (5.19′)) the relative velocity

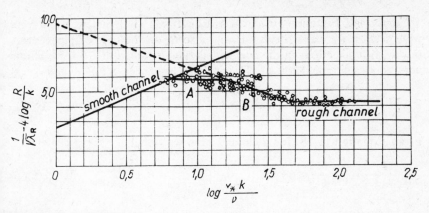

Fig. 6.5.

distribution for both cases can similarly be expressed by a single equation:

$$\frac{\bar{u}-v}{v\sqrt{\lambda}}=2\log\frac{y}{h}+0.88 \tag{6.61}$$

From experiments in straight rectangular flumes of varying roughness, formed by sand glued on the walls, Zegzhda (1938) derived equations expressing the relationship between $(1/\sqrt{\lambda_R}-4\log R/k)$ and $\log(v_*k/\nu)$ where $v_*=\sqrt{(\tau_0/\rho)}=v\sqrt{(\lambda/8)}=v\sqrt{(\lambda_R/2)}$ (*see* Equation (5.6) and Fig. 6.5):

for a smooth channel $(Re=vR/\nu)$

$$\frac{1}{\sqrt{\lambda_R}}=4\log Re\sqrt{\lambda_R}+2 \tag{6.62}$$

for the transitional region A,

$$\frac{1}{\sqrt{\lambda_R}}=4\log\frac{R}{k}+5.75 \tag{6.63}$$

for the transitional region B,

$$\frac{1}{\sqrt{\lambda_R}}=4\log\frac{R}{k}+9.65-4\log\left(\frac{v_*k}{\nu}\right)^{0.81} \tag{6.64}$$

for a rough channel and $Re>Re_{sq}$ where $Re_{sq}=63R/k\sqrt{\lambda_R}$ (*see* Equation (6.22)): i.e. for $v_*k/\nu>45$

$$\frac{1}{\sqrt{\lambda_R}}=4\log\frac{R}{k}+4.25 \tag{6.65}$$

(Keulegan (1938) analysing Bazin's data derived a similar expression with 4.4 as the additive constant.)

Comparing Equation (6.65) with Equation (6.60), where for a very wide section we can write $h \simeq R$ and also (as in the case of pipes) carry out minor corrections in the coefficients (i.e. 2 instead of 2.03) we obtain very good agreement for $\lambda = 4\lambda_R$ as from Equation (6.60)

$$\frac{1}{\sqrt{\lambda_R}} = 4 \log \frac{R}{k} + 4.22 \tag{6.60'}$$

From Equation (5.18) for a circular pipe we obtain

$$\frac{1}{\sqrt{\lambda_R}} = 4 \log \frac{R}{k} + 4.68 \tag{6.66}$$

The similarity of these equations must not be interpreted as dynamical similarity of flow in a circular pipe and rectangular channel, as follows from the comments in Sub-section 5.1.4 on the influence of the shape of the pipe cross-section on the friction coefficient. In a rectangular channel, just as in a non-circular pipe, there are secondary currents contributing to the increase in the friction coefficient—λ_R from Equation (6.65) or (6.60') is also greater than λ_R from Equation (6.66).

Experiments carried out by Komora (1957) and others, show also that in a flume with bed material of grains of the same size but different shape, e.g. coal and sand, we obtain results which give varying values of B' in the Prandtl–Karman Equation (6.21), of which Zegzhda's equation is an application. These experiments also confirmed Yassin's (1953) experiments on the influence of the flume width on the value of the additive 'constant', B', which may be regarded as a true constant for a given material only when the ratio of width to depth is $b/h \geqslant 10$. Further experiments show that even for a given size and shape of roughness its concentration also influences the value of B' (and even of the 'constant' A which embodies the 'universal constant' κ).

Measurements carried out by Martinec (1958) on Czech rivers of various types confirmed the unsuitability of mean velocity equations with a constant exponent of the hydraulic radius (e.g., Chezy, Bazin, Kutter, Manning, Strickler) for more accurate computations. This shortcoming is eliminated by the equation of Pavlovskij or Agroskin, which is a modification of the Prandtl–Karman equation; Martinec expressed the constant k' in Agroskin's Equation (5.27) as $(0.77 - \log d)$ which resulted in

$$v = 17.72 \left(\log \frac{R}{d} + 0.77 \right) \sqrt{(RS)} \tag{6.67}$$

or with simplified constants in

$$v = \left(18 \log \frac{R}{d} + 13 \right) \sqrt{(RS)} \tag{6.67'}$$

Martinec's measurements were carried out on rivers with a range $R = 0.15$ to 2.25 m, $S = 0.00004$ to 0.0039 and $d = 0.004$ to 0.25 m. If we introduce the expression $C = \sqrt{(2g/\lambda_R)}$ and for $17.72 = 4\sqrt{(2g)}$, from Equation (6.67) we obtain

$$\frac{1}{\sqrt{\lambda_R}} = 4 \log \frac{R}{d} + 3.08 \tag{6.68}$$

which, again, is an equation of type (6.21) or (6.65) with adjusted constant B'. The difference between (6.65), resulting from laboratory experiments, and (6.68), derived from prototype measurements, is no doubt primarily due to additional losses through minor changes of direction and cross-section, which are always present even in a very carefully selected natural river reach.

The Manning (Strickler) and Prandtl–Karman (Zegzhda) equations may be compared by expressing the term $1/\sqrt{\lambda_R}$ from both. Thus we can write for pipe flow:

$$\frac{1}{\sqrt{\lambda_R}} = \frac{1}{\sqrt{(2g)}} \frac{R^{1/6}}{n} = 4 \log \frac{R}{k} + 4.68 \tag{6.69}$$

and for open channel flow:

$$\frac{1}{\sqrt{(2g)}} \frac{R^{1/6}}{n} = 4 \log \frac{R}{k} + 4.25 \tag{6.69'}$$

If both types of equations were valid, the plot $\log R/k$ and $\log R^{1/6}/n$ would have to give a straight line with a slope of $6:1$.

In Fig. 6.6 the solid line illustrates Equation (6.69) and the dashed line (6.69'). The deviation of the slope of the curves from the straight line $6:1$ is an indication of the error introduced by the inaccuracy of Manning's equation. It is evident from Fig. 6.5. that the Manning (Strickler) equation is most reliable for the values of relative roughness giving a Chezy coefficient $C = R^{1/6}/n \simeq 50$. For considerably higher and lower values of C as frequently occur in practice with distorted models the deviations are considerable. For example, for a value of $n = 0.030$ and for $R^{1/6}/n = 70$, from Equation (6.69) we obtain $k = 141$ mm whereas for the same value of n but for $R^{1/6}/n = 20$, $k = 51$ mm. It follows from Equation (6.18) that in the above case an identical n in both cases means an identical d (64 mm) according to the Strickler equation. This is why the Manning or Strickler equations are unsuitable for the computation of river models, or rather they may be used only for an approximate calculation or for mean values of the coefficient C in the region of $50\,(\mathrm{m}^{1/2}/\mathrm{s})$.

Strickler (1923) put the coefficient $K' = 21.1/d^{1/6}$ in his equation (*see* Equation (6.16)), where d is the mean grain size of sediments in metres (i.e. c in Equations (6.16) and (6.18) is 21.1). With the use of the

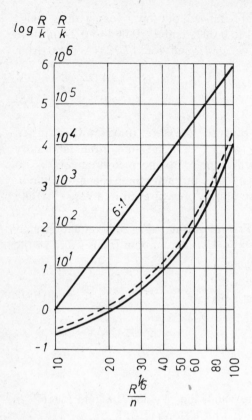

Fig. 6.6. [After Rouse (Ed.), 1950]

Strickler equation for the calculation of the roughness coefficient the question of what should be used as the decisive grain diameter d in the case of a sediment mixture arises. Strickler assumed $d = d_{50}$. Müller (1943), basing his conclusions on experience from Switzerland, showed that if the Strickler equation is changed to contain d_{90} the constant changes from 21.1 to 26. The advantage of this concept lies in the fact that, according to Müller, the average grain diameter of the covering layer of the sediment bed of rivers corresponds approximately to d_{90} of the total bed sample (armouring) so that d_{90} may be expected to characterize the decisive roughness k. In this case Strickler's modified equation is

$$v = K'R^{2/3}S^{1/2} = 26 \left(\frac{R}{d_{90}}\right)^{1/6} \sqrt{(RS)}$$

$$= 5.86\sqrt{(2g)} \left(\frac{R}{d_{90}}\right)^{1/6} \sqrt{RS} \tag{6.16'}$$

Müller's deductions were tested by an analysis of the gravel banks on Czech rivers carried out by Malíšek (1956) who reached the conclusion that d_{50} of the covering layer corresponds to d_{90} of the lower sediment layers (obtained after removing the covering layer) and not of the whole sample, and that this was only valid for mountain streams with sediments of a grain diameter above 100 mm. Malíšek found that d_{50} of the covering layer varied from d_{55} to d_{75} of the whole sample, and from d_{60} to d_{95} of the lower layers, as d_{50} of the covering layer varied from 10 to 180 mm.

To exclude the influence of the walls during experiments in comparatively narrow flumes it is necessary to assess the distribution of resistance and tangential stress between the bed and the walls of the flume, in particular if they have different roughness. According to experiments the simple method proposed by Einstein (1952) is sufficiently accurate. Einstein introduced the assumption that it was possible to divide the cross-section into components corresponding to parts of the wetted perimeter in such a way that the head losses in the various components of the cross-section corresponded to the actual distribution of these losses between the separate parts of the wetted flume perimeter. He introduced the assumption that the mean cross-sectional velocity was the same in all component parts of the section. If the parameters corresponding to the flume bed, the walls and the total section are marked by indices b, w and t respectively, then from the basic equation $\lambda_R = 2gRS/v^2$ and according to Einstein's assumptions

$$\frac{R_b}{\lambda_b} = \frac{R_w}{\lambda_w} = \frac{R_t}{\lambda_t} \quad \text{and} \quad A_t = A_b + A_w \qquad (6.70\text{a,b})$$

From these equations we obtain, for a rectangular channel,

$$\lambda_b = \lambda_t + \frac{2h}{b}(\lambda_t - \lambda_w) \qquad (6.71)$$

$$R_b = h\left(1 - \frac{2h}{2h+b}\frac{\lambda_w}{\lambda_t}\right) \qquad (6.72)$$

The value λ_w may be ascertained by measuring the resistance coefficient in the flume without a rough (sediment) bed, i.e. with the roughness of the bed practically the same as that of the walls. The mean value of tangential stress τ acting on the bed or the walls is then determined from $\tau = (\lambda/2)\rho v^2$.

Pantelopulos (1961) proposed another simple method for determining the distribution of tangential stress along the circumference of a flume from the velocity distribution along the wetted perimeter. The method is based on the equation $\tau = C\bar{u}^2$, which is valid for a hydraulically rough flow regime where C is a constant as long as $\bar{u}$ is measured at a constant distance from the surface. By measuring the velocity distribution in a flume with equally smooth bed and walls the constant C_w is found from equation

$$\bar{\tau}(b+2h) = C_w(b\bar{\bar{u}}_b^2 + 2h\bar{\bar{u}}_w^2) \tag{6.73}$$

For a rough bed in the same flume

$$\tau_t(b+2h) = C_b b\bar{\bar{u}}_b^2 + 2C_w h\bar{\bar{u}}_w^2 \tag{6.74}$$

After substituting for C_w from Equation (6.73) it is then possible to calculate C_b, from Equation (6.74), and to determine the tangential stress acting on the flume bed. In Equations (6.73) and (6.74) $\bar{\bar{u}}_b$ and $\bar{\bar{u}}_w$ denote the average of the mean local velocities measured in both cases at equal distances along the bed and the walls respectively.

6.3.2 Sediment transport

Problems connected with sediment movement are very important in engineering practice and have therefore long been the subject of research in the laboratory and in the field. Though much has already been achieved, due to its great complexity the problem is far from solved. Here only a concise statement of some approaches and of some factors influencing sediment movement will be highlighted with particular reference to their relevance to model studies and computation of sediment transport. For a more detailed study of the problem the reader is referred to the extensive literature, a small part of which is quoted here in the references.

There are various forms of bedload movement associated with different bed formations; incipient motion, movement in ripples, dunes, and antidunes. Parameters affecting sediment motion are the size and shape of sediment grains, their specific weight, grain size distribution, cohesion and natural angle of repose, tendency to form ripples or dune formations, and position of individual sediment grains on the channel bed. The hydraulic parameters influencing sediment movement are the slope of the energy line, discharge, depth, mean velocity and velocity distribution, turbulence and flow regime, and specific gravity and viscosity of water. It is evident that such a great number of parameters, many of which are interdependent, can be systematically investigated only by long-term laboratory research which in turn must be verified and supplemented by field measurements.

The equations expressing the laws of the beginning of bedload movement (incipient motion) and sediment transport vary due to the authors' different approach to the problem, their different assessment of the importance of individual parameters, and because empirical equations in particular have varying limits of validity. Furthermore, in the case of equations for incipient motion, different authors use different definitions for the beginning of movement. On the whole, every *empirical* or *semi-empirical* equation expresses incipient motion as a function either of the critical tangential stress, τ_d or the critical velocity near the bed, or the critical mean (cross-sectional) velocity. The law of bedload movement is then expressed by these types of equations as a function of the difference of the actual and critical tangential stress (e.g., Equation (6.48)) or the difference of the actual and critical discharge and slope, or the difference of the actual and critical velocity (mean or near the bed). Equations of this type have been proposed by Schoklitsch, Meyer–Peter, Kramer, Casey, Shields, Goncharov, Levi and others. Even though these equations are of an empirical or semi-empirical character and were not always based on a physical analysis, they are nevertheless of great importance both for sediment transport computations in prototype, where further basic data are often lacking, and for modelling and the calculation of scales of river models, where some of them have been found very effective. This holds good especially for Equation (6.48) proposed by Meyer–Peter; here the dimensionless constants are $A_1 = 0.047$ and $B_1 = 0.25$ when used for the calculation of bedload transport and $A_1 = 0.03$ for the end of sediment movement.

For

$$\frac{Q_s}{Q}\left(\frac{K_b'}{K_s'}\right)^{3/2} = 1$$

from Equation (6.48) for the specific sediment discharge we get the equation

$$g_s' = \frac{1}{\sqrt{(\rho B^2)}}(\tau_0 - \tau_c)^{3/2} \tag{6.75}$$

which for the quoted values of A_1 and B_1 and sediment specific gravity 2.65 gives the modified Meyer–Peter equation

$$g_s' = 0.253\,(\tau_0 - 755d)\ (\text{N/ms}) \tag{6.75'}$$

It is interesting to note that the criterion of bed stability ($g_s' = 0$) from equation (6.75') becomes

$$d = \frac{\tau_0}{755} = \frac{\gamma hS}{755} = \frac{10^3 9.81hS}{755} = 13hS \tag{6.76}$$

Equally using Shield's criterion for incipient motion (Fig. 6.4) and fully turbulent flow at the bed where $Fr_*^2 = 0.056$ (independent of Re_*) we get

$$0.056 = Fr_*^2 = \frac{u_*^2}{gd(S_s - 1)} = \frac{\tau_0}{\rho gd(S_s - 1)} = \frac{\tau_0}{\gamma_s'd} = \frac{hS}{d(S_s - 1)} \tag{6.76'}$$

and

$$d = 11 \, hS$$

Equation (6.76) can be combined for design purposes with the Manning–Strickler Equation (6.16') using for $n = (d^{1/6})/26 \simeq 0.04 d^{1/6}$ (with d in m).

Another and more modern approach to the problem of sediment transport is based on the *theoretical analysis* of the mechanism of the phenomena whereby all theories consider bedload movement either in jumps, or by rolling along the bed. Bearing in mind the fact that the form of sediment transport depends on its intensity, none of these theories can fully characterize the whole range of the movement. The theoretical approach to the problem can be based on probability (e.g., Einstein) or on the theory of turbulence (e.g., Kalinske). The concept of grain movement in jumps has been elaborated by Einstein, Velikanov and Yalin in particular and that of rolling along the bed by, e.g. White, Tison, Kalinske and Pantelopulos. Further approaches to the problem of sediment transport have been made by Bagnold, Ackers, Engelund and others.

Kalinske's equations (*see* Equations (6.46) and (6.50)) were discussed in Sub-sections 6.2.2 and 6.2.3. Figure 6.7 shows the relationship between $\bar{u}_d/\bar{u}_D$ and $(u_c/\bar{u}_D)^2$ as a function of $r = \sigma/\bar{u}$.

For the velocity near the bed, according to various data, the intensity of turbulence varies between $r = \sigma/\bar{u} = \frac{1}{3}$ to $\frac{1}{8}$ (usually $\frac{1}{6}$) and $K = (u_{max} - \bar{u})/\sigma = 3$. Therefore,

$$Kr = \frac{u_{max} - \bar{u}}{\bar{u}} \simeq \frac{1}{2} \quad \text{and} \quad \tau_{max} = \left(\frac{u_{max}}{\bar{u}}\right)^2 \bar{\tau} = (Kr + 1)^2 \bar{\tau} = 2.25 \bar{\tau}$$

(sometimes it attains a value of up to $3\bar{\tau}$). As $\bar{u}_D \propto u_*$ and

$$\frac{\bar{u}_d}{\bar{u}_D} = f\left(\frac{\tau_0}{\tau_c}\right) = f\left(\frac{\tau_0}{\gamma_s' d}\right) = f(Fr_*^2) = f\left(\frac{1}{\psi}\right)$$

we can write Equation (6.50) as

$$\frac{q_s}{u_* d} = f\left(\frac{1}{\psi}\right) \tag{6.77}$$

(ψ is often called the flow parameter.) A plot of experimental results shows that for higher values of q_s

$$\frac{q_s}{u_* d} = 10 \left(\frac{1}{\psi}\right)^2 \tag{6.77'}$$

with $1/\psi$ again approaching 0.056 for very low values of q_s (incipient motion).

The Einstein equation (1950) can be written in a very similar form as

$$\phi = \frac{q_s}{wd} = f(Fr_*^2) = f\left(\frac{1}{\psi}\right) \tag{6.78}$$

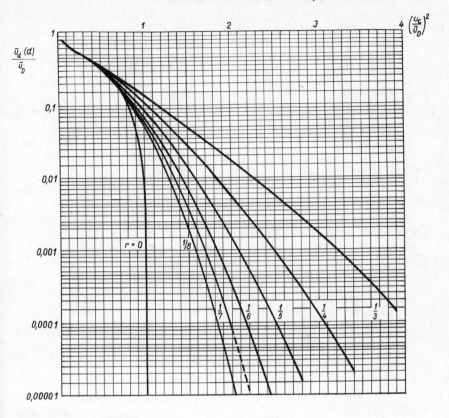

Fig. 6.7. [After Kalinske, 1947]

where ϕ is the transport parameter; for values of $\phi > 0.05$

$$\phi = 40 \left(\frac{1}{\psi}\right)^3 \tag{6.78'}$$

Kalinske considered the influence of turbulence in his equations but neglected the effects of hydrodynamic lift. Pantelopulos (1957) continued the work of Kalinske in his analysis but extended the theoretical analysis, supplemented by experiments carried out at the Water Resources Institute (VÚV) at Bratislava, to the influence of lift, vertical velocity pulsations and grain size distribution.

White *et al.* (1975) in a comprehensive review of sediment transport equations have shown that the Engelund–Hansen (1967) and the Ackers–White (1973) equations gave encouraging results when tested against a large number of flume and river data. The details of the derivation of these equations can be found in the relevant references and only the final results will be quoted here.

The Engelund–Hansen equation can be written as

$$\lambda\phi = 0.1 \left(\frac{1}{\psi}\right)^{5/2} \tag{6.79}$$

where the symbols have their previously stated definitions.
The Ackers–White equation is

$$G_{gr} = C_1 \left(\frac{F_{gr}}{A} - 1\right)^m \tag{6.80}$$

where

$$G_{gr} = \frac{ch}{s_s d} \left(\frac{v_*}{v}\right)^n \qquad \text{(dimensionless sediment transport rate)},$$

with c being the sediment concentration in ppm by weight ($= 10^6 g_s)/\gamma vh$; $n = 0$ for coarse sediment and $n = 1$ for fine sediment. Fgr, which Ackers and White denote as mobility number, is given by

$$Fgr = \frac{v_*^n}{\sqrt{(gd(s_s - 1))}} \left[\frac{v}{\sqrt{(32)} \log (\alpha h/d)}\right]^{1-n}$$

with $\alpha \simeq 10$. The values of C_1, A, m and n in Equation (6.80) are functions of the grain number $d_{gr} = d[g(s_s - 1)/v^2]^{1/3}$, and for $d_{gr} > 60$, $A = 0.17$, $m = 1.5$, $C_1 = 0.025$ (and $n = 0$).

From the above quoted equations (Einstein, Kalinske, Engelund–Hansen) it follows that for equal flow and transport parameters on the model and prototype ($M_\phi = M_\psi = 1$) the previously quoted similarity criteria (Equations (VI) and (VII)) apply. A less strict condition leading to some scale effects, which can be evaluated from the sediment transport equations, may be obtained, e.g. from the Engelund–Hansen equation, by using $M_\phi = M_\psi^{-5/2}$, assuming that this equation satisfactorily describes sediment transport both on the model and in prototype. This argument clearly underlines the need for a careful study of the limits within which each sediment transport equation applies, i.e. the conditions under which it has been derived.

The practical use of some of these equations, based on theoretical analysis of the mechanism of sediment movement, is hampered by the fact that the various coefficients and parameters, which are sometimes difficult to measure, are often unknown. When estimating them without sufficient data, errors are introduced into the results of the calculations, which considerably depreciates the value of theoretical derivation of the equations. It is necessary, therefore, to continue in theoretical and experimental research of sediment transport and to confront the results of laboratory research with results of field sediment measurements. These measurements are very valuable as laboratory research cannot include all factors acting in prototype.

It is necessary to realize, however, that from the point of view of instrumentation measurement of bedload on larger rivers involves great difficulties. The choice of suitable apparatus for bedload transport measurement is very important and its performance and especially efficiency can be ascertained only by laboratory experiments.

In the analysis no attention has so far been paid to limiting conditions where one form of sediment transport changes into another. This important problem has been dealt with, e.g. by Bogardi (1974) who has reached quantitative conclusions on the basis of studies by Liu and Hwang (1961), Simons and Albertson (1965), and Simons and Richardson (1966), and his own research and other Hungarian experiences. Bogardi plotted the results of theoretical and experimental work, originally expressed as

$$\frac{v_*}{w} = f\left(\frac{v_* d}{\nu}\right) = f(Re_*) \quad \text{or} \quad \frac{v_*}{w} = f\left(\frac{d}{\delta'}\right)$$

as a relationship $gd/v_*^2 = f(d)$ (*see* Fig. 6.8) where the limits between the various forms of bedload movement are shown ($v_* = \sqrt{(ghS)} = \sqrt{(\tau_0/\rho)}$).

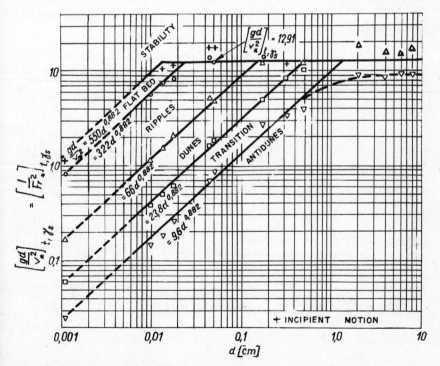

Fig. 6.8. [After Bogardi, 1974]

From Fig. 6.8 it is evident that all plots may be expressed by the equation

$$\frac{gd}{v_*^2} = \frac{1}{Fr_*^2} = \beta d^N \tag{6.81}$$

where $N = 0.882$ and β is a constant always characterizing a certain form of motion. β has the dimension $cm^{-0.882}$ (d in cm). Since Fig. 6.8 and Equation (6.81) are valid for the specific gravity of sediment, 2.65, and a water temperature, $t = 20°C$ (which influences viscosity and tangential stress), for a general value of γ_s and t

$$\left(\frac{gd}{v_*^2}\right)_{t,\gamma_s} = \frac{d}{hS}\frac{v_{20}^2}{v_t^2}\frac{\gamma_s - \gamma}{1.65\gamma} \tag{6.82}$$

It is not only the characteristic values for β (550; 322; 66; 23.8; 9.6) which are found from Fig. 6.8, but also the limiting value of the diameters of the grains, which under some conditions remain at rest or have the possibility of a certain form of motion. Thus, for example, for $1/Fr_*^2 > 13$ all grains are at rest and grains with diameter $d < 0.145$ mm may also be at rest at $1/Fr_*^2 < 13$. From this, for the boundary between rest and bedload motion for $d > 0.145$ mm, we again get Equation (6.76). Figure 6.9 shows the relationship between τ_0 ($= \tau_c$) and d for the critical stability condition, which may again be generalized for various water temperatures and sediment specific gravity.

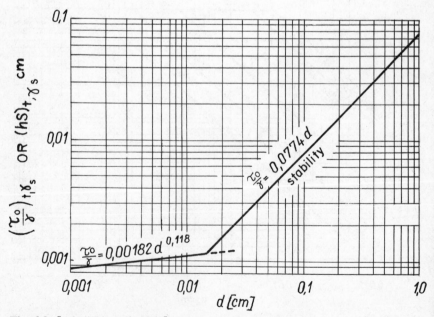

Fig. 6.9. [After Bogardi, 1959]

The size of dunes and their effect on the friction coefficient was also investigated by Knoroz (1951), who suggested the following empirical relationship

$$\lambda_D = 0.205 \frac{H_D}{L_D} \left(\frac{H_D}{h}\right)^{0.25} + \lambda_s \left(1 - 10 \frac{H_D}{L_D}\right) \tag{6.83}$$

where H_D is the height of the dune, L_D the length of the dune, λ_D the total friction coefficient and λ_s the friction coefficient given by sediment size only. Further

$$H_D = \frac{3.5 R \left(\frac{v - v_c}{v}\right)^{2/3}}{\log \frac{h}{d} + 6} \tag{6.84}$$

$$L_D = \frac{2.8 h v}{v - v_c} \tag{6.85}$$

where v_c is the critical velocity for incipient motion.

An analysis of the total sediment carrying capacity of a river (sediment movement along the bottom and in suspension) has been carried out, e.g. by Laursen (1958). He expressed the dimensionless parameter L as a function u_*/w

$$L = \frac{\bar{c}}{\sum p \left(\frac{d}{h}\right)^{7/6} \left(\frac{\tau_0}{\tau_d} - 1\right)} = f\left(\frac{v_*}{w}\right) \tag{6.86}$$

where p is the proportion by weight of fraction diameter d present in the bed material, and $\bar{c}(\%) = (q_s/q)(\gamma_s/\gamma)100$, ($q_s$ is the total specific sediment discharge (m^2/s)). On the basis of this analysis and Fig. 6.8 Bogardi produced the relationship between u_*, d and L on Fig. 6.10. Figures 6.9 and 6.10 permit a speedy calculation of practical problems, as the following example shows.

We are looking for the value hS which must not be exceeded for the stability of sediments with $d = 1$ mm and specific gravity 2.78 in a flow of water at a temperature $t = 12°C$. According to Fig. 6.10 and Equation (6.76)

$$hS \leqslant 0.0077 \frac{v_{20}^2}{v_{12}^2} \frac{2.78 - 1}{1.65} \leqslant 0.0077 \left(\frac{0.0101}{0.0124}\right)^2 \frac{1.78}{1.65} \leqslant 0.0055 \text{ cm}$$

Further if we want the river to transport a load of 1.20 N/m^3 of a diameter $d = 0.05$ mm for a slope $S = 0.55 \times 10^{-4}$ (i.e. for $h = 100$ cm)

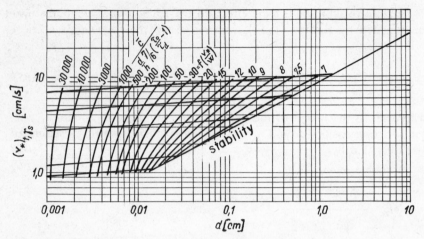

Fig. 6.10. [After Bogardi, 1959]

without sedimentation, we can continue with the calculation as follows:

$$v_* = \sqrt{(ghS)} = \sqrt{(981 \cdot 0.0055)} = 2.32 \text{ cm/s}$$

$$(v_*)_{t,\gamma_s} = 2.32 \sqrt{\left(\frac{v_{12}^2}{v_{20}^2} \frac{1.65}{2.78-1}\right)} = 2.75 \text{ cm/s}$$

From Fig. 6.10 we find that for $v_* = 2.75$ cm/s and $d = 0.005$ cm the value $L = 470$. From Fig. 6.9 we find τ_d/γ for 0.0005 cm $= 0.00102$ cm, which transformed to the given temperature and specific gravity gives

$$\left(\frac{\tau_{d_{\text{tys}}}}{\gamma}\right) = 0.00102 \frac{v_{12}^2}{v_{20}^2} \frac{1.65}{1.78} = 0.00143 \text{ cm}.$$

From Equation (6.86) we find

$$L = 470 = \frac{\bar{c}}{\left(\dfrac{0.005}{100}\right)^{7/6}\left(\dfrac{0.0055}{0.00143}-1\right)}$$

Thus $\bar{c} = 0.0126\%$. The total volume of transported sediment C' in N/m^3 is therefore $C' = \bar{c} \cdot 10^3 \cdot 9.81 = 1.26$ N/m^3, which corresponds to the required value.

Another concept of channel stability is that the channel cross-section remains unchanged even if there is sediment transport, i.e. if the bed (and sides) of the channel are 'live'; the criterion is now not bed stability but channel stability, i.e. a channel of constant section. This concept is the basis of the regime theory developed originally by Kennedy from observations of Indian silt-carrying rivers and irrigation canals. The main contributors to the theory were Lindley, Lacey (1946) and later Blench

(1969). In the form presented by Blench the resultant equations can be summarized as follows:

$$b = \sqrt{\left(\frac{f_b}{f_s} Q\right)} \tag{6.87}$$

$$h = \sqrt[3]{\left(\frac{f_s Q}{f_b^2}\right)} \tag{6.88}$$

$$S = \frac{f_b^{5/6} f_s^{1/12} v^{1/4}}{3.63 g Q^{1/6} \left(1 + \dfrac{c}{2330}\right)} \tag{6.89}$$

where h and b are the mean channel depth and width in ft and c the sediment concentration in ppm by weight, $f_b = v^2/h = 9.6\sqrt{d}(1+0.012c)$ is the 'bed factor' and $f_s = v^3/b =$ is the 'side factor'. For slight cohesiveness of the banks $f_s = 0.1$ and for high cohesiveness $f_s = 0.3$. (Q is in ft^3/s and the grain diameter d in inches.) It is interesting to note the powers of the discharge in equations (6.87) to (6.89):

$$b \propto Q^{0.5}; \qquad h \propto Q^{0.33}; \qquad S \propto Q^{-0.166}$$

These powers are comparable with the powers in the equations for the width, depth and slope scales for $M_d = M_{\gamma_s'} = M_{\gamma_{col}'} = 1$ (*see* Equations (6.58 a–c)). On the other hand, from Equation (6.76) and the Manning–Strickler equation the bed stability criterion results in powers

$$b \propto h \propto Q^{0.46}; \qquad S \propto Q^{-0.46}$$

By the analysis of total sediment carrying capacity we have already touched on the problem of suspended sediment transport. The laws of sediment transport in suspension have been elucidated better (though not completely) than those of bedload transport thanks to numerous theoretical and experimental studies (Goncharov, Velikanov (1946), Makavejev, Kolmogorov, Vanoni (1946), Kalinske, Lane, Knapp, Ippen (1971) and others; *see* Bogardi (1974) and Vanoni (1975)) carried out both in the laboratory and in prototype.

As stated earlier most studies set out from the theory of turbulent flow, the logarithmic velocity distribution law and the findings presented in Sub-section 5.1.1; the resultant equation for the distribution of sediment concentration along a vertical in an open channel is given by Equation (6.55). As this equation results in a zero concentration at the water surface (for $y = h$, $C'/C_a' = 0$) and in infinitely high concentration at the bed for $y = 0$ for all values of z, in Equation (6.54) it is better for ε_y to use the mean value in the vertical

$$\bar{\varepsilon}_y = \frac{\kappa v_* h}{6} = \frac{v_* h}{15} \qquad \text{(for } \kappa = 0.4\text{)}$$

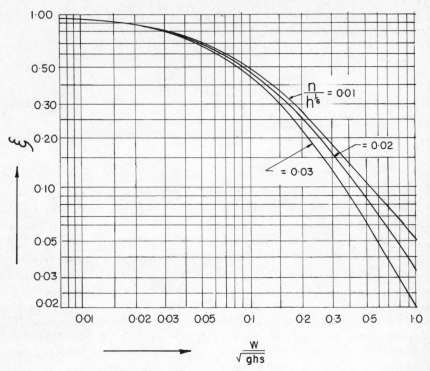

Fig. 6.11. [After Rouse (Ed.), 1950]

which results in the equation

$$\frac{C'}{C'_a} = e^{-15(w/v_*)[(y-a)/h]} \tag{6.90}$$

Together with the logarithmic velocity distribution, this in turn, after integration, gives the equation for the suspended sediment specific discharge (Kalinske, 1947)

$$q_s = qC'_a \xi e^{-15wa/v_* h} \tag{6.91}$$

where ξ is a function of w/v_* and the relative bed roughness $n/h^{1/6}$ (see Fig. 6.11).

In conclusion it is worth noting some further implications of theoretical and experimental studies of sediment transport for research on models of rivers. It follows from Bogardi's work that the parameter β in Equation (8.81), characterizing the form of bedload motion, may replace the condition of similarity for the beginning of sediment movement (Equation (VI) in Sub-section 6.2.2). In this case β also determines the ratio of the grain size and the laminar sub-layer since from Equations (6.23), (6.81) and (6.82) it follows that:

$$\frac{d}{\delta'} = \frac{1}{11.6\beta} \frac{gd^{(2-N)}}{v_* \nu} \frac{\gamma_s - \gamma}{1.65\gamma} \tag{6.92}$$

This method assumes the same parameter β on the model and in prototype, even if it is possible to admit a small difference between these two values. It follows at the same time that the same sediment may be used on the model and in prototype (same specific weight and dimensions).

Pantelopulos (1957), setting out from his preceding studies, showed that for the ratio of discharges of a sediment mixture (g'_{s_s}) and of sediment diameter $d(g'_{s_d})$ the following equation is valid:

$$\frac{g'_{s_s}}{g'_{s_d}} = \frac{\bar{K}_s}{\bar{K}_d} \frac{d_k}{d} = \text{const.} \tag{6.93}$$

where d_k characterizes the sediment mixture. In Equation (6.93) $\bar{K} = \frac{2}{3}\psi p \bar{u}_D / \sqrt{(\tau_0/\rho)}$ for both cases and d is the sediment diameter for which the critical tangential stress is identical with the mean critical tangential stress for the grains of the mixture. Thus Equation (6.93) opens the way to replacing the actual mixture by a single diameter material on the model whilst preserving the same law for sediment transport (except for the above mentioned constant) on the model as in prototype. This permits a simplification of modelling technique so that it is not necessary to model the entire range of the grain size distribution curve, which sometimes causes difficulties, especially for small grain diameters.

Similarity of suspended sediment requires similarity of velocity distribution and of concentration on the model and in prototype and identity of the values of exponent z in Equation (6.55) (*see* Equation (6.56)). Modelling of suspended sediments in river models is difficult as their choice on the model is limited by the bedload transport (which mostly must be modelled simultaneously), by the influence of the lateral walls of the model and by other factors as well. Since the methods of computation of suspended load sedimentation and transport are reasonably well elaborated, the sedimentation of suspensions in reservoirs and river reaches is modelled only in exceptional cases and mathematical methods accompanied by laboratory studies of the physical properties of the suspended sediment (*see* Equation (6.53)) are usually used. The problems of similarity of movement of suspended particles for studies of sedimentation tanks are discussed in greater detail in Chapter 9.

In the case of unsteady or nonuniform flow the problem of sediment transport is naturally even more complicated and the subject of further research.

The special case of local erosion is discussed briefly in Chapter 7.

6.4 Design of River Models

6.4.1 Prototype information and model validation

For the calculation of a river model at least a minimum of prototype data must be available. These include, sufficiently frequent cross-sections of the river reach under consideration, the discharge rating curve, the longitudinal section of the river bed and water levels at least for one discharge under consideration, but if at all possible for the entire discharge range to be modelled. In rivers with bedload movement the sediment grain size distribution curve, the sediment specific and volumetric weights and the characteristic grain form are also needed. Data on the quantity of moving bedload in prototype are usually not known, but sometimes at least the approximate discharge corresponding to the beginning of bedload movement may be obtained. All these data are necessary not only for the correct determination of scales and model operation, but also for carrying out the proving experiments on the model as the first stage of experimental work. By reproducing on the model a phenomenon known in prototype it is possible to test the validity of the calculations of the model scales during the proving experiments. After an adjustment of the model, where necessary, the research work proper on the model with the planned structures and channel changes can proceed.

6.4.2 Choice of model scales

The equations given in Sub-section 6.2.4 (Equations (I) to (VII) and the limiting conditions (a) to (e)) permit a complete computation of model scales both for fixed and movable bed models. Equations (6.36) and (6.57) give the scales of time for the water and sediment discharges. In practice the length and width scales M_l and M_b in most cases are determined by the laboratory space available and the length of the river to be reproduced. The third remaining scale, which may be chosen, is usually the roughness size k (fixed bed models) or sediment size d (movable models) which has to be selected in such a way that after the computation of the remaining scales from Equations (I) to (VII) the limiting conditions (a) to (e) are observed, where relevant. Alternatively the depth scale M_h is chosen and the roughness and/or sediment size computed.

The friction coefficient λ and its dependence on the roughness size is best determined by a preliminary experiment in a tilting flume, whilst eliminating the influence of the walls (*see* Sub-section 6.3.1, Equations (6.71) to (6.74)). If such experiments cannot be undertaken or are not necessary, e.g. if the roughness can easily be corrected on the model proper during its proving, the coefficient λ is determined by computation.

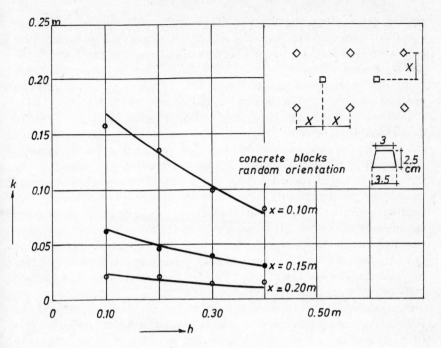

Fig. 6.12. [After de Vries, 1977]

Equations (6.62) to (6.65) or Fig. 6.2 (Fig. 6.5) are most suitable for the computation of the friction coefficient. For an approximate computation of flow in the region of rough turbulent flow the Manning–Strickler Equation (6.16) or Müller's modification of it (6.16′) for a bed with sediment can also be used especially if the values of the Chézy coefficient are in the region of $50 \, \text{m}^{1/2}/\text{s}$. Figure 6.12 gives some guidance on the equivalent roughness value k of concrete blocks regularly placed with random orientation on a fixed bed model (de Vries (1977)).

It is worth noting that for large values of vertical exaggeration the roughness elements required for the model could be so large with respect to depth as to completely distort the flow field. In this case it is preferable to replace the required bed shear stress by the resistance of a number of vertical bars or strips acting in the whole fluid body. The number n of bars, e.g. of circular section diameter D, can be approximately estimated from

$$n = \frac{2g}{C_D h D} \left(\frac{1}{C^2} - \frac{1}{C_1^2} \right) \tag{6.94}$$

where C and C_1 are the required model Chézy coefficient and the actual coefficient of the (concrete) bed without roughness and C_D is the drag coefficient of the individual bar. The number of roughness elements actually required and their spacing and positioning on the model may best be determined during the model proving tests. In movable bed models the bed roughness is primarily provided by the bed forms; should additional roughness be required in very special circumstances a small number of artificial roughness elements (bars or strips) may be used.

It will be recalled that the scale of hydraulic radius M_R is a function of depth and that therefore, strictly speaking, similarity for a vertically exaggerated model is possible only for one depth (or a constant depth/width ratio) (*see* Equation (6.30)). The proving tests should, therefore, first of all be carried out for the depth which was chosen for the model computation and then the whole relevant range of discharges and depths should be explored. In practice, particularly in relatively wide channels, it will frequently be seen that no further adjustment of roughness need be made. However, should it be necessary, this may easily be done for higher stages than the one the model computation was based on by increasing the bed roughness in parts of the model submerged at these higher discharges (e.g. the flood plain).

Even though the great importance of the correct determination of the roughness coefficient in a river model is evident, this does not mean that in some cases correct results might not also be obtained on models where the roughness has not been ascertained so carefully. This holds good in particular for models of rivers which meander strongly and where considerable losses of head occur due to changes in cross-section and direction; since these losses in prototype may amount to up to 50% of all losses, including friction losses (*see* Equation (6.1)) and normally are in the region of 20 to 30% and further because in strongly distorted models they may amount to up to 75%, a small error in the roughness of the model cannot, in such a case, really substantially influence the experimental result.

Sub-section 6.3.2 deals with some basic equations for sediment transport and their implications for similarity of models with movable beds. Very often the prototype data for sediment discharge are not available and we then have to use the quoted equations for its computation. Theoretical and experimental studies of sediment transport are valuable for the elucidation of basic principles and form the basis of mathematical modelling of rivers with sediment. Often, however, they cannot give a satisfactory quantitative (sometimes not even qualitative) answer to engineering problems, which must be solved by scale models designed and operated according to the principles discussed in Sub-sections 6.2.4 and 6.3.2.

The following sections give some examples of these model studies together with a brief description of the techniques used.

6.5   Models of River Training Schemes

River training schemes have been studied on models in practically all hydraulic laboratories all over the world. The models often represent very extensive reaches and tens and sometimes even hundreds of kilometers of rivers. Though they sometimes occupy a large area their scales may be very small and distortion can be considerable. For example the Water-ways Experiment Station laboratory at Vicksburg, USA, built a model for the study of the floods and flood protection in the lower reaches of the Mississippi representing in prototype an area of 40 000 km². The model was built on a site of 1 ha with a horizontal scale 1 : 2000 and vertical scale 1 : 100. Another model of the entire Mississippi basin, built to the same scale, covered an area of 100 ha and its construction required the shifting of 50 000 m³ of soil. In the following examples taken mainly from the author's own experience in Czechoslovakia (Novak (1951–1967)) some methodological problems will also be pointed out.

To facilitate the study of the training and improvement of the naviga-tion channel in a difficult reach of the Danube on the Czechoslovak–Hungarian border near the confluence with a strong river branch a model (Fig. 6.13) was constructed in the Hydraulic Research Institute (VÚV) laboratory in Prague with a horizontal scale 1 : 300 and vertical scale 1 : 100. The discharges on the model reproducing 5 km of the river were undistorted, i.e. they were modelled according to the Froude law of similarity. Based on Equations (I) to (VII) and limiting conditions (a) to (e) in Sub-section 6.2.4 the sediment bed on the model was simulated by coal of specific gravity = 1,386 with $d_{90} = 2.4$ mm, $d_s \simeq 1.15$ mm.

The model sediment discharge could not be determined from Equation (VII) as the sediment transport in the part of the Danube under consider-ation was not known in prototype. However, since echosounder data of the Danube bed recording its changes over a certain period were availa-ble, it was possible to verify the calculated time scale of sediment movement during the proving experiments, and use the result for a correction of the experimentally found sediment discharge curve on the model. This was established as follows: the model with the bed set according to prototype (for a certain date) was operated with a constant water discharge without supplying sediment for a period of thirty minutes. After this experiment the sediment (coal) retained in the settling tank at the end of the model was removed and the experiment continued (with-out changing the bed) for the same water discharge, but now with the dosing of trapped sediment at the model inlet, again for a period of thirty minutes (the dosing being spread uniformly over this period). The quan-tity of sediment retained in the settling tank after this second 'round' was compared with the dosage. If both were approximately the same the

Fig. 6.13. Model of a Danube reach. [Novak, 1966]

result represented one point in the required sediment discharge curve, if not the experiment was continued until good agreement between the sediment retained in the settling tank in two consecutive 'runs' was obtained. A similar procedure was chosen for further values of water discharge to obtain the function $g_s = f(q)$.

The above mentioned procedure may be used only for relatively short models. The duration of the experiment (in the given case 30 minutes) must then be sufficiently long for a representative movement of the sediment (dunes, etc.) from the model to the settling tank to take place, but not so long as to considerably scour the movable bed in the first 'round' of the experiment when water without the sediment dose passes through the model. In the case of longer models it is better to operate them without interruption over a long period in such a way that the sediment is returned throughout from the end of the model to the inlet in a closed circuit provided with an ejector, in a similar way as in a tilting flume (*see* example in Section 6.6). The law of bedload movement obtained in such a way may be compared with the theoretical calculation for a straight channel, either for the model or the prototype.

The time scale of bedload movement was only approximately determined by calculation in this case as $M_{t_s} = 800–1200$, because the value of $M_{\gamma' vol}$ in Equation (6.57) could also be determined only approximately. For the model experiments the actual sequence of discharges on the Danube was reproduced (according to the records of daily water levels in Bratislava) over a period of 1050 days and the intitial and final state of the model bed was compared with the prototype sounding records. It was found that when the sediment was dosed into the inlet on the model according to the experimentally ascertained relationship the time scale $M_{t_s} = 1200$ was best suited. For experiments carried out according to these parameters very good qualitative and quantitative agreement in the configuration of the model and prototype river bed was obtained. If this resultant time scale is compared with the time scale for water movement according to the Froude law (Equation (6.36)) $M_t = M_l/M_h^{1/2} = 30$, it will be seen that the use of coal and other model parameters speed up the channel forming process on the model about forty times. Thus it was possible to represent a phenomenon taking nearly three years in prototype within 21 hours on the model.

On the basis of the analysis of flow and the bed formation various river training schemes were then studied on the model to find a reasonably economical solution that would considerably improve the navigable depth in the reach under consideration and stabilize the flow. For the chosen alternatives experiments were carried out with the same discharges in the same sequence as for the proving experiments, i.e. a comparative forecast was made assuming the same discharges for the river over a period of 1050 days, both without improvements and after the completion of the training works. On the basis of the model study a scheme was then proposed consisting of an alteration of the already existing works, the construction of new groynes, the dredging of a certain reach and, lastly, a partial closure of the branch confluence (Fig. 6.13). The measures carried out on model studies according to these recommendations proved successful and the resultant prototype bed configuration for the considered period corresponded well, on the whole, with the model results. Smaller differences which occurred could be attributed to the fact that the prototype discharge sequence on the Danube during and after the completion of the training works differed somewhat from the discharges assumed on the model in the period chosen for its proving tests.

For model studies involving groynes and sills (as, e.g., in the above example), it is also necessary to weigh up carefully the advantages and disadvantages of model distortion, which, if too large, could distort the function of the groynes on the model. There are various views on the permissible limit of distortion in such a case; some laboratories do not permit any distortion, others report satisfactory results obtained on river models with groynes where the distortion was as much as eightfold (Vicksburg). Experiments carried out at VÚV Prague (Novak, 1954) show that with a mild distortion (up to 2 and for $M_{S_0} = 1$) sufficiently good results may be expected when investigating the depth and extent of scour at groynes; with increasing distortion gradually greater deviations from prototype behaviour occur. For a fixed bed model greater distortion is permissible, but it must be realized that to obtain the correct ratio of the discharge in the free channel to the flow over the groynes, distortion of the Froude number is not permissible, and that therefore Equation (I) must be preserved. The reason for this is that for a similarity of overfall Q' over groynes $M_{Q'} = M_b M_h^{3/2}$ (where b is the groyne length). Even under these circumstances, however, considerable distortion of models with sills and groynes cannot be recommended.

For models simulating both the river channel and the flood plain, as has been the case in the model study of river training near the outflow from a power station into the River Váh, carried out at the VÚV Prague laboratory (Novak, 1954) (see Fig. 6.14), it is necessary to take into consideration in model computations the difference in roughness of the flood plain (fixed bed) and the river channel (movable bed). With the use of the Strickler equation the total coefficient K', on the model and in prototype, will be given approximately by the equation

$$K' = \frac{A_1 K_1' \left(\frac{A_1}{P_1}\right)^{2/3} + A_2 K_2' \left(\frac{A_2}{P_2}\right)^{2/3}}{(A_1 + A_2)\left(\frac{A_1 + A_2}{P_1 + P_2}\right)^{2/3}} \tag{6.95}$$

where index 1 refers to the channel and index 2 to the flood plain. The equation is derived in a similar way as outlined for the exclusion of the influence of the flume walls in Sub-section 6.3.1.

The undistorted model of the River Otava at Písek, built to a scale of 1 : 60 for a study of the most suitable flood protection scheme in an urban region with low weirs and a historically valuable bridge (Čábelka and Novák, 1964) (Fig. 6.15), is a typical example of a fixed bed river model.

Fig. 6.14. Model of river training at a power station canal outfall (River Váh). [Novák, 1954]

An interesting feature of the model are the roughness elements on the river bed; the regularly spaced ceramic bricks glued to the concrete gave good agreement between the model and prototype water levels during the proving experiments.

The model of the Vltava cascade, constructed at VÚV Prague (Novak, 1965) ($M_l = M_b = 700$ and $M_h = 80$) and simulating 180 km of the Vltava River and the confluences of the main tributaries (Fig. 6.16), is an example of an extensive river model with fixed bed. The aim of research here *inter alia* was to ascertain the influence of reservoirs and the

Fig. 6.15. Model of a flood protection scheme with a bridge (River Otava). [Čábelka and Novák, 1964]

Fig. 6.16. Model of the Vltava cascade. [Novak, 1965]

operation of the dams on the progress of flood waves and to elucidate the movement of a flood wave through a deep reservoir of complicated shape. Since the flow on the model was unsteady and nonuniform, Equation (II) was observed and the model could not be tilted. Therefore it was also necessary to use considerable roughness on the model and this was achieved by using wire mesh strips. The model was provided with a long-distance control device for the regulation of discharges (Sub-section 4.4.2) and float limnigraphs with resistance transmitters (Sub-section 4.3.2). Figure 6.17 shows a detail of the model of the river with the wire mesh roughness elements.

Fig. 6.17. Vltava cascade (detail). [Novak, 1965]

6.6   Models of River Intakes

Offtakes from rivers with sediment transport are frequently studied by means of scale models. In essence, the problem is to divide the channel flow in such a way that the bulk of the sediment proceeds along the river and very little enters the intake structure. The branching of sediment-carrying flow has been studied theoretically and experimentally in a general way and many suitable types of intakes have been proposed for various conditions (mountain or lowland rivers, large or small sediment transport or various grain size, various winter regimes, etc.). Most intakes depend for satisfactory performance upon the utilization of transverse circulation, induced either by river training upstream of the intake or by the intake itself.

General relationships for dividing the flow derived on the basis of theoretical and experimental work usually include as parameters the angle α between the two channels (or the angle under which the subsidiary channel branches off the main), the ratio of widths b_0/b and discharges Q_0/Q in both channels, the ratio of width and depth of the main channel, the relative roughness of both channels, the sediment parameters and the Reynolds and Froude flow numbers.

Transverse circulation is caused by the transverse component of flow in open channels and is, in turn, the cause of spiral flow in the bends and the meandering of rivers in general. There is a very close connection between transverse circulation and the 'laws' of channel formation formulated by Fargue on the basis of observations on the Garonne river.

Among the general principles for the design of intakes at weirs on sediment transporting rivers, the following may be stated:

(a) if possible the intake should be placed on the concave bank;

(b) in case of a weir with gates the weir pier between the first and second section next to the intake should be extended sufficiently far upstream to protect the intake inlet;

(c) the space between this pier and the intake sill with rack should narrow in plan in the downstream direction;

(d) if possible the (fixed) weir sill should be at the level of the upper reservoir bed in all weir sections, but particularly in the section adjacent to the intake;

(e) the contours of the intake structure should be rounded to prevent contraction of the flow;

(f) the intake sill should be placed above the upstream reservoir bed and its edge should be rounded.

These practical measures help to reduce the intrusion of sediment into the intake to a minimum, especially if a suitable operation of the weir gates facilitates the flushing of sediment from the upstream reservoir. At lower upstream water levels the sediment is flushed by opening the adjacent weir gate, but at higher levels with intensive sediment transport the gates adjacent to the opposite bank should be opened first to assist in the formation of an artificial concave upstream of the extended weir pier. Models of rivers, where the flow near intake structures in particular is being observed, are mostly undistorted or only slightly distorted, since both river training measures and the flow at a hydraulic structure are studied at the same time.

The following are two examples of model studies of inlet structures carried out in the Prague laboratory (VÚV) in Czechoslovakia.

On a model of scale 1 : 75 the intake into a canal conveying water to a group of hydroelectric power stations on the River Váh together with the adjacent weir and the training of the river in the upstream reach was investigated (Novák, 1954). The aims were to determine an optimum lay-out of the whole structure, to propose suitable river training measures and the form and shape of the intake structure, (which consisted of a flow regulating structure, an intake sill with skimmer wall, a settling reservoir for sediment and a dividing wall for the navigation inlet into the canal), and to propose the most suitable operation for the weir, the details of which were studied on a separate model. It was also necessary to ensure the good functioning of the whole structure for a variable ratio of discharges in the river Q and through the inlet Q_0 within the range 0 to 17. The model included a length of about 2 km of the river upstream of the inlet and sediment was modelled by sand. Figure 6.18 shows that in the original design a considerable amount of sediment entered the navigation inlet, due especially to an unsuitable right river bank line upstream of the intake and unfavourable effects of an old groyne in the river upstream of the weir on the left bank. Through river training and a change in the whole intake layout as well as in some of its details considerably improved results were obtained and at the same time the model study contributed to a notable reduction in construction costs, e.g. by shortening the intake sill and the submerged skimmer and dividing walls. The sill of the navigation inlet was designed with sharp contours in the plan (saw-teeth pointing upstream) which cause vortices with a vertical axis encouraging the transport of bedload along the sill and into the adjacent weir section.

The second example (Fig. 6.19) shows a model study of an intake of cooling water to a thermal power station on the River Elbe where undisturbed intake of water from the river had to be ensured for Q/Q_0 ranging from about 4 to 40 for two different levels of the inlet sills beyond which there are sediment settling tanks. The model scale was 1 : 60 and the sediment which was mainly sand in prototype was represented by coal. A suitable solution was obtained by using two bed sills

Fig. 6.18. Model of an intake into a power station canal (River Váh). [Novák, 1954]

Fig. 6.19. Intake to a thermal power station (River Elbe). [Čábelka and Novák, 1964]

(in prototype sheet piles) which introduced a transverse circulation and prevented the silting up of the intake by bedload. This circulation, however, tends to float debris and ice towards the intake which must be protected by a floating boom.

6.7 Models of Cofferdams

Hydraulic models are also used to observe the influence of the proposed construction procedure on the flow regime at hydraulic structures, particularly on sediment carrying rivers (problems of raising of water level, sediment transport and ice passage, etc.), and on local scour and deposits at the proposed cofferdams. As in the case of bridge piers undistorted or only very slightly distorted models are used.

A model of scale 1:70 was used in the VÚV laboratory, Prague to study the construction method and particularly the order of sinking of caissons used for the foundation of gate piers of a barrage on the River Váh (Fig. 6.23) where the situation was further complicated by the presence of old bridge piers. A similar model of the river was also constructed in a provisional field laboratory directly on the construction site to permit quick and detailed testing of various alternate solutions and suggestions occurring during construction.

On a model of a reach of the Bistrica River in Roumania, built in the Prague laboratory to a scale of 1:60, the shape, slope, width, inlet and outlet of a bypass channel were tested for the construction procedure of the Bicaz dam. The aims were to minimize the scour near the cofferdam, improve conditions for the navigation of rafts during construction, reduce the backwater effect and preserve the sediment transport during construction. Figure 6.20 shows the original proposal after a discharge of 800 m³/s has been passed through the construction site and Fig. 6.21 the final solution after the laboratory research, from which not only the considerable reduction of scour near the outlet from the flume is evident but also the undisturbed bedload movement through the flume. The investigations also showed the danger of instability of the flow regime and great scour in the case of flumes curved in plan and flowing with near critical depths, and also that the flow regime is the most important factor for controlling scour at the outflow from the bypass flumes. A method which gives good results for supercritical flow (e.g. flow distributing walls) is not necessarily effective for subcritical flow.

Flow diversion and construction site protection is particularly important in the case of earth and rockfill dams. Frequently a by-pass tunnel is used. However, this is uneconomical in shallow wide valleys where it is better to use a concrete tunnel passing directly through or under the body of the dam and used for other functions after completion of the dam,

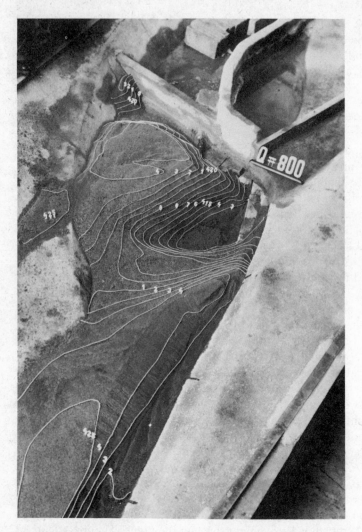

Fig. 6.20. Model of a cofferdam on the Bistrica River (original design). [Čábelka and Novák, 1964]

e.g. for permanent reservoir outlets or even power station penstocks. Figure 6.22 shows an example of a power station intake and by-pass tunnels which were used to pass discharges up to 550 m³/s during the construction stages of the barrage on the River Váh (at Liptovska Mara). After the completion of the dam the tunnels were used for the installation of permanent reservoir outlets. The design was tested in the hydraulic laboratory in Bratislava and by adjusting the inlet and invert of the tunnels to the shape shown in Fig. 6.22 good results were obtained and

Fig. 6.21. The same cofferdam as in Fig. 6.19 after design modifications. [Čábelka and Novák, 1964]

even the maximum discharge could be passed through the tunnels with free water surface flow. The inlet had to be protected by a series of sheet piles arranged in a fan-like shape in front of the inlet to act as a boom against the intrusion of large floating debris into the tunnels.

6.8 Sedimentation in Reservoirs

Reservoir silting can also be studied on extensive river models. As has already been mentioned in Sub-section 6.3.2 this is usually limited to studying silting up by bedload, as the problem of sedimentation of suspended load is easier to handle by computation. On the model the time of advance of gravel banks in the reservoir as well as the possibility of their flushing by the operation of the outlet gates of the hydraulic structure are usually studied. Since for studies of sedimentation in reservoirs a model with nonuniform flow is used, the model cannot be tilted and the conditions given by Equation (II) must be preserved, unless we are limiting ourselves to the region at the end of the backwater.

Thus for studying the sedimentation in a reservoir on the Váh River a distorted model, scale $M_l = M_b = 250$ and $M_h = 100$, was used in the

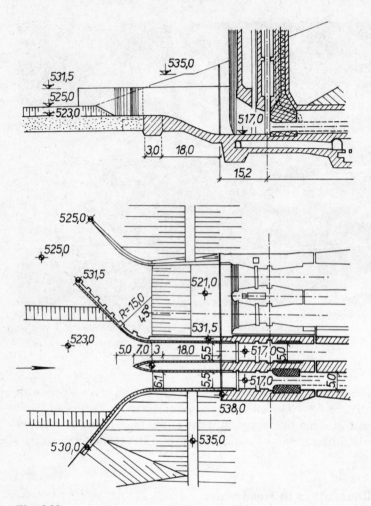

Fig. 6.22.

VÚV laboratory, Prague (Pantelopulos (1961)). The bedload was simulated by coal, $M_d = 11$, with a specific gravity of 1.4. The scale of the bedload discharge was $M_{g_s'} = 290$ and the time scale for the development of the bed formation $M_{t_s} = 400$, i.e. 21 hours on the model corresponded to one year in prototype. A section of over 6 km prototype of the river was reproduced on the model which was equipped with a sediment recirculation system (*see* Section 4.1). At the end of the model the water and sediment passed into a tank with a bottom shaped like a hopper and provided with waste overfalls maintaining a constant water level (pressure). Part of the water discharged over the waste overfalls into the laboratory sump, but the greater part, together with sediment, was transported with the aid of an ejector from the bottom of the tank back to the inlet tank of the model, which again was fitted with overfall waste channels. The water and sediment entered the model from the bottom of this tank through a pipe with a regulating valve. The discharge of water and sediment was measured by opening a trap door in the outlet diverting the water with bedload into a measuring tank with a triangular notch for water discharge measurements; the discharge of the transported bedload was measured by retaining it in a wire mesh basket near the inlet into this measuring tank. In this way it was possible to find on the model the law of sediment discharge in a free river channel, without any backwater caused by the planned barrage. For the study on sedimentation and flushing the barrage was then built on the model, and the bedload was dosed into inflowing (clean) water above the end of the backwater (at the model inlet) according to the law determined in the first stage of the experiments.

The research confirmed some generally valid conclusions known from previous experiments and prototype observations. For a considerable rise of the water level the bedload in the reservoir settles at its upstream end and is gradually transported into the reservoir in the shape of large banks. The material is sorted as first naturally coarser bedload settles and then in the direction towards the barrage gradually finer grains settle in the reservoir; thus on a similar basis, for similarity of reservoir sedimentation a prototype mixture should not be replaced by a single grain material on the model. Further bedload then advances over the new bed up to the barrage and during higher discharges may be passed through it downstream. Flushing, especially during the first years of the barrage operation, influences only a small area upstream of its gates or at most reduces the height of the sediment banks by spreading them along a greater length of the reservoir. It cannot, however, completely eliminate the bedload settled in the reservoir without a considerable lowering of the water level and without great water losses and thus usually also losses in power production. This holds good, even more so, for cases where the river also carries a considerable amount of sediment in suspension, total discharge of which is sometimes ten times that of bedload, and which also partly settles in the reservoir and 'cements' the sediment banks.

In the case under consideration the power loss was compared with the possible effect of flushing and it was recommended not to open the barrage gates at certain discharges as the original operating rules suggested (unless for reasons of flooding) but to dredge the settled material. The model was also used to suggest places most suitable for dredging.

Another case on the Váh River (Nosice) involved the study of a 20 m high dam and the first task of the laboratory was to propose a suitable type of outlet installation designed to permit on the one hand the passage

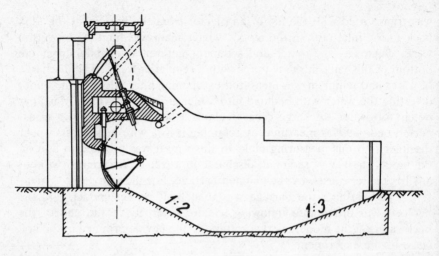

Fig. 6.23.

of discharge and ice floes over the spillway, and on the other hand the complete emptying of the reservoir and passage of floods with the smallest possible backwater effect in order to limit sedimentation in the reservoir to a minimum even during floods. As the result of model studies carried out at the VÚV laboratory, Prague (Novák, 1956) on a two-dimensional model of scale 1:35 and a three-dimensional dam model of scale 1:70, the author developed the type illustrated in Fig. 6.23. The shape of the flap gates and spillway, of the inlets to the bottom tainter gates, the function of the stilling basin and aeration vents, and the capacity of the entire outlet structure and its optimum operation, all were investigated in detail. The model also illustrated that, due to the flow contraction, the sediment flowing through the outlet tended to pass through the centre of the section keeping clear of the piers. This phenomenon is sometimes utilized in intakes on sediment-bearing rivers. The outlet structure is similar to that used at Verbois on the Rhone in Switzerland, but contains a number of new features particularly because of the high tail water level in the case of the Nosice dam. Figure 6.24 illustrates one of the experiments dealing with the outlet operation and shows the influence of uneven opening of the outlets when only three gates were opened resulting in great scour downstream of the shut tainter gates and at the banks.

On a model of the 20 km long reservoir of this dam, scale $M_l = M_b = 400$ and $M_h = 80$, the area of sediment deposition for various reservoir water levels, the proposed training of the Váh River at the end of the backwater and, partly also, bedload movement in the reservoir were studied. As the investigation was mainly directed to the end of the

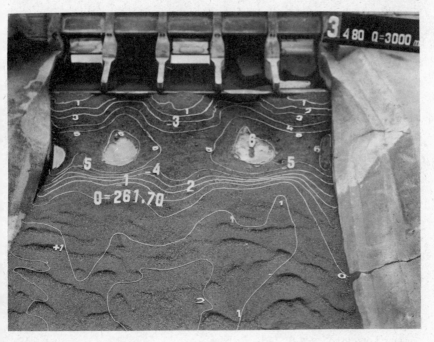

Fig. 6.24. Model of erosion at the outlet works of the Nosice dam (River Váh). [Novak, 1956]

reservoir a model with a fixed bed was chosen and only its upstream end had a movable bed using sand $d_{90} = 1.5$ mm, which was also dosed at the model inlet. The slope of the model was reduced by half, i.e. $M_S = 2.5$ instead of 5, and the discharges were distorted by 10% against the Froude law of similarity.

The examples in this chapter do not exhaust in any way the subject of studies on river models and many more from prominent laboratories all over the world (Wallingford, Delft, Chatou, Leningrad, etc.) could be quoted. They show, however, the type of problems solved on these models and the economic importance of these investigations.

References

Ackers, P. and Charlton, F. G. (1970). Dimensional analysis of alluvial channels with special reference to meander length, *J. Hydraul. Res. IAHR*, **8** No. 3, pp. 287–315.

Ackers, P. and Charlton, F. G. (1970a). The geometry of small meandering streams, *Proc. ICE*, Paper 7328S, pp. 289–317.

Ackers, P. and Charlton, F. G. (1970b). The slope and resistance of small meandering channels, *Proc. ICE*, Paper 7362S, pp. 349–370.

Ackers, P. and White, W. R. (1973). Sediment transport: new approach and analysis. *Proc. ASCE, J. Hydraul. Div.* **99**, No. HY11, pp. 2041–2060.

Alam, A. M. Z. and Kennedy, J. F. (1969). Friction factors for flow in sand bed channels, *Proc. ASCE, J. Hydraul. Div.*, **95**, No. HY6, pp. 1973–1992.

Allen, J. (1938). Experiments on waves of translation in small channels, *Philosophical Magazine Ser. 7*, **25**, pp. 754–768.

Allen, J. (1947). *Scale Models in Hydraulic Engineering*, Longmans, Green & Co., London.

Allen, J. and Shahwan, A. (1954). The resistance to flow of water along a tortuous stretch of the river Irwell, *Proc. ICE*, Paper 5914, Part III, pp. 144–165.

Allen, J. R. L. (1970). *Physical Process of Sedimentation*, Allen and Unwin, London.

Altunin, S. T. and Orlov, I. J. (1949). Modelling of erodible rivers, (in Russian), *Gidrotechnicheskoje stroitelstvo*, No. 12, pp. 11–16.

American Society of Civil Engineers. (1963). Friction factors in open channels. *Proc. ASCE, J. Hydraul. Div.*, **89**, No. HY2, pp. 97–143.

Bagnold, R. A. (1951). The movement of a cohesionless granular bed by fluid flow over it, *Brit. J. Appl. Phys.*, **2**, No. 2, pp. 29–34.

Bagnold, R. A. (1956). The flow of cohesionless grains in fluids, *Phil. Trans. Roy. Soc. (London), Series A*, **249**, No. 964.

Barr, D. I. H. and Herbertson, J. G. (1968). A similitude framework of regime theory, *Proc. ICE*, **41**, pp. 761–781.

Blau, E. (1957). Die Bedeutung und die Aufgaben der Geschiebeforschung für den Flussbau, *Wasserwirtschaft-Wassertechnik*, No. 10.

Blench, T. (1955). Scale relations among sand bed rivers including models, *Proc. ASCE*, **81**, Paper No. 667, 16 pp.

Blench, T. (1969). *Mobile-bed Fluviology*, University of Alberta Press, Alberta.

Bogardi, J. (1959). Neuere Erkenntnisse auf dem Gebiete der Geschiebeforschung; *Oesterreichische Wasserwirtschaft*, No. 11, pp. 286–294.

Bogardi, J. (1965). European concepts of sediment transportation, *Proc. ASCE, J. Hydraul. Div.*, **91**, NHY1, pp. 29–54.

Bogardi, J. (1974) *Sediment Transport in Alluvial Streams*, Akademiai Kiado, Budapest.

British Hydromechanics Research Association (1976). *Proceedings of the International Symposium on Unsteady Flow in Open Channels*, BHRA, Fluid Engineering, Cranfield, UK.

Čábelka, J. and Novák, P. (1964). *Hydraulic Research 1 – Research on Models*, (in Czech), SNTL, Prague.

Chow, Ven Te. (1959). *Open-Channel Hydraulics*, McGraw-Hill, New York.

Cheong, H. F. and Shen, H. W. (1976). Stochastic characteristics of sediment motions, *Proc. ASCE J. Hyd. Div.*, **102**, No. HY7, pp. 1035–1049.

Cioc, D. and Spartaru, A. (1957). Distortions et déformations des modèles a fond fixe, *Proc. 7th General Meeting IAHR, Lisbon*, Vol. II, Paper D49, 8 pp.

Dunne, T. and Leopold, L. B. (1978). *Water in Environmental Planning*, W. H. Freeman and Co., Reading, U.K.

Einstein, H. A. (1942). Formulas for the transportation of bed load, *Trans.*

ASCE, pp. 561–573.

Einstein, H. A. (1950). The bed-load function for sediment transportation in open channel flows, *U.S. Dept. of Agriculture Technical Bulletin.*

Einstein, H. A. and Banks, R. B. (1950). Fluid resistance of composite roughness. *Trans. American Geophysical Union*, **31**, pp. 603–610.

Einstein, H. A. and Barbarossa, N. L. (1952). River Channel Roughness, *Trans. ASCE*, **117**, pp. 1121–1146.

Einstein, H. A. and Chien, Ning. (1956). Similarity of distorted river models with movable beds, *Trans. ASCE*, **121**, pp. 440–457.

Einstein, H. A. and Müller, R. (1939). Über die Ähnlichkeit bei flussbaulichen Modellversuchen, *Schweizer. Archiv*, No. 8.

Elata, C. and Ippen, A. T. (1961). *The Dynamics of Open Channel Flow with Suspensions of Neutrally Buoyant Particles*, Technical Report, No. 45, Hydrodynamics Laboratory, Massachusetts Institute of Technology, Cambridge, Mass.

Engelund, F. and Hansen, E. (1967). *A Monograph on Sediment Transport in Alluvial Streams*, Teknisk Forlag, Copenhagen.

Francis, J. R. D. (1973). Experiments on the motion of solitary grains along the bed of a water stream, *Proc. Roy. Soc. (London)*, *Series A*, **332**, pp. 443–471.

Graf, W. H. (1971) *Hydraulics of Sediment Transport*, McGraw–Hill, New York.

Henderson, F. M. (1966). *Open Channel Flow.* Macmillan, New York.

Hino, M. (1963). Turbulent flow with suspended particles, *Proc. ASCE, J. Hydraul. Div.* **89**, No. HY4, pp. 161–185.

Inglis, Sir Claude. (1949). *The Behaviour and Control of Rivers and Canals*, Research Publication, No. 13, Central Water Power Irrigation and Navigation Report, Poona Research Station, India.

Ippen, A. T. (1971). A new look at sedimentation in turbulent streams, *J. Boston Soc. Civil Eng.*, **58**, No. 3, pp. 131–163.

Iwagaki, Y. (1954). On the laws of resistance to turbulent flow in open rough channels, *Proc. 4th Japanese National Congress of Appl. Mech.* pp. 245–250.

Jansen, P. Ph. *et al.* (1979). *Principles of River Engineering: The non-tidal alluvial river*, Pitman, London.

Jegiazarov, I. V. (1958). *Modelling of River Processes*, (in Russian), ANSSR, Moscow.

Kalinske, A. A. (1947). Movement of sediment as bed load in rivers, *Trans. Am. Geophys. Union*, **28**, No. 4, pp. 615–620.

Kellerhals, R., Church, M. and Bray, D. I. (1976). Classification and analysis of river processes, *Proc. ASCE, J. of the Hyd. Div.*, **102**, No. HY7, pp. 813–829.

Kennedy, J. F. (1963). Mechanics of dunes and antidunes in erodible-bed channels, *J. Fluid Mech.*, **16**, Part 4, pp. 521–544.

Keulegan, G. H. (1938). Laws of turbulent flow in open channels, Research Paper, RP1151, *Journal of Research, US National Bureau of Standards*, **21**, No. 6, pp. 707–741.

Knoroz, V. F. (1951). Free surface hydraulic transport and its computation, (in Russian), *Izv. VNIIG*, **44**, pp. 112–142.

Komora, J. (1957). The use of Prandtl–Karman equations for the computation of scales of river models with movable bed, (in Slovak), *Vodohospodársky časopis SAV*, No. 2, pp. 89–103.

Lacey, G. (1946). A general theory of flow in alluvium, *J. ICE*, **27**, pp. 16–47.

Lane, E. W. (1955). Design of stable channels, *Trans. ASCE*, **120**, pp. 1234–1279.

Larras, J. (1972). *Hydraulique et Granulats—Collection due Centre de Recherches et D'Essais de Chatou*, Eyrolles.

Laursen, E. M. (1958). The total sediment load of streams. *Proc. ASCE, J. Hydraul. Div.* **84**, No. HY1, pp. 1530–1536.

Leopold, L. B. and Maddock, T. (1953). *The Hydraulic Geometry of Stream Channels and Some Physiographic Implications*, Professional Paper 252, U.S. Geol. Survey.

Leopold, L. B., Wolman, M. G. and Miller, J. P. (1964). *Fluvial Processes in Geomorphology*, W. H. Freeman and Co., San Francisco.

Levi, I. I. (1960). *Modelling of Hydraulic Phenomena*, (in Russian), Gosenergoizdat, Moscow.

Liu, H. K. and Hwang, S. Y. (1961). Discharge formula for straight alluvial channels, *Trans. ASCE*, **126**, Part I, Paper 3276, pp. 1787–1822.

Losievskij, A. I. and Letnev, M. V. (1953). *Laboratory Studies of Rivers*, (in Russian), Gosenergoizdat, Moscow.

Luque, R. F. (1974). *Erosion and Transport of Bed-Load Sediment*, Krips Repro B.V.-Meppel, Netherlands.

Maddock, T. (1973). A role of sediment transport in alluvial channels, *Proc. ASCE, J. Hydraul. Div.*, **99**, pp. 1915–1931.

Mahmood, K. and Yevjevich, V. (1975). *Unsteady Flow in Open Channels*, Vols I and II, Water Resources Publications, Fort Collins, Colorado.

Malíšek, A. (1956). Investigations of gravel banks (in Czech), *Vodní hospodařství*, No. 12, pp. 312–314.

Marchi, E. (1957). Experienze di moto uniforme su correnti a pelo lobero in modelli di canali artificialmente scabri, *At. del V. Congresso di Idraulica*, Turin.

Martinec, J. (1958). *Effect of Channel Roughness on River Flow*, (in Czech), Práce a štúdie No. 96, VÚV, Prague.

Meyer–Peter, E. and Müller, R. (1948). Formulae for bedload transportation, *Proc. 2nd General Meeting IAHR, Stockholm*, **III**, pp. 39–64.

Müller, R. (1943). Theoretische Grundlagen der Fluss- und Wildbachver-bauungen, *Mitteilungen aus der Versuchsanstalt für Wasserbau ETH, Zurich*, No. 4.

Nalluri, C. and Novak, P. (1977). Turbulence characteristics in smooth open flow channels, *5th Biennial Symposium on Turbulence, University of Missouri, Rolla*, Paper II–3, 14 pp.

Novák, P. (1951). *Similarity in Experiments with River Models*, (in Czech), Práce a štúdie No. 86, VÚV Prague.

Novák, P. (1954). Investigations on river models, (in Czech), *Vodní hospodářství*, No. 10, pp. 291–303.

Novák, P. (1956). Outlet works on sediment transporting rivers, (in Czech), *Vodní hospodářství*, No. 9, pp. 235–240.

Novak, P. (1965). Model research on flood waves passing through a series of reservoirs and a river channel, *Proc. 11th Congress IAHR, Leningrad*, **III**, Paper 3.27, 10 pp.

Novak, P. (1966). A study of river regulation with extensive bed load movement, *Golden Jubilee Symposia (Model and prototype conformity)*, Poona, **1**, pp. 9–13.

Novak, P. (1967). Model similarity and training of rivers with large channel irregularities, *Proc. 12th Congress IAHR, Fort Collins*, **I,** Paper A47, pp. 379–388.

Novak, P. and Nalluri, C. (1975). Sediment transport in smooth fixed bed channels, *Proc. ASCE, J. Hydraul. Div.*, **101,** HY9, pp. 1139–1154.

Pantelopulos, J. (1957). Etude experimentale du mouvement par charriage de fond d'un melange de matériaux, *Proc. 7th general meeting IAHR, Lisbon,* **II,** Paper D30, 24 pp.

Pantelopulos, J. (1961). Influence de la turbulence sur la repartition de la force tractrice entre les matériaux d'un fond mobile *Proc. 9th Congress IAHR, Dubrovnik*, pp. 98–109.

Pantelopulos, J. (1961a). Quelques resultats expérimentaux sur l'engravement et les possibilités de degravement d'une retenue par un barrage en lit de rivière, *Proc. 9th Congress IAHR, Dubrovnik*, pp. 1128–1133.

Raudkivi, A. J. (1976). *Loose Boundary Hydraulics*, 2nd Edn, Pergamon Press.

Rohan, K. (1960). *Head Losses in Nonuniform Flow in Prismatic Channels*, (*in Slovak*), Práce a štúdie No. 10, VÚV Bratislava.

Rouse, H. (1950). (Editor) *Engineering Hydraulics*, John Wiley and Sons, New York.

Schlichting, H. (1958). *Grenzschicht Theorie*, Braun Verlag, Karlsruhe.

Shen, H. W. (Ed.) (1971). *River Mechanics*, Water Resources Publications, Fort Collins, Colorado.

Shields, A. (1936). *Anwendung der Aehnlichkeitsmechanik und der Turbulenz-forschung auf die Geschiebebewegung*, Mitteilungen der Preuss Versuchsanst. f. Wasserbau, Berlin 26.

Simons, D. B. and Albertson, M. L. (1963). Uniform water conveyance channels in alluvial material, *Trans. ASCE*, **128,** Part I, Paper 3399, pp. 65–107.

Simons, D. B. and Richardson, E. G. (1961). Forms of Bed Roughness in Alluvial Channels, *Proc. ASCE, J. Hydraul. Div.*, **87,** No. HY3, pp. 87–105.

Simons, D. B. and Richardson, E. V. (1966). Resistance to Flow in Alluvial Channels, Professional Paper 422-J, US Geological Survey.

Simons, D. B. and Sentürk, F. (1977). *Sediment Transport Technology*, Water Resources Publications, Fort Collins, Colorado.

Smutek, R. (1959). *Theory of Flow in Rectangular Conduits*, (in Czech), Rozpravy ČSAV, Řada technických věd, Nakl. ČSAV, No. 5, Prague.

Štich, O. (1958). *On Sediment Transport*, (in Slovak), Práce a štúdie No. 2, VÚV, Bratislava.

Strickler, A. (1923). *Beiträge zur Frage der Geschwindigkeitsformel und der Rauhigkeitszahlen für Ströme, Kanäle und geschlossene Leitungen*, Mitteilungen des Eidg. Amt für Wasserwirtschaft, No. 16, Bern.

Sumbal, J. (1959). *Similarity of Open Channel Flow with Movable Bed*, (in Slovak), Práce a štúdie, No. 4, VÚV Bratislava.

Sumer, M. (1970). Model Similarity Concerning the Transport of Suspended Matter in a Turbulent Flow Field, *J. Hydraul. Res. IAHR*, No. 3, **8,** pp. 357–364.

Thomas, Z. (1970). *Similarity of Flow in Conduits and Open Channels*, (in Czech), Práce a štúdie No. 127, VÚV Prague.

Vanoni, V. A. (1946). Transportation of suspended sediment by water, *Trans. ASCE*, **111,** Paper 2267, pp. 67–133.

Vanoni, V. A. (Ed.) (1975). *Sedimentation Engineering*, American Society of Civil

Engineers Task Committee for the preparation of the manual on sedimentation, ASCE, New York.

Vanoni, V. A. and Nomicos, G. N. (1959). Resistance Properties of Sediment-Laden Streams, *Proc. ASCE, J. Hydraul. Div.*, **85,** No. HY5, pp. 77–107.

Velikanov, M. A. (1946). *Dynamics of Rivers*, (in Russian), Gidrometeorizdat, Leningrad.

Vries, M. de (1977). *Scale Models in Hydraulic Engineering*, International Institute for Hydraulic and Environmental Engineering, Delft.

Vries, M. de and Zward, J. J. van der. (1975). *Mobile Bed River Models*, Publication No. 156, Delft Hydraulic Laboratory, Delft.

Watkins, R. D. and Brebner, A. (1954). Model-scale relations for open channels with non-uniform flow, *Proc. ICE*, **3,** pp. 183–215.

White, C. M. (1940). Equilibrium of Grains on the Bed of a Stream, *Proc. Roy. Soc. (London), Series A*, **174,** pp. 322–338.

White, W. R., Milli, H. and Crabbe, A. D. (1975). Sediment transport theories: a review, *Proc. ICE, Part 2*, pp. 265–292.

Wisner, P. (1955). Contribution to the modelling of scour in natural rivers, (in Roumanian), *Energetica si Hidrotehnica*, No. 5.

Yalin, M. S. (1965). *Similarity in Sediment Transport by Currents*, Hydraulic Research Paper No. 6, HMSO, London.

Yalin, M. S. (1971). *Theory of Hydraulic Models*, Macmillan, London.

Yalin, M. S. (1977). *Mechanics of Sediment Transport*, 2nd Edn, Pergamon Press, Oxford.

Yang, C. T. (1976). Minimum unit stream power and fluvial hydraulics, *Proc. ASCE, J. Hydraul. Div.*, **102,** No. HY7, pp. 919–934.

Yassin, A. M. (1953). Mean roughness coefficient in open channels with different roughnesses of bed and side walls, *Mitteilungen aus der Versuchsanstalt für Wasserbau und Erdbau ETH, Zurich*, No. 27.

Zegzhda, A. P. (1938). *Theory of Similarity and Computations of Hydraulic Models*, (in Russian), Gosstrojizdat, Moscow.

7 Models of Weirs, Dams and Hydroelectric Power Stations

7.1 General

7.1.1 General considerations and criteria of similarity

It is impossible in this book to cover the many problems investigated on models of weirs, dams and power stations in hydraulic laboratories throughout the world. We can only attempt to show some of the main results and contributions of experimental work attained in recent years in the solution of important hydrodynamic problems in this field of hydraulic structures. The experimental solution of hydraulic problems described here may be classified as follows:

(a) Low-head hydraulic structures, and problems connected with their general layout, passage of ice over weirs, etc.
(b) Dam spillways, i.e. overfall, chute, side channel, shaft, and siphon spillways.
(c) Dam outlets, culverts, inverted siphons, etc.
(d) Energy dissipation and stilling basins, local scour downstream of stilling basins, etc.
(e) Gates used in hydraulic structures, i.e. investigation of their shapes, hydrodynamic pressures, oscillation, etc.

In modelling these structures the *Froude law of similarity is almost exclusively used.* Sometimes, however, it is necessary to model phenomena where some further conditions must be fulfilled to achieve similarity, the study of *vortices, aeration and cavitation* being the most prominent ones. Similarity and methods of modelling cavitation have been discussed in Chapters 2 and 4 and aeration will be discussed briefly in Sub-section 7.3.3. As vortices occur at all types of structures some general points and a brief discussion of their modelling is included here.

7.1.2 Similarity of vortices

A vortex with air nucleus occurs frequently in hydraulic structures mainly at the outflow from an orifice in the bottom or the walls of a reservoir, at outflows under a movable spillway crest gate, at a transition from free water surface flow to flow under pressure, i.e. at inlets of siphons, conduits, culverts, etc., at shaft and siphon spillways, at pump intakes, etc. The vortices here usually have an unfavourable effect, such as, lowering discharge capacity, increase of bed disturbance near the structures, deterioration of turbine efficiency and of the filling of locks, etc. On the other hand the properties of vortices may be used to pass debris and smaller ice flows over hydraulic structures, e.g. vortices intentionally induced by flow rotation may be used for this purpose.

For model research of vortices the criteria of similarity are complicated by the fact that fundamentally they are a two-phase phenomena (water–air). This is why neither the laws of formation of vortices and of the velocity distribution in the rotating flow, nor problems of similarity have so far been fully solved. That this is so is shown by the difference in opinion on model similarity of vortices. Originally it was assumed that for fully developed turbulence of flow (high Reynolds number) it was possible to use the Froude law, especially as far as velocities and discharges were concerned. This opinion was held, e.g. by Blau, Escande, Camichel, Bratosin, Dobos, Szolnoky and others. According to them the velocity scale of the rotating flow is therefore

$$\frac{v_p}{v_m} = M_l^{1/2} \tag{7.1}$$

It has been shown, however, that apart from forces of gravity, viscous forces and, to a smaller extent, surface tension also affect the vortices. Modelling with a constant Reynolds number, where

$$\frac{v_p}{v_m} = \frac{\nu_p}{\nu_m} M_l^{-1}$$

can be considered, however, only for flow in closed sections, where vortices are of no particular importance. The effect of the joint action of viscosity and surface tension with the gravity force is expressed by some later authors in various methods of extrapolation of the velocity of rotation of the vortex from model to prototype:

$$\text{Brkich (1953):} \qquad \frac{v_p}{v_m} = M_l^{0.36} \tag{7.1'}$$

$$\text{Fraser (1953):} \qquad \frac{v_p}{v_m} = M_l^0 = 1 \tag{7.1''}$$

$$\text{Denny–Young (1957):} \qquad \frac{v_p}{v_m} = M_l^n \qquad \text{where } 0 \leqslant n < 0.5 \tag{7.1'''}$$

On the basis of their experiments Poliakovskij and Perelman (1959) prove the possibility of local modelling of vortices according to the Reynolds law whilst simultaneously preserving the Froude law for the whole flow. As a determining factor for the characterization of the vortex and the velocity field surrounding it they use the Reynolds number as $Re = v_r r/v$, where v_r is the circumference velocity at a radius r. These authors state that for $Re > 2.5 \times 10^5$, for a radius $r \leq 50$ cm, and for practically important depths the phenomenon is automodelling, i.e. independent of Re. For smaller values of Re ($4 - 5 \cdot 10^{-4}$) quantitative similarity may be achieved by an artificial increase of the circumferential velocities, e.g. by a tangential supply of a supplementary stream of liquid.

Jain *et al.* (1978) have studied the vortex formation at vertical pipe intakes and found that the critical submergence for vortex formation with an air core, S_c above a pipe intake, diameter d, is a function of a viscosity parameter $N_v(g^{1/2}d^{3/2}/v)$, circulation $N_r(\pi D_0 v_\theta S_c/Q)$ and the Froude number $(v/\sqrt{(gd)})$. No surface tension effects were evident ($We = \rho v^2 d/\sigma > 1.2 \times 10^2$). For $N_v > 5 \times 10^5$ viscosity had no effect and thus the vortex could be modelled using Froude similarity only.

7.2 Models of Low-Head Structures

7.2.1 General layout

When designing a more complicated hydraulic structure it is advisable to compare several alternative layouts as well as the placing and design of its individual components. This investigation, which is to help in the assessment of the influence of various alternative designs on the flow regime, the passage of ice, the local morphology of the river bed and possibly also on navigation, can be carried out on hydraulic and/or aerodynamic models. The choice of the type and scales of the model depends on the problems to be dealt with.

Investigations into the conceptional solution of the Bratislava–Wolfsthal Danube barrage may serve as an example (Gallay and Vincent, 1960). The distorted model scales 100/450 represented a 24 km long section of the Danube, i.e. the entire reservoir with the proposed barrage (Fig. 7.1). The movable bed on the model was formed by a coal mixture of specific gravity 1.33, which at a scale 1 : 10 represented the gravel material of the Danube.

On this model ten different alternatives of the whole layout of the barrage with hydroelectric development and navigation locks were investigated and the most suitable solution selected, especially from the point of view of flow, morphological changes and discharge capacity of the channel and flood plain upstream of the barrage, for a maximum discharge $Q = 14\,000$ m^3/s. Research showed that the centre of the barrage

Fig. 7.1. Model of the Danube barrage at Bratislava-Wolfsthal. [Gallay and Vincent, 1960]

must be placed approximately in the streamline of the flow, to pass this discharge safely and not to prevent the passage of ice and sediment. It was found advantageous to divide the hydroelectric power station into two parts, southern and northern placed on either side of the barrage in slight cuts into the banks, so achieving better protection against moving ice. The placing of the locks on the concave side in the streamline was found unsuitable both for navigation (strong transverse surface currents upstream of the lock approach) and because of morphological changes upstream of the barrage. Therefore, in the resulting design (Fig. 7.1) the locks are situated on the convex side. However, the guide wall of the upstream approach must not be full, but must contain openings to prevent sediment deposition. The flow upstream of the barrage was improved by retaining the right bank of the present channel in the reservoir (Fig. 7.1). Model investigation has shown that part of the sediment load of the Danube especially within discharges of 900 to 6000 m³/s will be deposited in the reservoir, especially at its upstream end.

The distorted model results were complemented by further investigations on a non-distorted model of scale 1:60, on which the construction stages of the barrage, the passage of ice from the reservoir (Sub-section 7.2.3), the design of the upstream lock approaches (Sub-section 8.2.2), translation waves and measures to reduce them (Sub-section 8.3.2), etc., were studied.

7.2.2   Low-head power stations at weirs

Low-head power stations adjoining weirs on smaller or medium sized rivers are usually placed in a cut into the bank and have the power house built as a direct continuation of the weir. In the majority of power stations of this type built prior to the Second World War a number of operational drawbacks have been found, caused, on the one hand, by their incorrect positioning in the river (inlets and outlets of the power plants placed in the straight sections or in the convex sides of the bends are being silted up), or, on the other hand, by a hydraulically unsuitable layout and inlet (outlet) shape in the form of a 90° bend with a very small radius (Fig. 7.2).

The unsuitability of this shape of inlet from the hydraulic point of view has been proved by model investigations and prototype measurements. Figure 7.2 (Čábelka, 1950) shows a great vortex region beyond the head of a long narrow pier separating the weir from the inlet to the first turbine, the efficiency and performance of which is thereby greatly reduced. A further disturbance in the flow occurring in the inlet beyond the perpendicular junction of the inlet wall with the river bank causes sedimentation and reduces efficiency and performance of the turbine adjacent to the bank. An unfavourable influence on the flow in the inlet is also exerted by unsuitable supports of the inlet bridge and the screen protecting it against floating debris and ice. To improve the unfavourable inlet layout, reducing the possible annual output of the power plant by about 10%, an effective reconstruction based on model investigations on a three-dimensional model of scale 1:35 was suggested.

The three Francis turbines were replaced by one Kaplan turbine of the same capacity and the design of the head and tailrace of the power station

Fig. 7.2. Model of an old power station inlet. [Čábelka, 1950]

was changed (Fig. 7.3). Since the space taken up by two Francis turbines adjoining the bank is sufficient for the placing of one Kaplan turbine, it was possible to close the inlet and outlet of the Francis turbine next to the weir. The pier was enlarged and the power station inlet given a hydraulically effective, unsymmetrical streamlined shape, around which water flowed without separation at all discharges. The inlet was extended in a funnel-like configuration at its entry and was fitted with an inlet sill and a bridge with a coarse rack in direct continuation of the line of the bank. The inlet bridge was supported on long thin streamlined piers forming guide walls. Most of the coarse debris and ice flows are retained by the rack and are passed below the weir over a lowered segment in the weir section adjacent to the power station.

In general, the power station can be suitably placed in the concave bank of the river bend next to the weir (Fig. 7.4), which is usually situated beyond the vertex of this bend. In this position only a little sediment is deposited in front of the inlet and outlet and is more easily washed away, due to transverse flow circulation, which is further increased by an artificial concave formed by turning the inlet sill and the bridge with

Fig. 7.3. Model of reconstructed power station inlet.

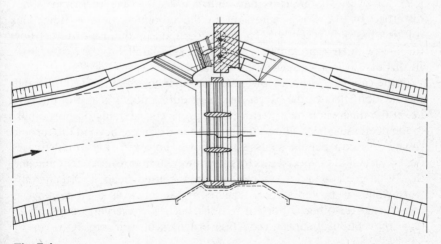

Fig. 7.4.

coarse rack in the downstream direction round the head of the dividing pier.

The fundamental feature of this solution is the realignment in plan of the axes of both the inlets to the turbines and of their draft tubes by turning them about 20° round the vertical axis of the turbines in the direction towards the river channel. This realignment simplifies the hydraulically effective solution of a funnel-shaped inlet and outlet from the power station, especially when it is placed in the concave bank. The solution has the following characteristics:

(a) A small excavation required by the power station inlet and outlet in the river bank;
(b) An even and undisturbed flow into the inlets and from the outlets of all turbines of the power station, and smooth flow of water round all parts of its sub-structure;
(c) Small energy losses in the power station inlet and outlets;
(d) Good efficiency and working characteristics of all installed turbines;
(e) Low silting up of inlet and outlet by sediment;
(f) Low construction, operational and maintenance costs.

It is suitable especially for smaller power stations where one or two vertical turbines are installed. In the case of a power station with one turbine this solution saved a full 10% of the construction costs, somewhat less than that in the case of power stations with two turbines.

The outline of the dividing pier between the power station and the weir recalls an aerofoil section. The pier head is not only a hydraulically effective, unsymmetrical streamlined shape, but also forms a suitable and not too long projection upstream of the weir ensuring that the flow in the inlet for every discharge is perpendicular to the fine rack and is not disturbed by the flow depression in the adjoining weir section. This solution has only recently been improved upon by the use of direct flow turbines with an approximately horizontal axis parallel to the axis of flow. In this case it is advisable to use the design shown in Fig. 7.3.

In the case of low-head power stations an increase of the head through the ejection effect of the excess discharge during floods is also of interest, i.e. at the time when their performance drops considerably proportionally to the decreasing head due to the increase in discharge beyond the turbine capacity. A cost-benefit analysis has shown, however, that in most cases the construction of special ejectors for power stations is not economic and that to use ejection for an increase in the used head is usually only worthwhile in power stations where an outlet with ejecting flow is constructed for other important reasons, such as preserving continuity of flow, prevention of surges, reduction in length of weir, etc.

7.2.3 Winter regime

The problem of model investigation of winter regime may be divided roughly into two groups, according to whether it is or is not possible to ignore the direct influence of frost on the studied phenomenon. Research work that can be carried out only in an ice laboratory equipped with a closed re-circulating hydraulic flume with freezing installation must be included in the second group. Here, for example, the formation of ice and its shape and physical properties, are investigated as well as the static and dynamic effect of ice on hydraulic structures, the protection of racks in inlet structures against ice formation and barring by frazil ice, ice formation on the walls of pipes, protection against ice by compressed air, etc. (*see* Section 12.5).

The other group of studies comprises problems in the solution of which it is possible to ignore the direct influence of frost on the studied phenomenon and to replace ice with another suitable material of similar properties (specific gravity, strength, friction, etc.). This type of research may be carried out in any hydraulic laboratory and is used, e.g., for studying suitable layouts of low-head power stations which would simplify the flow of ice through the construction site, the protection of power stations and the upper lock approaches against the direct pressure of ice floes, the manipulation of barrage gates and outlets of hydraulic structures during the passage of ice from the reservoir, steady and unsteady flow of water beneath the ice, etc. (*see also* Section 12.5).

As the movement of floating ice floes is influenced mainly by gravity, the Froude law is applied with such a scale of geometric reduction of the ice floes and the structure as to preserve turbulent flow on the model and reduce the influence of surface tension.

As the specific gravity of the material of the ice floes on the model must be identical to that of ice, i.e. about 0.917, wood and some porous materials are suitable for use, but paraffin or a mixture of paraffin and wax with the specific gravity of about 0.92 is best.

To investigate the breaking of ice floes during their passage over the weir on the model similarity of the strength of ice must be observed in the model material. From the Froude law of similarity we find the scale of stress and thus also strength. If we set out from the expression for stress, $\tau = M'/W$, where M' is the bending moment and W the section module (first moment) the scale for τ will be

$$M_\tau = \frac{M_p'/W_p}{M_m'/W_m} = \frac{M_l^4}{M_l^3} = M_l \qquad (7.2)$$

If this condition is to be fulfilled small slabs of real ice are used on the model, during the production of which kitchen salt is added to the

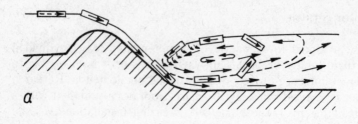

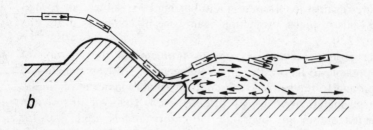

Fig. 7.5. Passage of ice flows over weirs. [after Bjeljashevskij, 1953]

freezing water, so reducing their strength; before use on the model their real strength is measured.

Bjeljashevskij (1953) dealt with passing ice floes over weirs and studied the most suitable weir design on two-dimensional models (Fig. 7.5).

For a weir with a bottom roller in the stilling basin the ice floes return to the weir in the hydraulic jump, rotate and assemble there, bump against the spillway and the stilling basin surface and tend to damage it; apart from that they make the passage of further floes from the upstream reservoir over the spillway more difficult (Fig. 7.5a). Better conditions for undisturbed and harmless passage of ice floes is given by a surface flow with a non-submerged hydraulic jump (Fig. 7.5b). However, in this case the apron below the weir is under great strain. This is why Bjeljashevskij recommends a slight submergence of the hydraulic jump as shown on Fig. 7.5c; this is suitable with respect to both the passage of ice and the forces acting on the apron. During laboratory experiments ice floes of prototype dimensions 1.5×2.0 m, 4.0×5.0 m and 0.5 m thick were used.

In the hydraulic laboratory at Gdansk, Poland, (Cebertowicz, 1958) experiments were carried out on a model of a barrage and power station on the Visla River to examine the passage of ice floes and the protection of the power station inlet from the direct pressure of ice. It was found that for directing the ice floes to the barrage a firm concrete guide wall is better suited than a floating elastic boom and a decrease in the operation of the power station is also advantageous. The ice floes were represented on the model (scale 1:50) by irregular slabs made from a mixture of wax and paraffin 0.3 to 1 cm thick with an area of up to 100 cm^2.

In Czechoslovakia a study was carried out on the passage of ice through a three-dimensional model (scale 1:60) of the proposed Bratislava–Wolfsthal barrage on the Danube. The passage of the ice was achieved in one of two ways, i.e. by overfall over the lowered upper part of double segments of two or all the six barrage sections, or by passing it through two completely opened central sections (Fig. 7.6; Sikora, 1962).

From the experimental results the relationship $Q_p = f(Q)$ was established (Fig. 7.7a) between the discharge Q_p needed for floating the ice from a 1 m^2 area of the upstream reservoir and the discharge Q over the weir, through which the ice floes are passed.

Fig. 7.6. Passage of ice through a model of the Danube barrage. [Sikora, 1962]

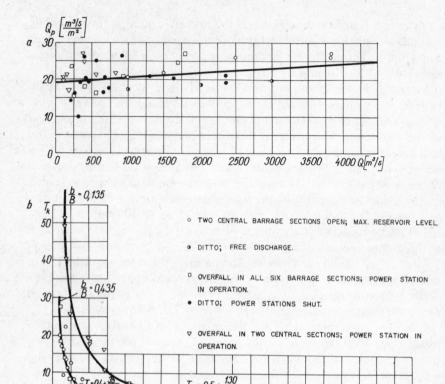

Fig. 7.7. [After Sikora, 1962]

The following important more general conclusions were deduced from the study:

(a) The discharge Q_p needed for passing ice from a $1\,m^2$ area of the reservoir increased slightly with the increasing discharge Q over the barrage.

(b) The manner of the operation of the gates exerted only a small influence on the value Q_p which was about 20 to $35\,m^3/s$.

(c) If the ice floes were passed through all completely opened barrage sections without appreciable backwater effect, the value Q_p dropped below $20\,m^3/s$; this state approached the normal passage of ice on a free river.

(d) Great difficulty was experienced in passing even slightly heaped-up ice floes over the barrage with an overfall jet height $H \leqslant 1\,m$, especially during frost.

The results of the experiments were also plotted as $T_k = f(q)$, where T_k is the time necessary (hrs) for the passing of ice floes from 1 km^2 of the reservoir and q is the specific discharge over the barrage (m^2/s). Figure 7.7b shows two graphs, one for the ratio $b/B = 0.435$ and the other for $b/B = 0.135$, where b is the length of the barrage sections with piers and B the width of the upstream reservoir. The greater value of the ratio represented the passage of the ice floes over the lowered segments of all six sections and the smaller value that over the two central sections. The following conclusions may be drawn from the above graphs:

(1) Time T_k decreases very rapidly with increasing specific discharge q through the barrage sections, across which the ice is passed.
(2) Time T_k also decreases with increasing ratio of b/B (effect of reduced contraction).

7.3   Models of Spillways

7.3.1   Overflow spillways

The study of overflow weirs is one of the oldest and most widespread fields of hydraulic research. Basic studies on weirs of various shapes were carried out by Bazin at the end of the last century and continued by other scientists. Their aim was to determine above all the values of the coefficients necessary for the calculation of the discharge Q, over weirs and notches of various shapes and types and under various conditions, as stated in greater detail in textbooks of hydraulics. Bazin's rectangular notch may be be regarded as the basic shape. Here water flows over a vertical wall with a horizontal sharp edge of varying height S above the bottom of the flume, without lateral contraction and with a perfectly aerated space beneath the overfalling nappe, of which the width B is equal to the width of the experimental flume which has vertical (smooth) lateral walls. For an overfall height H in the range 0.1 to 0.6 m Bazin adjusted Weisbach's equation so that the influence of the velocity of approach was included in the coefficient C as follows:

$$Q = \tfrac{2}{3}C\sqrt{(2g)}BH^{3/2}\left(1+\alpha\frac{k'}{H}\right)^{3/2} \tag{7.3}$$

where $k' = v_0^2/2g$ is the approach velocity head. On the basis of further experiments Bazin derived an expression for the influence of the velocity of approach

$$\left(1+\alpha\frac{k'}{H}\right)^{3/2} = 1+0.55\left(\frac{H}{H+S}\right)^2 \tag{7.4}$$

and expressed the coefficient $m_0 = \frac{2}{3}C$ as:

$$m_0 = \frac{2}{3}C = 0.405 + \frac{0.003}{H} \tag{7.5}$$

If we put

$$m = m_0 \left[1 + 0.55 \left(\frac{H}{H+S} \right)^2 \right],$$

we obtain Bazin's classic equation for an overfall in the simple shape

$$Q = m\sqrt{(2g)}BH^{3/2} \tag{7.6}$$

Further studies of the overfall of Bazin's type have shown that several limiting conditions influence the value of the discharge coefficient. Apart from the obvious effects of surface tension for small heads and viscosity for low Reynolds numbers these are, primarily, the velocity distribution and the degree of turbulence of flow upstream of the overfall, which are conditioned by the length of the approach flume and the mode of its inlet, the roughness of the upstream face of the spillway wall (plate), the rounding of the 'sharp' spillway edge and, finally, the pressure conditions in the space below the overfall jet.

With the aid of Bazin's overflow and the results of his measurements it is possible to measure the discharge accurately and also to determine the shape of the streamlined spillway surface of dams and weirs and of their gates by measuring the shape of free (fully aerated) nappes falling over a sharp-edged vertical and inclined thin plate, as was already done by Bazin and later supplemented and extended by further researchers.

Spillways on the crests of gravity dams or side channel spillways of earth or rockfill dams used to be designed in various hydraulically more or less effective shapes. Often they were not suitable for the flow of the overfall jet which caused various unfavourable phenomena, reaching dangerous levels with increase in size of hydraulic structures where spillways had to be designed for large discharges. This is why Creager, (Creager et al., (1945)) suggested the shape derived from the lower envelope of a free, perfectly aerated overfall jet, falling over a horizontal, straight sharp edge of a high spillway wall, for the crest as well as the entire surface of an overflow spillway of a high gravity dam. For this he used extrapolated shapes of nappes measured by Bazin on his overfall with a vertical weir plate as well as with one inclined at 45° in the direction of flow. Creager, formed the spillway surface of the dam in such a way that he pressed it slightly into the lower envelope of a free overfall nappe of equal overfall height as the maximum overfall height on the spillway of the dam.

Thus a streamlined spillway surface was formed which has considerable hydraulic and economic advantages, such as:

(a) A favourable value of the overfall coefficient, permitting a reduction in the length of the spillway;
(b) Favourable and smooth distribution of hydraulic pressures along the spillway surface and exclusion of dangerous negative pressures;
(c) Reduction of the spillway volume.

These advantages led to speedy application in practice and to further theoretical and experimental studies.

Already Bazin proved that on one and the same sharp-edged overfall the shapes of the nappes measured for a head $H \geq 0.1$ m are geometrically similar and that, thus, the influence of viscosity and surface tension is negligible. These shapes may therefore be recalculated from the nappe of an overfall head with $H = 1$ (e.g., 1 m), i.e., the unit overfall nappe which may be analytically expressed by the equation $y = mx^n$; the origin of the $x - y$ coordinates is placed on the spillway crest. The shape of the unit nappe may then be recalculated according to geometric similarity for any design head H_d.

Bazin also found that the shape of the unit nappe and thus also of its lower envelope changes with every change in the upstream slope and shape of the overfall wall, as well as with every change in the height of the horizontal sharp overfall edge above the bed of the experimental flume, which causes a change in the approach velocity. The influence of the approach velocity was particularly evident for $S < 2H$, which applies usually to weirs and low dams.

As Bazin's experiments did not cover the range of shapes and heights required in practice they were supplemented by numerous further studies. Of these the most important were investigations by Scimemi (1937), Smetana (1945), Oficerov and particularly the US Bureau of Reclamation Laboratory (1965). Scimemi and Smetana measured the shape of the overfall nappe flowing over a sharp-edged high perpendicular wall (i.e. negligible influence of inlet velocity). Scimemi expressed his results for the lower envelope of the 'unit' nappe as $y = 0.5x^{1.85}$ (Fig. 7.8 − spillway surface: 1 − with negative pressures, 2 = atmospheric (zero) pressures, $y = 0.5x^{1.85}$, 3 − positive pressures, $y = 0.46108x^{1.85}$). The Bureau of Reclamation experiments covered a whole series of shapes of unit overfall nappes for various heights of the overfall wall (large and small, i.e. with and without the influence of approach velocities) and for various slopes and shapes (see Fig. 7.9). The results of these measurements are available in graphs and tables.

In the design of streamlined spillway surfaces the choice of the design

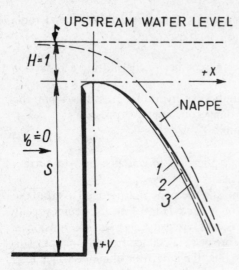

Fig. 7.8.

head H_d is important. Three possibilities exist:

(1) $H_d > H_{max}$
(2) $H_d = H_{max}$
(3) $H_d < H_{max}$

where H_{max} is the maximum overfall head that may be expected during the flood. (Note that H is now measured from the crest of the spillway.)

The first solution with $H_d > H_{max}$ results in a streamlined spillway with

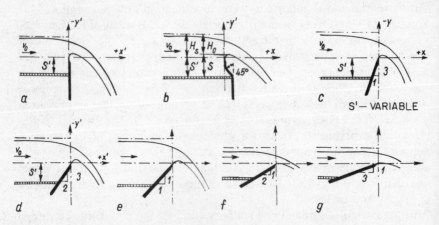

Fig. 7.9. [After US Bureau of Reclamation, 1965]

positive pressures at all discharges and this was used by Creager and Smetana for the design of high dam spillways with vertical upstream walls (Creager also used this criterion for spillways with the upstream face inclined at 45°). Even the maximum overfall nappe is slightly supported and thus exerts a smoothly distributed low pressure on the spillway surface which slowly increases with the reduction of the overfall head H, i.e. with the increase of the measure of support given by H_d/H. The discharge coefficient C, which for $H_d/H = 1$ may reach the favourable value $C = 0.75$, decreases with the growing measure of support of the nappe with a limit at about 0.58 (C for a broad crested weir).

For Creager's streamlined spillway surface with positive pressures Scimemi used the expression $y = 0.47x^{1.8}$; for the transition from the vertical upstream dam face to the spillway crest he suggested a circle of radius $0.4H_d$. The spillway shape investigated by Smetana for the design head $H_d = 1.1H_{max}$ is more rational and smoother than Creager's design and is given by $y = 0.46108x^{1.85}$. According to the same principle it is also possible to express streamlined spillway surfaces for lower dams and weirs with various slopes and shapes of the upstream face. Thus it is also advantageous to use these surfaces for barrage gates in order to prevent both negative pressures caused by the overfall jet and gate oscillation.

The second solution with $H_d = H_{max}$ gives a streamlined spillway surface with atmospheric pressures. The highest overfall nappe follows the spillway surface and theoretically neither positive nor negative pressures occur. The lower nappes are supported, however, by the spillway surface and exert a slight pressure on it just as in the preceding case. This spillway surface is more suitable than the one with positive pressures, since it results in higher values of the discharge coefficient and thus a smaller spillway.

The third solution with $H_d < H_{max}$ gives a streamlined spillway surface with negative (below atmospheric) pressures. It causes a depression and therefore an increased curvature of the nappe on the spillway crest resulting in negative pressures there. These disappear as soon as the head decreases to $H \leqslant H_d$. The negative pressure on the streamlined surface of the spillway crest increases with the increase of the head H above the value H_d. This increases the value of the discharge coefficient which reaches a value $C = 0.825$ for head $H \simeq 2H_d$. However, the nappe remains stable and in contact with the spillway surface only up to an overfall head $H = 1.65H_d$ for which the discharge coefficient attains a value of $C_d = 0.81$. This applies only if there is no access of air beneath the nappe into the sub-atmospheric pressure region (e.g. at piers), for otherwise the jet might occasionally separate from the spillway surface and again be sucked back to it, which might lead to its oscillation. If air is excluded then, according to Escande, one may permit a maximum overfall head $H_{max} = 1.65H_d$, i.e. design the spillway for the design head

$H_d = 0.6H_{max}$. It is advisable in this case to test on a spillway model that the pressures, in prototype, do not fall to a point where water vapour pressures result in cavitation with all its unfavourable effects. A certain safety factor should also be considered so that accidental and small irregularities on the spillway surface do not cause an increase in local negative pressures up to the cavitation value (Escande regards as sufficient a remainder of at least 10% atmospheric pressure). This type of streamlined spillway surface is very acceptable hydraulically and economically and is used ever more frequently for free overfall spillways. The case for its use is further supported by the fact that the occurrence of high (catastrophic) overfall discharges, during which the highest head, H_{max} occurs, is very rare and of a short duration.

The values of the coefficients for irregularly shaped spillways were investigated by Bradley (1952).

If there are gates on the overfall spillway it is advisable as indicated by model studies carried out by Lískovec and Weigl (1958) to place the sills at a distance of about $0.2H_d$ downstream from the spillway crest. This considerably reduces the tendency towards negative pressures on the crest occurring when discharging under partly raised gates. For gated overflow spillways, models are also used to determine the rating curve and coefficients for flow under the gates for various water levels in the reservoir. The results are usually given in nomographs or by a set of curves expressing the relationship between the discharge, the water level in the reservoir and the opening of the gate. If the spillway has several gated sections, the operational procedure at which the permitted stilling basin loading is not exceeded and which does not cause excessive downstream scour is also studied on the model.

Models are also used to study the shape of transition between the lower part of the spillway and the horizontal apron or stilling basin bed. Since a junction with an obtuse angle causes a sudden local pressure rise and pressure fluctuations, a smooth transition curve is frequently used. More recently various experimentally tested sills, baffles and ski jumps have been used in conjunction with streamlined overfall spillways to increase the dissipation of excess energy of the overfall jets (*see* Sub-section 7.5.1).

For movable weirs scale models are used to investigate pressures exerted by the overfall nappe on the spillway surfaces (*see also* Sub-section 7.6.2) and the influence of the height and shape of their fixed sill or of the lowered gates on the discharge capacity of the weirs, i.e. on the upstream water level and on the passing of ice and sediments during floods. According to Jambor's (1959) and Laco's (1963) experiments the influence of the raised sill crest on the discharge capacity is negligible up to about the value of $S = (0.15 \text{ to } 0.2)h$, where h is the depth of water above the weir. The raised sill must be rounded and joined to the

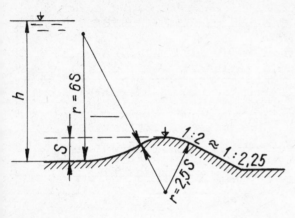

Fig. 7.10.

upstream bed by a smooth curve and to the stilling basin at a slope of between 1:2 and 1:2.25 (Fig. 7.10).

Piers and the resulting lateral contraction influence the discharge capacity of the spillway, the shape of the overfall nappe and the resultant pressures on the spillway surface. The lateral contraction of the overfall nappe depends on the shape of the piers, the ratio of the spillway width, B, to the upstream channel width, B_c, and the ratio, H_0/B (here H_0 is the overfall head including the velocity head). Figure 7.11 shows the relationship between $(1 - B/B_c)$, H_0/B and the contraction coefficient C_c for low weirs as determined experimentally by Laco.

Lateral contraction at the upstream head of piers also depends on their position relative to the upstream side of the spillway and the ratio of their width to the length of the spillway (weir) sections. Contraction and the resulting unfavourable effects (Fig. 7.12) may be excluded, or at least considerably diminished, by forming the upstream pier head in a stream-lined symmetrical or asymmetrical shape (good results are normally achieved for a length of the streamlined pier head equal to the pier width), and, in the case of a high sub-structure, by advancing the pier head upstream of the spillway crest into the more slowly flowing water.

In the case of low weirs where the downstream part of the piers is usually submerged by the tail water and where during floods the overfall is drowned, the shape of the downstream end of the piers exerts a greater influence on the discharge capacity than that of the upstream part (the same as in the case of bridge piers). Therefore, the downstream end of piers at low weirs should also be streamlined. This reduces both the backwater effect upstream of the weir and the loading of the apron and river bed.

The most suitable shape and position of spillway piers and the values of

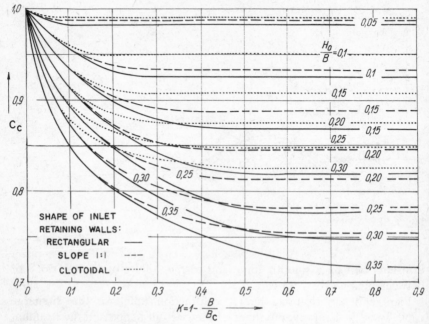

Fig. 7.11. [After Laco, 1963]

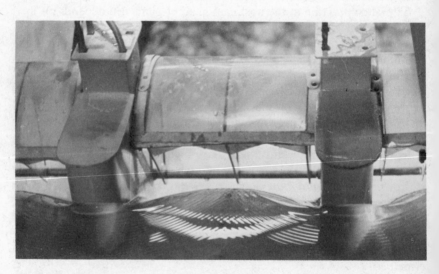

Fig. 7.12.

the coefficient of their lateral contraction are best investigated by model studies. For drowned overfalls the coefficient σ_z which is necessary for the calculation of the discharge according to Bazin's modified equation

$$Q = \sigma_z m \sqrt{(2g)} B H^{3/2} \tag{7.7}$$

is also determined for various spillway designs. The influence of the lateral contraction on the discharge over the spillway is expressed by the coefficient of contraction C_c which is included in Equations (7.6) and (7.7).

The spillways proper of the side channel spillways from which the discharge is conveyed downstream, usually by a chute (*viz.* Sub-section 7.3.3), are solved in a similar way as the direct overflow spillways.

7.3.2 Shaft spillways

(a) *General and similarity conditions*
Shaft spillways are used to pass floods from reservoirs where it is not possible or economical to use a simpler overfall or side channel spillway. A shaft spillway consists of the funnel-shaped spillway proper which is most frequently circular in plan, a vertical (in exceptional cases sloping) shaft, the shaft bend and the almost horizontal outlet tunnel terminating in the river channel below the dam. Excessive energy of the water flowing out of the tunnel is usually dissipated before entry into the river in a stilling basin. The shaft spillway is sometimes used as a combined structure with the valves of the bottom outlets and possibly also the turbines of the hydroelectric power station placed in its lower part and with their outflow terminating at the base of the vertical shaft and discharging into the outlet tunnel. Depending on their mode of operation shaft spillways are either free (automatic) or gated (regulated) with gates at the crest of the spillway. Gated shaft spillways are normally used only to pass large discharges (over $700 \text{ m}^3/\text{s}$).

In shaft spillways with a great head the velocity of flow at the point of transition from the vertical shaft to the horizontal conduit attains considerable values (sometimes more than 50 m/s). Under certain conditions this may cause cavitation and pressure fluctuations with all their unfavourable effects on the structure and these must be eliminated by a suitably designed shape and by aeration of the shaft bend.

A number of problems connected with the design of shaft spillways are solved by model studies. For example: the dimensions and shape of the cut into the bank of the valley for a shaft spillway with anti-vortex protection; dimensions and shape of the crest of the spillway and the funnel-shaped spillway surfaces; shape of the bend (elbow) of the vertical shaft; elimination of vacuum and of cavitation; placing and dimensioning of aeration vents; distribution of pressures and pressure fluctuations in the shaft and bend; influence of the inlet vortex and the flow rotation in the shaft; values of the discharge coefficient and spillway capacity; dissipation of excess kinetic energy of the water flowing out of the outlet conduit; possibility of passing larger (longer) floating objects (rafts) through the shaft spillway, etc.

The hydraulic phenomena in shaft spillways, as a whole, are modelled according to the Froude law of similarity, since the flow is influenced mainly by gravity. To be able to ignore the other simultaneously acting forces, the conditions given in Section 2.8, as well as some further limiting conditions, must be preserved on the model. According to Wagner (1956) the influence of surface tension on the value of the discharge coefficient is evident for an overfall head $H \leqslant 50$ mm. The model of the spillway must therefore have a scale of M_l such that the overfall head is greater than the limiting value, especially for a discharge decisive for the dimensioning of the shaft spillway.

The influence of the approach velocity, v_0, on the investigated shape of the shaft spillway and the discharge coefficient may be ignored if $S \geqslant D_c$, where S is the height of the spillway crest above the bed of the reservoir near the shaft spillway and D_c the diameter of its circular spillway crest. These cases occur at spillways placed upstream of the dam in a deep reservoir where the approach velocity to the spillway is very low. The influence of the approach velocity cannot be neglected in the case of shaft spillways situated in comparatively shallow cuts in the side of the valley upstream of the dam where $S < D_c$. According to Wagner the overfall at a shaft spillway is free, i.e. not drowned, if $H_S/D_c \leqslant 0.225$, where H_S is the overfall head on the sharp edged circular spillway from which the shape of the spillway is derived (Fig. 7.16). If the ratio H_S/D_c rises above the value 0.225, the overfall changes into a partly drowned one and the value of the discharge coefficient decreases. If $H_S/D_c > 0.5$, the water level above the spillway is practically horizontal and the overfall is completely drowned.

During the drowning of the shaft spillway a funnel-shaped vortex with an air core occurs in its axis (Fig. 7.13). This considerably decreases the discharge capacity, since part of the flow section of the vertical shaft and bend is filled with air. During the resulting spiral flow in the shaft shear stresses are more pronounced. All this necessitates an increase in the cross-sectional area of the shaft to guarantee the required discharge capacity of the drowned spillway. Such a vortex in the drowned shaft spillway and its unfavourable effects on the discharge capacity may be prevented by placing piers on the spillway crest which usually extend into the shaft inlet. Their function may be replaced by other types of anti-vortex devices such as ribs or thin vertical walls in varying positions, number, shape and length. Anti-vortex protection should be used above all in the case of shaft spillways placed at the side of the valley where the

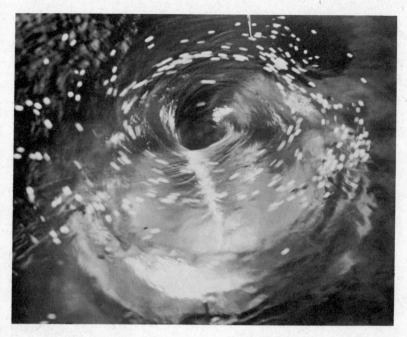

Fig. 7.13.

entire shaft and outlet tunnel are cut in the rock and by-pass the earth dam.

In the case of shaft spillways placed in a deep reservoir it is usual not to try to prevent the formation of a vortex and spiral flow in the shaft of the drowned spillway, but on the contrary, to encourage it. Spiral flow results in the elimination of negative pressures likely to cause cavitation, in more even pressure distribution on the walls of the inlet, shaft and bend, in considerable decrease (up to 50%) of pressure fluctuations in the shaft bend, which in turn limits the occurrence of vibrations of the structure, and in easier and harmless passing of large floating objects (such as logs) from the reservoir through the core of the vortex into the shaft and through the bend into the outlet conduit (Haindl and Doležal, 1961). These favourable effects are specially welcome in the case of tower shaft spillways which are placed on the upstream slope of higher earth dams founded on non-rocky substrata. Conditions for the occurrence of spiral flow in the shaft are also artificially created in the case of free overfalls, by placing low walls of a helical shape into the funnel of the spillway (Fig. 7.14). (According to its place of origin and most frequent use the name 'Prague Type' is applied to this type of shaft spillway (Čábelka and Novák, 1964). The optimum dimensions, number and shape of vanes placed on the shaft spillway crest may change according to specific

Fig. 7.14. Shaft spillway at the Hracholusky dam (Czechoslovakia).

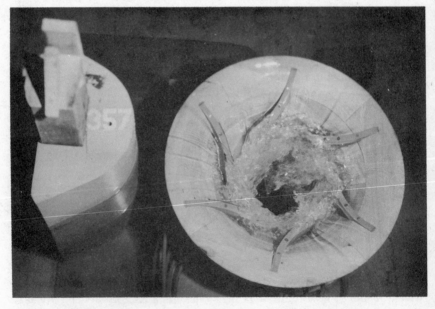

Fig. 7.15. Model of shaft spillway. [Čábelka and Novák, 1964]

conditions and should be ascertained experimentally. Figure 7.15 shows the flow through the shaft.

During model studies the influence of spiral flow in the shaft on discharge capacity of a shaft spillway of this type was also observed. Its increase for the same dimensions of the vertical shaft could be obtained by covering (eliminating) the air core of the vortex whilst preserving the spiral flow of water in the shaft.

The results of model and prototype studies show that with the admission of air into the zones where the flow separates from the walls of the shaft spillway, the total dynamic load of the corresponding parts of the structure and the intensity of pressure fluctuations on the walls are considerably reduced and the flow through the structure becomes more stable. Since during the free overfall the water cushion in the vertical shaft of every shaft spillway is intensely aerated, and since during the submerged flow over a shaft spillway without anti-vortex protection a vortex with an air core entraining a large quantity of air into the shaft is formed, two more similarity problems must be borne in mind during model studies (Haindl *et al.* 1962):

(1) Similarity of height of aerated water cushion in the vertical shaft of the spillway;
(2) Similarity of discharge through the shaft during a vortex regime.

(The general problem of similarity of vortices has already been mentioned in Section 7.1.)

(1) From Bernoulli's equation for sections 1 (vertical shaft) and 2 (end of shaft bend) we may express the head z of the water level of the water cushion above the outlet from the shaft bend for a free overall over the spillway crest as

$$z = \frac{1}{2g}(v_2^2 - v_1^2) - \left(\frac{p_1 - p_2}{\gamma}\right) \tag{7.8}$$

where p_1 and p_2 are the air pressure intensities above the water level and v_1 and v_2 are the mean cross-sectional velocities in Sections 1 and 2. If $p_1 = p_2 = p_0$ (atmospheric pressure), Equation (7.8) is simplified to

$$z' = \frac{v_2^2 - v_1^2}{2g} \tag{7.8'}$$

With a negative pressure $\Delta p/\gamma$ in section 2 the height of the water cushion will be

$$z = \frac{1}{2g}(v_2^2 - v_1^2) - \frac{\Delta p}{\gamma} = z' - \frac{\Delta p}{\gamma} \tag{7.8''}$$

With the discharge of water, air is entrained into the shaft; the mean velocity of the mixture of air and water may be regarded as being the same as the mean velocity of non-aerated flow in the shaft. From continuity $q = \rho_1 vA$, where

$$\rho_1 = \frac{Q_{\text{water}}}{Q_{\text{mixture}}}$$

Thus from Equation (7.8) we obtain for the head z^+ of the aerated water cushion

$$z^+ = \frac{1}{2g} \frac{Q^2}{\rho_1^2} \left(\frac{1}{A_2^2} - \frac{1}{A_1^2} \right) = z' \frac{1}{\rho_1^2} \tag{7.9}$$

e.g., for $\rho_1 = 0.8$ we obtain $z^+ = 1.57z'$. However, ρ has different values on the model and in the prototype. If we write the quantities for the model with index m and for prototype with index p, we get, with the use of the Froude law, the relation

$$z_p^+ = z_p' \frac{1}{\rho_{1p}^2} = z_m' M_l \frac{1}{\rho_{1p}^2} = z_m^+ M_l \left(\frac{\rho_{1m}}{\rho_{1p}} \right)^2 \tag{7.10}$$

i.e. the water cushion in prototype will be higher than the corresponding model value ($\rho_{1m} > \rho_{1p}$).

(2) The discharge through a shaft with a vortex is expressed by the relation

$$Q_p + Q_p^+ = (Q_m + Q_m^+) M_l^{5/2} \tag{7.11}$$

where Q is the discharge of water and Q^+ the discharge of air. If D is the diameter of the vertical shaft, D^+ the diameter of the vortex air core and v the vertical component of the water velocity in the vortex and of air in the vortex core, Equation (7.11) may be written for $M_l = D_p/D_m$ as

$$Q_p = Q_m M_l^{5/2} + v_m \frac{\pi}{4} D_m^{+2} M_l^{5/2} - v_p \frac{\pi}{4} D_p^{+2} \tag{7.11'}$$

If $D_p/D_p^+ = c_p$ and $D_m/D_m^+ = c_m$ we obtain

$$Q_p = Q_m M_l^{5/2} + v_m \frac{\pi}{4} \frac{D_m^2}{c_m^2} M_l^{5/2} - v_p \frac{\pi}{4} \frac{D_p^2}{c_p^2}$$

$$= Q_m M_l^{5/2} + \frac{\pi}{4} v_p D_p^2 \left(\frac{1}{c_m^2} - \frac{1}{c_p^2} \right)$$

By introducing for $c_p/c_m = \alpha$ we get

$$Q_p = Q_m M_l^{5/2} + \frac{\pi}{4} v_p D_p^2 \frac{1}{c_p^2} (\alpha^2 - 1)$$

Since $v_p(D_p^2/4)\pi = Q_p$ the resultant relation will be

$$Q_p = Q_m M_l^{5/2} \frac{c_p^2}{c_p^2 + 1 - \alpha^2} \tag{7.12}$$

It was found experimentally that ratio c_p has an order of ten and the ratio α an order of one $(\alpha > 1)$. Therefore the expression

$$\frac{c_p^2}{c_p^2 + 1 - \alpha^2}$$

is only slightly larger than one so that it changes the modelled discharge only very slightly. Thus the discharge through the shaft spillway may also be extrapolated according to the Froude law of similarity for a flow with a vortex.

(b) *Shape of the spillway surface of a shaft spillway*

The shapes of the spillway surfaces and the discharge coefficients of shaft spillways were studied in great detail by Wagner (1956) on a circular sharp-edged weir diameter $D_c = 508$ mm. On this perfectly aerated weir he measured the shapes of the overfall jets, the values of the discharge coefficients and the influence of the approach velocity for various overfall

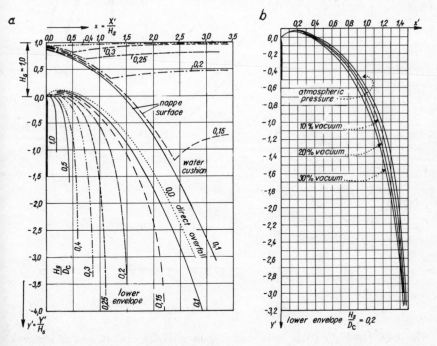

Fig. 7.16. Shapes of shaft spillways. [After Wagner, 1956]

heads. Since the shapes of fully aerated overfall jets from sharp-edged circular weirs are similar if they have the same ratio H_s/D_c (H_s is the head over the spillway and D_c the diameter of the spillway crest) Wagner investigated the shapes of the unit overfall for a number of values of the ratio H_s/D_c (Fig. 7.16a); using the lower envelopes the shape of the spillway surface for any overfall head and any spillway crest diameter can be designed. Wagner also investigated the influence of negative pressures (10% to 50% vacuum) below the overfall jet on its shape. Figure 7.16b shows the results for the ratio $H_s/D_c = 0.2$ and Fig. 7.17 shows the variation of the coefficient of discharge m (Equation (7.6)) with H_0/R_s and S/R_s.

The use of Wagner's streamlined shape of the spillway crest and funnel-shaped inlet into the vertical shaft is especially suitable for shaft

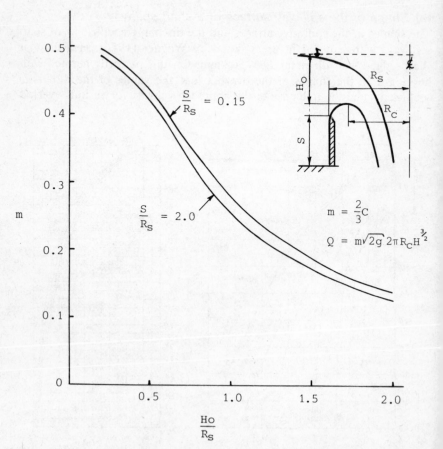

Fig. 7.17. Discharge coefficients of shaft spillways. [After US Bureau of Reclamation, 1965]

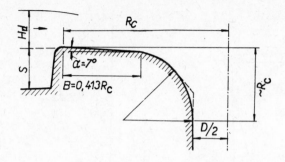

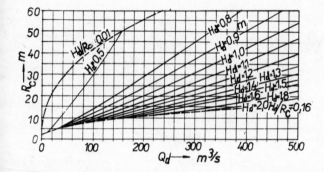

Fig. 7.18. Shaft spillway with wide crest. [After Blau, 1970]

spillways in deep reservoirs. For shaft spillways placed in the cut into the slope of one of the sides of the valley upstream of the dam it is suitable according to Bollrich (1965) when its main parameters lie within the range $0.1 < H_s/D_c < 0.25$. For the ratio $H_s/D_c < 0.1$ a shaft spillway with a flat (wide) crest, investigated by Blau (1970), is used. The results of this study are shown on Fig. 7.18 for $0.01 < H_d/R_c < 0.16$, where H_d is the design overfall head and R_c is the radius of the circular shaft spillway crest. Q_d is the design discharge of the shaft spillway.

(c) Shape and dimensions of the cut into the valley for the shaft spillway and the anti-vortex devices

To achieve the greatest discharge capacity of a shaft spillway placed in the cut at the side of the reservoir upstream of the dam a smooth flow of water from the reservoir must be ensured over the entire circumference of the circular spillway and the occurrence of a vortex with an air core for the submerged overfall should be excluded. This problem has been dealt with experimentally by Mojs (1970) who developed similar work by other

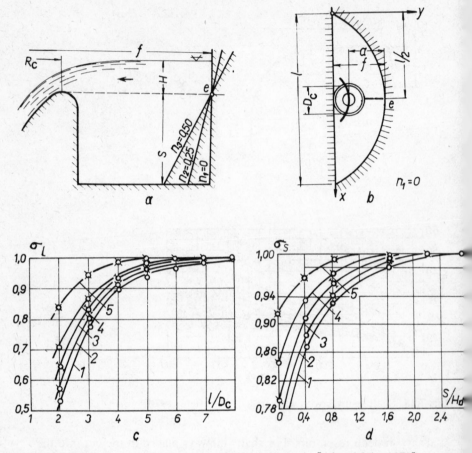

Fig. 7.19. Shaft spillway near the bank of the reservoir. [After Mojs, 1970]

authors. By extensive research he showed that the most effective vortex prevention of all those investigated (piers on the crest of the shaft spillway of various length or vertical walls in the shape of a cross, at angles, rounded, etc.) was a thin vertical curved wall, as shown in Fig. 7.19b, with its top above the maximum water level in the reservoir and its bottom edge reaching into the funnel of the spillway by $0.25 R_c$ below the level of the spillway crest. The anti-vortex effect of this wall could be increased further by another vertical straight wall leading radially from the spillway crest in the shortest line to the cut into the bank (point e in Fig. 7.19b, the axis of the wall indicated by broken lines). This additional wall is useful also for carrying a communication bridge from the bank to the spillway.

Suitable shapes and dimensions of the cut into the bank established by model studies are shown in Fig. 7.19a, and b. The bottom of the cut around the spillway is horizontal at such a depth S below the crest that $S/H_d > 1.6$; at the crest level the end is limited by a parabola

$$y = \frac{4x(l-x)f}{l^2}$$

where $f = 1.75D_c$. The ratio $f/D_c = 1.75$ has been found to be the optimum for all shaft spillways throughout the range of H/R_c from 0.1 to 0.8. The value of l is usually given by $l/D_c > 6$. Mojs' study further showed that the slope of the cut, within a range from $n = 0$ to $n = 0.5$ (Fig. 7.19a), does not influence the discharge capacity of the shaft spillway.

Wagner and others have shown that for free standing shaft spillways, with streamlined spillway surface, the value of the discharge coefficient $m = \frac{2}{3}C_d$ is not constant but depends generally on the degree of support of the overfall jet H_d/H (*see* Sub-section 7.3.1) and on the value of the ratio H/D_c. In the case of shaft spillways placed in a cut into the bank the discharge coefficient is also influenced by the ratios l/D_c and S/H, i.e. by the width and depth of the cut. Figure (7.19c,d) give the values of the correction factors σ_l and σ_s to be applied to the corresponding values of the free spillway discharge coefficient m as determined by Mojs for values of $H/R_c = 0.2$, 0.3, 0.4, 0.5 and 0.6 (curves 1 to 5).

Figure 7.20 illustrates schematically the three regimes for a shaft spillway, without gates, placed in a cut in the bank. The rating curve is composed of three parts, as in the case of a free standing spillway (*see* 7.3.2(a) above)

(1) Free overfall over the spillway crest

$$Q = m'L\sqrt{(2g)}H^{3/2} \tag{7.6'}$$

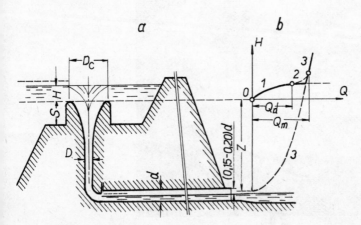

Fig. 7.20.

where L is the total length of the spillway crest ($=2\pi R_c$), H is the overfall head and $m' = m\sigma_l\sigma_s$.

(2) Transition region between the free and submerged spillway.

(3) Submerged shaft spillway with Q given by

$$Q = C_d A \sqrt{(2g(H+Z))} \tag{7.13}$$

where A is the cross-sectional area of the constricted shaft bend, Z the height of the spillway crest above the ceiling of the shaft bend and C_d the coefficient of discharge determined (on the model) for the given shaft spillway.

In the case of some shaft spillways a certain part of the spillway crest can be out of action (Fig. 7.21) because of the proximity of a tower with

Fig. 7.21. Model of a 'partial' shaft spillway. [Čábelka and Novák, 1964]

the regulating valves of the bottom outlets leading into the horizontal outlet tunnel. In this case, the distribution of pressures on the spillway surface and in the vertical shaft is not even and the pressures and their fluctuations should, therefore, be measured on the model for a greater number of points than for a symmetrical overfall of water over the entire circumference of the shaft spillway crest. Greater care must also be devoted to the study of effective aeration.

(d) Losses in the constricted bend of the spillway shaft

Research on losses caused by the curvature and constriction of the shaft bend was carried out by Gardel (1949). He took measurements for various values of the ratio r_c/D where r_c is the radius of curvature of the axis of the bend in the vertical section and D is the diameter of the shaft. During the model studies he also varied the value of the constriction e at the end of the bend, i.e. ratio e/D.

The discharge through a submerged shaft spillway without a vortex is given by Equation (7.13); for $C_d\sqrt{(Z+H)} = C_d\sqrt{H_b} = \sqrt{H^+}$;

$$Q = A\sqrt{(2gH^+)} \tag{7.13'}$$

Gardel investigated the relationship of the coefficient $\eta = C_d^2 (= H^+/H_b)$ and ratio H_b/D of the shaft spillway for various values of the ratio r_c/D and e/D of the bend. From the results it follows that the coefficient η is almost constant in the investigated range of the ratios H_b/D (5 to 11) and e/D (0.18 to 0.50) with values as follows: for $r_c/D = 1$, $\eta = 0.67$; $r_c/D = 1.5$, $\eta = 0.735$; and for $r_c/D = 2$, $\eta = 0.80$. The resistance coefficient of the bend ξ_b may then be expressed as

$$\xi_b = \frac{H_b - H^+}{H^+} = \frac{1}{\eta} - 1 \tag{7.14}$$

(e) Aeration of the bend and outflow conduit of the shaft spillway

At higher discharges and velocities sub-atmospheric pressures may occur on the inner (convex) side of the shaft bend and the beginning of the outlet conduit of the shaft spillway that may cause cavitation and vibration of the entire structure. This may be prevented by the access of air through suitably designed aeration vents (Fig. 7.22) (Haindl, 1957). The quantity of air necessary depends not only on the dimensions and shape of the bend but, above all, on the regime of flow in the outlet tunnel. Figure 7.23 shows the four characteristic flow regimes in the tunnel, which are similar to those in a bottom outlet with a regulating gate at the beginning or in the middle of the outlet:

(i) Pressure flow regime which occurs in the case of equal cross-section of

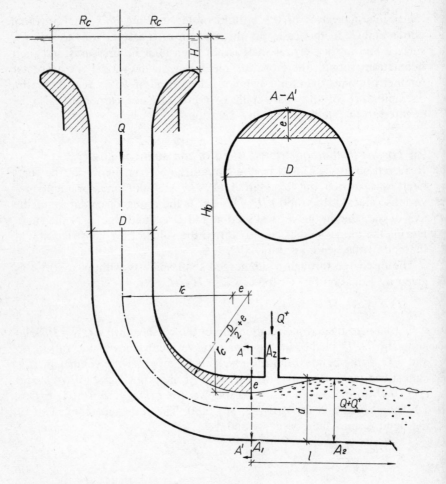

Fig. 7.22. [After Haindl, 1957]

the vertical shaft, bend and outlet tunnel terminating below the down-stream water level (the bend is not aerated in the region of negative pressure and there is no hydraulic jump in the tunnel). With respect to the discharge capacity of the shaft spillway, this pressure regime is the most efficient. However, it is undesirable because of low stability of flow and because of the danger of great negative pressures, cavitation and vibration, and therefore it is used only for shaft spillways built in the rock outside the body of the earth dam.

(ii) Pressure flow regime with a hydraulic jump at the beginning of the outlet tunnel downstream of the point of constriction provided with aeration. This regime occurs where the outlet tunnel is comparatively

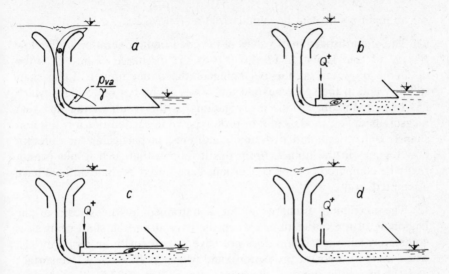

Fig. 7.23.

long or terminates below the downstream water level. Even with sufficient aeration at the point of contraction it may cause vibration of the structure because of the pulsation of the hydraulic jump in the tunnel. Therefore, it should only be used with very good dam foundations, or when the outlet tunnel by-passes the dam itself laterally.

(iii) Flow with free surface and with a free hydraulic jump, which does not fill the cross-section of the outlet tunnel. Aeration is provided downstream of the contraction.

(iv) Flow with free surface and without a hydraulic jump in the outlet tunnel. This regime is the most favourable from the hydraulic point of view and safest for the shaft spillway and the dam. Therefore it may also be used in cases of poorer dam foundations and if the tunnel passes through the body of an earth dam. To assure the stability of this regime the discharge of air into the outlet tunnel downstream of the constriction must be correctly determined and the aeration pipe designed accordingly.

Sikora (1965) carried out a series of measurements on three geometrically similar models of shaft spillways with the scale ratio $1:2:4$. He concentrated mainly on the air entrainment by the flow over the crest of a shaft spillway, the determination of discharge of air entrained by the flow at the beginning of the outlet tunnel and the dimensioning of the aeration vent, and on model similarity of entraining air and the possibility of extrapolating the results from the model to prototype.

The main results can be summarized as follows:

(1) The great dispersion of values of the coefficient of aeration of the flow $\beta = Q^+/Q$ (*see* Equation (7.17)) (Q^+ is the discharge of air, Q is the discharge of water) at the beginning of the outlet tunnel of the shaft spillway and in the space beyond the valves of the bottom outlets, which has been found in various investigations, is the result of the fact that measurements on models and in prototype were carried out for different shapes, dimensions and hydraulic conditions, in particular for different flow regimes in the tunnel. From this it follows that such results cannot really be compared nor the conclusions generalized as some authors have attempted to do.

(2) The maximum discharge of air is entrained by the stream at the beginning of the outlet tunnel when the overfall on the shaft spillway is completely submerged and does not have a vortex with an air core (e.g., when using anti-vortex protection), and when the flow has a free surface without hydraulic jump in the whole tunnel (Fig. 7.23d). The aeration vents at the beginning of the outlet tunnel should be designed for this maximum air discharge.

(3) The expression for the coefficient of aeration $\beta = Q^+/Q$, which was derived analytically and verified experimentally, is

$$\beta = \frac{A_2}{A_1} \sqrt{\left| \left(\frac{1 - \xi_1 - \dfrac{\Delta p}{\gamma} \dfrac{2g}{v_1^2}}{1 + \sum\limits_{2}^{n} \xi} \right) - 1 \right|} \tag{7.15}$$

where:

A_1 is the cross-sectional area at the point of contraction,

A_2 is the entire cross-sectional area of the outlet tunnel,

ξ_1 is the resistance coefficient (coefficient of losses) in the hydraulic jump downstream of the contraction,

$\sum\limits_{2}^{n} \xi$ is the sum of resistance coefficients (coefficients of losses) in the remaining length of the tunnel,

$\dfrac{\Delta p}{\gamma}$ is the difference in pressures beyond the contraction and at the end of the outlet tunnel,

$\dfrac{v_1^2}{2g}$ is the velocity head at the contraction.

This relationship is valid for the pressure flow regime in the tunnel with a hydraulic jump at its beginning (Fig. 7.23b) and for the case of pressure flow where the mixture of water and air completely fills the flow cross-section throughout the whole length of the tunnel.

It follows from Equation (7.15) that the maximum value of the coefficient of aeration β_{max} approaches the value of the ratio of cross-sectional areas

$$\beta_{max} = \frac{A_2 - A_1}{A_1} \qquad (7.15')$$

(4) From the analysis of parameters influencing the air entrainment at the beginning of the outlet tunnel the coefficient of aeration β can be expressed in the non-dimensional form

$$\beta = f\left(\frac{p'/\gamma}{v_1^2/2g}, Fr, \frac{l}{d}\right) \qquad (7.16)$$

which has been verified by model experiments; in Equation (7.16) p' is the negative pressure beyond the contraction and l/d is the relative length of the outlet tunnel.

(5) If there is free surface flow throughout the outlet tunnel, the coefficient of aeration β is given by a relationship which is valid for the aeration of a stream of water in open channels as given in Sub-section 7.3.3. Here β is expressed by the density, ρ_1, of the air-water mixture in the whole section as

$$\beta = \frac{Q^+}{Q} = \frac{Q^+ + Q}{Q} - 1 = \frac{1}{\rho_1} - 1 = \frac{1 - \rho_1}{\rho_1} \qquad (7.17)$$

where $\rho_1 < 1$ (the weight of air in the mixture is ignored).

If the value of coefficient β according to Equation (7.17) is greater than the value β_{max} from Equation (7.15') then Equation (7.15) is valid.

(6) Sikora found that both the beginning of air entrainment by the water and the coefficient of aeration, β, are functions of the Froude number at the point of contraction. When the models were operated according to the Froude law the results of all the models were practically identical, after extrapolation according to their scales. In contradiction to previous views, he arrived at the conclusion that the results of model studies of aeration of shaft spillways at the beginning of the outlet tunnel, where appropriate limiting conditions are observed, may be extrapolated into prototype according to the Froude law ($\beta_m = \beta_p$). The discharge of air entrained by the flow into the shaft spillway outlet tunnel for which the aeration vent must be designed is given by $Q^+ = \beta Q_d$, where Q_d is the design discharge falling over the shaft spillway; for the coefficient of aeration β the greatest value that might occur in the given case must be considered. The necessary cross-section A_z of the aeration pipe is given by

$$A_z = \frac{Q^+}{v^+} = \frac{\beta Q_d}{v^+}$$

The velocity of air flow in the prototype aeration pipes should have the value $v_p^+ \leqslant 50$ m/s to exclude dynamic stresses, according to Martins (1959) and Goljevscek; usually $v_p^+ = 45$ m/s.

To dissipate the excess energy of the water flowing from the shaft spillway outlet tunnel measures may be used as discussed in Sub-section 7.5.3.

7.3.3 Side channel, chute and siphon spillways

(a) *Side (channel) spillways*
The term 'side spillway' usually refers to two different hydraulic structures having a similar purpose, i.e. drawing off water from a channel or reservoir, but different hydraulic properties and designs. The classic *side* or *lateral weir* draws off part of the discharge from *a channel with a free surface* if in a certain section the discharge is to be limited or divided, or if a certain water level is to be maintained.

The spillway crest of a lateral weir is usually parallel to the axis of the channel, or slightly inclined towards it. The crest can be horizontal or also slightly sloping in the direction of flow. The overfall head at the weir changes along the spillway crest. The channel flow at the weir is a spatially varied nonuniform flow conditioned by the division of the flow between the main channel and the weir, which further changes with varying crest shapes and with different positions of the side weir, i.e. in a straight channel or in a bend. It is therefore difficult to compute the flow theoretically with any safety and for the design of large and important side channel weirs it is best to investigate the flow, discharge condition and design details on scale models.

Many scientists have dealt with the theoretical and experimental solution of the classical side weir. Zschiesche (1954) carried out a large number of experiments with side weir crests of various shapes. De Marchi (*see* Chow, 1959) worked out an approximate solution of the differential equation for the water levels along the side weir. Kunštátský (1956) continued de Marchi's solution, systematically analysed Zschiesche's measurements, which he supplemented by his own experiments, and elaborated a theoretically founded method of hydraulic computation of side weirs.

The second type are *side channel spillways* for passing flood discharges from *reservoirs*. They are mainly used when it is not possible to have a direct overfall spillway on the dam, usually at earth, rock-fill, buttress or arch dams. They are placed on the valley slope at the side of the dam and their solution depends on the morphology, geological conditions, the height and type of the dam, the operation of the reservoir, etc. A side channel spillway has the following main parts: the spillway proper, the flume (trough) downstream of the spillway, a steep chute, a sloping shaft or a cascade, and finally the energy dissipator.

Model studies of side weirs and side channel spillways are carried out according to the Froude law of similarity with the limiting conditions stated in Section 2.8. The modelling of aeration of the free surface flow occurring mainly on long, steep chutes, however, is not determined by the Froude law.

The spillway itself is usually free, without gates and with a horizontal crest at the highest normal water level in the reservoir. To prevent the reservoir water level from rising too much during floods the spillway crest is usually fairly long, having a streamlined cross-section and slight negative pressures, and the spillway flume is designed so that even the high discharges pass over it as a free overfall. The side channel spillway may also be provided with movable gates to control the reservoir volume within their height.

In relation to the axis of the chute, which is usually approximately perpendicular to the axis of the dam, the spillway can be placed not only as a side channel spillway, with the crest perpendicular to the dam (*see* Fig. 7.24), but also upstream of the dam, with the spillway crest straight or slightly curved or in direct continuation with the dam axis. The frontal spillway is perpendicular to the axis of the chute, and since its length is limited it is usually provided with gates. It is very similar to a low dam or weir followed by a chute. A spillway crest, which is curved in plan, is used as a frontal spillway if its length is to be increased and if this is possible with regard to the terrain of the reservoir. The plan of the curved crest, usually without gates, may vary in shape, e.g., it may form part of a circle or ellipse, a horseshoe or a deformed wave. For these types of spillway, model studies are used to develop a comparatively short energy dissipator which must be designed so as to ensure a free overfall over the whole length of the spillway crest and an even distribution of the discharge along the entire width of the chute.

The side channel spillway proper, with its horizontal crest parallel to the axis of the chute, i.e. approximately perpendicular to the axis of the dam, has a flume formed by a long, usually straight channel cut in the side of the valley, with the chute as its direct continuation. Figure 7.25 indicates the great complexity of the spiral flow in the spillway flume with a gradually increasing discharge in the direction of the flow, which is unevenly aerated, its fluctuating velocities are unevenly distributed and the water level is irregular and unsteady. The theoretical solution of this flow, directed towards determining the dimensions of the flume and the water level in it, is difficult and possible only with the introduction of simplifying assumptions (Hinds, Favre and Li). It is therefore often verified experimentally.

A number of principles for the design of side channel spillway flumes

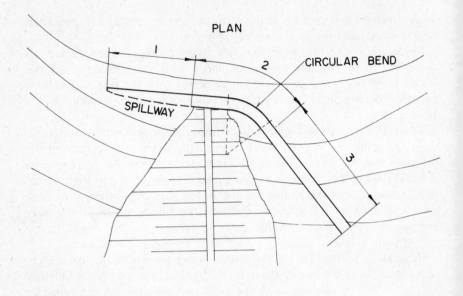

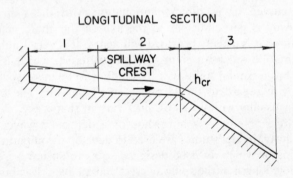

Fig. 7.24.

may be derived as a result of model studies. The longitudinal slope of the bottom should be greater than 2% and can be either constant or increase slightly in the direction of flow. The most suitable cross-section of the flume is a rectangle, or trapezoid with steep sides. The slope of the side of the flume adjoining the spillway is adapted to the solution of its spillway crest. If possible the slope of the side of the flume opposite the spillway should be vertical or very steep in order to decrease the height of the 'run-up' wave caused by the cross flow from the overfall. The height of this wave for a milder slope of this side wall can be decreased by a longitudinal step in the invert of the flume. The depth, width and bed slope of the spillway flume must be designed in such a way that even the maximum flood discharge passes with a free overfall over the entire

Fig. 7.25. Flow in a model of a side channel spillway. [Čábelka and Novák, 1964]

spillway crest; therefore, the width of the flume roughly doubles in the direction of flow. At the end there should be a control section of the same width as the chute to guarantee an even distribution of flow. At the beginning of the spillway flume the spillway crest ((1) in Fig. 7.26a) should not be straight, but in a quarter circle. Model studies have shown that in this solution more favourable flow conditions occur at the beginning of the flume (2) because the water overfalling at the head of the flume increases the flow velocity there. If the spillway crest is to remain straight, e.g. in a gated side channel spillway as used on the Hoover Dam, it is advisable to design the beginning of the flume according to Fig. 7.26b. Near the dam the spillway crest is usually terminated by a pier with an asymmetrically rounded face.

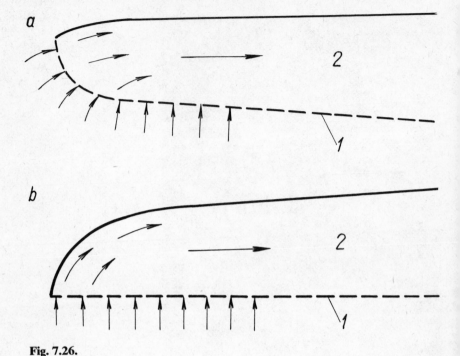

Fig. 7.26.

(b) *Chutes*

The chute should be smoothly connected to the energy dissipator of a frontal spillway or continue directly from the side channel spillway flume. For economic as well as hydraulic reasons it should be straight, with a supercritical bed slope continuing from the energy dissipator or the spillway flume, where subcritical flow usually occurs (Fig. 7.24). The morphological and geological conditions of the valley slope, which the chute should follow, may result in a chute that is curved in plan and also in changes of its slope. A bend of the chute with supercritical as well as unsymmetrical inflow of water from the spillway, or badly designed piers on a gated spillway usually cause transverse interference waves along the water surface in a direction oblique to the axis of the chute. Under certain conditions during supercritical flow translatory waves, approximately perpendicular to the axis, may also occur. Both these types of waves cause an uneven distribution of discharge along the width and length of the chute, a considerable raising of the water level in it, and unsymmetrical and unsteady loading of the stilling basin. Further, most chutes are associated with aerated flow which increases the depth and necessitates raising of the lateral walls.

An example of transverse *interference waves* on a chute with supercritical flow is shown on Fig. 7.27. In a straight chute the slope of the bed may gradually change and the cross-section may have any shape suited to local conditions. However, if a bend in the chute is necessary it is advisable to place it immediately downstream of the spillway and to give it a gentle, subcritical slope, passing into supercritical slope only at the end of the bend (Fig. 7.24), because in subcritical flow conditions the bend does not cause interference waves. If the bend is placed in the part of the chute with a supercritical slope, the occurrence of interference waves may be avoided by the use of a compound bend with a transverse

Fig. 7.27. Interference waves on a model of a chute. [Čábelka and Novák, 1964]

bottom slope or by dividing the chute with longitudinal sills or guide walls at the bend (Ippen, 1949). The cross-section of the chute should be rectangular or trapezoidal with steep sides.

On the basis of detailed research Arsenishvili (1961) gives the following two empirical criteria for the rise of *translatory waves* on rectangular or trapezoidal chutes with a supercritical slope and normal roughness of bed and walls:

the range of the slopes where waves may occur

$$0.02 < S < 0.35 \tag{7.18}$$

waves do not occur even for a slope defined by Equation (7.18) if

$$\frac{h}{P} \geqslant 0.10 \tag{7.19}$$

where h is the water depth and P the wetted perimeter.

The unfavourable results of translatory waves may be prevented by reducing their occurrence by the choice of such geometric and hydraulic parameters of the flume as to fulfil criterion (7.19): by using a triangular, semicircular or parabolical cross-section by artificially increasing the roughness of the bed and the walls of the chute along its entire length or in the sections tending to form waves; or, finally, by interpolating reaches with small slopes between those with great slopes. If the formation of translatory waves cannot be prevented by the use of some of these measures, they must be taken into account in the height of the lateral walls of the chute flume and in the design of the energy dissipation facilities downstream of it.

The problem of similarity of translatory waves on models of chutes has not yet been fully solved. For the occurrence of the waves a considerably greater length is usually necessary than can be obtained on models. Therefore if they are to be reproduced on the chute model, they must be produced artificially by disturbing the water level of the supercritical flow.

In the design of longer chutes, *aeration* of the supercritical flow is of great importance, since it influences velocity, depth and energy dissipation. The first systematic research was carried out in the Vienna Federal laboratory by Ehrenberger (1930) on steep wooden flumes. Then followed research in the laboratory and measurements on prototype chutes supplemented by theoretical studies on aeration. Michels and Lovely attempted a classification of aerated flows into seven types according to the degree of aeration. Further research by Lane, Hickox (1942), Halbronn *et al.* (1953), Straub and Anderson (1958) etc., has shown that aeration of supercritical flows begins at the surface and only at a certain distance, l, from the beginning of the chute (Fig. 7.28). This surface aeration is

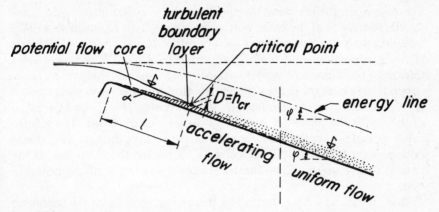

Fig. 7.28.

accompanied by aeration from the sides of the chute, especially if they are very rough, uneven or contain grooves.

Surface aeration does not occur immediately at the beginning of the chute because here the flow still has a low velocity and weak turbulence. A strongly turbulent layer is only found along the bottom and walls; the rest of the flow forms a potential core uneffected by turbulence. During the accelerating flow on the chute the depth of the flow gradually decreases whereas the thickness of the turbulent boundary layer increases, until at the critical point it affects the entire depth of the flow (Fig. 7.28). From this point onwards conditions for surface aeration of the stream exist. In a strongly turbulent flow the vertical velocity components at the surface are sufficient to separate drops of water from the flow and project them into the air, i.e. to overcome gravity, viscosity and surface tension acting against their separation. When falling back onto the water surface the drops cause the separation of further drops and simultaneously entrain air bubbles into the flow. Due to strong turbulence these bubbles are carried deeper into the flow and also driven back to the surface, disturbing it violently and thus contributing to further, still more intense aeration. During accelerated flow on a long chute the flow aerates gradually in depth until the air and water mixture reaches the bottom. Beyond this section there is uniform flow on a chute with constant slope during which neither velocity, flow depth nor the composition of the mixture changes.

On the basis of observations on models and prototypes of concrete chutes and overflow dam spillways, Hickox (1942) established a correlation between the distance of l (m) of the critical point from the spillway crest and the specific discharge q (m³/s/m), which may be expressed by the empirical equation

$$l = 14.7q^{0.53} \tag{7.20}$$

The distance l, for the same specific discharge q, is shortened by increasing the roughness of the chute bottom as follows from Kratochvil's (1948) measurements on the spillway of the Brno dam, and from Bayer's laboratory measurements of angle, α, of the growth of the turbulent layer thickness on flumes of various slopes and bed roughness. Angle α depends above all on the bed roughness (for a very smooth glass surface $\alpha = 0.006$, for a very rough bed $\alpha = 0.01$), considerably less on the slope of the flume and only very slightly on the specific discharge. The inverse value of angle α approximately expresses the relative distance l/h_{cr}, of the critical point from the spillway crest (h_{cr} is the depth of the flow at the critical point) which, according to Hickox's measurements, approaches 100.

Two criteria have been derived by theoretical analysis for the beginning of aeration of a flow with free surface by Govinda Rao and Rajaratnam (1961). With a number of simplifying assumptions they considered the equilibrium of forces (motion and surface tension) acting on a drop of water at the moment of its separation from the surface of the flow and obtained the first dimensionless criterion

$$\psi = \frac{U\sqrt{h}}{\sqrt{(\sigma/\rho)}} > 465 \qquad (7.21)$$

for the beginning of aeration, where U is the surface velocity of the flow. For the derivation of the second criterion they started from Richardson's empirical equation for the mean size of drops during the disintegration of a jet and the equilibrium of forces acting on the separating drop. Thus they obtained

$$\frac{U\nu^{1/5}}{\sigma/\rho} > 60 \qquad (7.22)$$

These criteria confirm Halbronn's theory that aeration of a supercritical flow begins at the point of the chute where the turbulent bottom layer penetrates as far as the surface.

Hino (1961) started from a similar consideration of the equilibrium of forces acting on a water particle carried from the bed to the surface of the flow by a vortex-like movement, and arrived at a simple approximate condition

$$hS > \text{const.} \approx 0.015 \text{ (m)} \qquad (7.23)$$

the fulfilment of which is necessary for the aeration of the stream. Another important quantity for the design of the chute is the velocity of the steady aerated flow. From his work on wooden flumes Ehrenberger suggested the empirical equation for velocity v (m/s)

$$v = 55R_1^{0.52}S^{0.40} \qquad (7.24)$$

suitable also for chutes of greater dimensions with relatively smooth bed and sides. The greater the roughness, the smaller are the flow velocities. For a chute with walls of quarry-stone Nichiporovich (1934) recommends a coefficient of 37 (instead of 55) in the Ehrenberger equation (index 1 marks the aerated flow parameters if they differ from the unaerated flow parameters which are without index).

Some authors recommend the computation of the velocity of the aerated flow on a steep chute of rectangular cross-section from an equation of the Manning type (Hall, 1942)

$$v = \frac{1}{n_c} R^{0.67} S^{0.50} \qquad (7.25)$$

where $n_c < n$.

The depth of the aerated uniform flow h_1(m) on a chute of rectangular section can be calculated from De Lapp's equation

$$h_1 = c \left(\frac{q^2}{g} \right)^{1/3} \qquad (7.26)$$

where the coefficient c has the value 0.316 to 0.372.

Air concentration in the aerated flow is usually expressed by the ratio of the discharge of water to the total discharge of the mixture, i.e. by the coefficient $\rho_1 < 1$, expressed as $\rho_1 = Q/A_1 v$ (*see* Equation 7.17). If the weight of air in the mixture is neglected ρ_1 expresses the specific gravity of the water and air mixture. From extensive measurements on chutes and dam spillways Hall determined the mean value of the coefficient ρ_1 as a function of the Froude number:

$$\beta = \frac{1 - \rho_1}{\rho_1} = c_1 \frac{v^2}{gR} = c_1 Fr^2 \qquad (7.27)$$

where the coefficient c_1, expressing the influence of the wall roughness, has the mean value for concrete chutes $c_1 = 0.006$.

Jevjevich and Levin (1953), using measurements on two chutes with very rough walls, supplemented this relationship by the influence of the roughness of the bed (ψ') and the velocity distribution and aeration in a vertical (α_a):

$$\frac{1 - \rho_1}{\rho_1} = c' Fr_1^2 \psi' \alpha_a \qquad (7.28)$$

where $c' = \text{const.} = 0.175 \pm 10\%$, $Fr_1 = v/\sqrt{(gR_1)}$, $\psi' = (n/R_1^{1/6})\sqrt{g}$ and

$$\alpha_a = \frac{\displaystyle\int_0^{h_1} \rho_h u_h^3 dh}{\rho_1 v^3 h_1} \qquad (7.29)$$

ρ_h and u_h are the density of the mixture and its velocity at a height h above the bed, h_1 is the depth of flow of the mixture, ρ_1 the mean density and v the mean cross-sectional velocity.

From the velocity of the aerated flow and the air content, which can be easily found from the above equations, the depth of the aerated flow and the necessary height of the lateral walls of the chute are determined. Aeration of the supercritical flow does not cause any special difficulties in the design or operation of the chute. Its great advantage is that it increases the effectiveness of the energy dissipation in the stilling basin downstream of the chute by compressing the air bubbles contained in the mixture.

Finally the problem of model similarity for the aeration of supercritical flow with a free surface must be mentioned. For the various forces coming into play during aeration, i.e. during the ejection of the water drops from the surface, different laws of similarity are valid: for gravity the Froude law, for surface tension the Weber law, and for viscosity the Reynolds law. This fact causes difficulties during model research on aeration, where influence of the scale is very much in evidence. The velocity, the forces and the energy of the flow with a free surface are controlled by the Froude law. If the model scale is M_l the scale of kinetic energy of the water drops causing their separation from the surface of the flow, according to the Froude law, is M_l^4. On the other hand, e.g., the magnitude of the work of the surface forces acting against their separation decreases according to the Weber law by only M_l^2. This great discrepancy explains, why, for example, on a prototype of a chute, aeration occurs where at the corresponding point on the model turbulence produces only a disturbance of the surface but does not achieve separation of the drops. The surface of a supercritical flow on the model is therefore more stable than in prototype. The Froude similarity fully applies, however, for the position of the critical point at which a surface disturbance of the water appears on the model and aeration of the flow on the prototype.

(c) Siphon spillways

Siphons are closed conduits in the form of an inverted U. Initially, the discharge is given by the head above the crest and the 'weir' equation (Equation (7.6)). With further increase of head and discharge, air in the bend at the crest is gradually exhausted and after priming the siphon operates under the full head and the discharge is given by the 'pipe' equation (Equation (7.13)). Siphon spillways usually have an inlet, short upper leg, a throat (control section), lower leg and outlet. A siphon breaker (air vent) controls the action of the spillway so that it ceases to function if the reservoir level falls below a predetermined value, as the inlet is usually well submerged (to prevent the formation of vortices and entrance of ice or floating debris). The outlet may be free discharging or submerged.

The main advantages of siphon spillways are their large capacity at low reservoir levels and automatic operation. The disadvantages are the danger of clogging or freezing, difficulties in regulating the discharge, particularly with a single siphon, and the possibility of cavitation and vibration. Modern design based on laboratory investigations, and the use of air-regulated siphons can overcome at least the main disadvantages. The design and associated laboratory studies of the Spelga Dam in

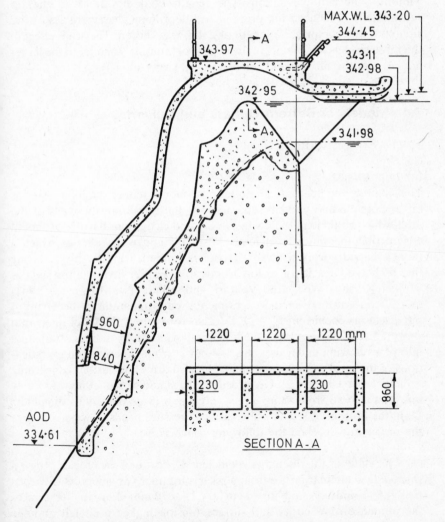

Fig. 7.29. Spelga Dam—siphon profile. [Poskitt and Elsawy, 1976]

Northern Ireland (Poskitt and Elsawy, 1976) serve as an example. The 30 m high gravity dam has 4 batteries of 3 siphons each on its crest; a section through the siphons is shown in Fig. 7.29.

As the siphons discharge into the atmosphere (on the spillway) the exit was formed so as to aid priming and oppose ingress of air downstream. The upstream horizontal lip, or 'ducksbill', placed at the entrance above the crest level produces stable air control and flow conditions (stepped levels aid regulation of the outflow). Model tests carried out at Queen's University, Belfast on three models, $M_l = 7$, 10, 20, confirmed that the maximum negative pressure at the crest (-7.8 m) was still acceptable without danger of cavitation. The length (and elevation) of the lip substantially influenced the priming and depriming characteristics of the siphons and a compromise length of 2.4 m was chosen. The scale effect in the three models was mainly in the degree of 'hunting' (smaller in the larger model) and the air demand (higher in the larger model).

7.4 Models of Bottom Outlets and Culverts

7.4.1 Bottom outlets

(a) *Inlet shape*
The shape of the inlet into an outlet pipe should reduce the inlet losses as far as possible and prevent separation of the flow from the walls of the inlet, which could lead to flow instability and cavitation. Further, it should ensure that the water level in the reservoir above the inlet at which a funnel-shaped vortex with an air core is formed, considerably reducing the discharge capacity, is as low as possible. Earlier investigators such as Winkel, Castel, Weisbach, Venturi and others (*see* Lískovec, 1961) mostly concentrated on the experimental determination of the value of the discharge coefficient $C_d = Q/A\sqrt{(2gh)}$ for various shapes of inlets into short pipes. Lískovec (1961) dealt in detail with the hydraulics of the inlet into pipes flowing under pressure and, apart from experimental investigations of the most suitable inlet shape, he also drew conclusions concerning similarity (*see* Chapter 2). He measured the shape of the jet flowing freely into atmosphere from sharp-edged circular orifices of various diameters D' in the bottom of a tank using various pressure heads of water h above the orifice and reached the following conclusions:

(1) The value of the discharge coefficient C_d for the flow of water from a sharp-edged circular orifice from a reservoir under varying pressure heads h is 0.597 and constant for diameters $D' \geqslant 70$ mm. For smaller orifices the influence of viscosity and surface tension makes itself felt and the value of C_d increases till for $D' = 10$ mm it reaches the value 0.656.

(2) The shapes of outlet jets are geometrically similar for $D' \geqslant 60$ mm and $h \geqslant 6D'$.

These conclusions give limiting conditions of similarity for outflows through circular orifices.

(3) The basic shape of the outlet jet, which represents the optimum shape of the inlet into a pipe flowing under pressure, is a body formed by the rotation of a part of a strophoid (Fig. 7.30)

$$y = (0.683 - x)\sqrt{\left(\frac{0.874 - x}{x - 0.492}\right)} \tag{7.30}$$

round the y axis (which is the pipe axis). This shape is valid for the outlet pipe of diameter $D = 1$. For another value of D we obtain the optimum shape of the inlet by multiplying the coordinates x and y by this value of D as long as the above stated limiting conditions are observed. Lískovec proposes length L of the inlet piece as $L = 1.25D$.

(4) For $D_1 = 1.366D \geqslant 70$ mm we obtain a further limiting condition of model similarity for the model pipe diameter $D \geqslant 50$ mm.

(5) For an inlet designed in this way the coefficient of discharge C_d in relation to the cross-section A of a pipe, diameter D, is $C_d = 0.979$ for a head $h \geqslant 3D$.

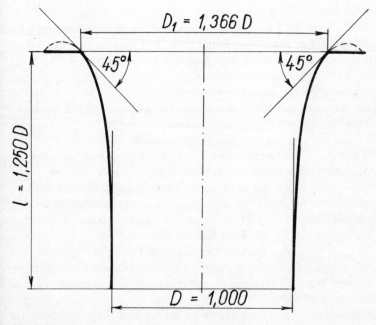

Fig. 7.30.

Only positive pressures act on the wall of such an inlet at all heads above the inlet.

The coefficient C_d may further be expressed by the product of the coefficient of contraction C_c and the velocity coefficient C_v

$$C_d = C_c C_v = \frac{C_c}{\sqrt{(1+\xi)}} \quad (\textit{see also } (7.14)) \qquad (7.31)$$

where ξ is the head loss coefficient. In the given case $\xi = 0.043$ and $C_c = 1.000$.

(6) Any widening of the inlet above the dimensions stated in Fig. 7.30 does not increase its discharge capacity and is therefore unnecessary (e.g., the shape marked in a broken line above the level of the wall on Fig. 7.29). If the inlet is closed by a gate then an increase of the inlet area only makes the gate unnecessarily expensive.

(7) The above conclusions are valid for every position of the inlet, i.e. with a vertical, inclined or horizontal axis. Nor did the experiments show any difference in the discharge capacity of the inlets with various positions of the axis for heads $h \geqslant 6D$. At this level a funnel shaped vortex begins to form above the inlet with a vertical axis which considerably reduces its capacity, as against an inlet with a horizontal axis where no vortex forms even with considerably smaller pressure heads.

(b) *Space in front of the inlet*

In front of the inlet into an outlet pipe there are usually screens with supports, temporary or regulating outlet gates and frequently also an inlet sill, raised above the bottom of the reservoir. Perpendicular lateral wing walls upstream of the dam face and usually connected with a ceiling are used as supports for the inlet screens and for the gate grooves. Model experiments were carried out to determine the influence of the position, shape and length of these inlet walls, the inlet sill and ceiling, and also of the entire screen cage, on the discharge capacity and function of the outlet and pressures in the inlet proper. This problem was also investigated by Lískovec on a scale model with outlet diameter 100 mm. The results showed that when the inlet of the outlet pipe is formed with an optimum shape, the height of the inlet above the bottom of the reservoir, the position and shape of the vertical lateral inlet walls, and the position and slope of the ceiling above the inlet had no measurable influence on the discharge capacity of the outlet. On the other hand in the case of hydraulically unsuitably designed inlets with an inlet contraction, all these parameters can have a favourable influence on the increase of the discharge capacity of the outlet.

To reduce velocities and thus losses in the screens the vertical lateral inlet walls may be opened funnel-wise in the upstream direction at an angle of about 8° from the pipe axis and connected directly to the edge of the inlet. Similarly, but using a greater angle (about 30°) the ceiling of the space in front of the inlet should be raised.

During research carried out by Novák and Wisner (1952) on a model of scale 1:25 for the design of a bottom outlet of the high Bicaz dam in Roumania, it was found that at a ratio $h'/D = 1.1$, where h' is the depth of the bottom of the screen cage beneath the axis of the outlet conduit with diameter D (2.50 m prototype; Fig. 7.31) a drop in pressure occurs in the inlet, especially at lower heads. Even though this drop in pressure is not dangerous, it is better to avoid this ratio and in the given case a ratio $h'/D = 1.4$ was chosen. Model tests also showed that, with a properly designed inlet and the screen placed sufficiently far in front of it, the size and shape of the screen cage hardly influences the capacity of the outlet and no shortcomings occur, even if the screens are partially blocked. As far as the pressures in the inlet are concerned, of all the parameters considered the inlet cage floor exerted the greatest influence.

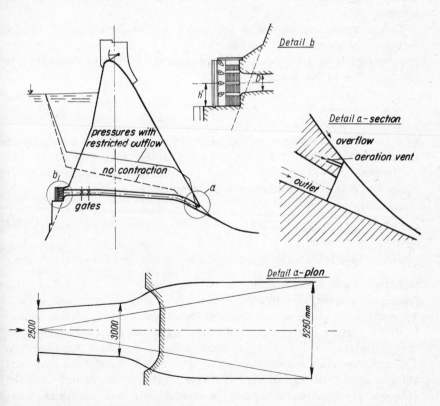

Fig. 7.31. Bicaz Dam—outlet works.

(c) *Pressures in the outlet*

The capacity of the outlet and the pressures in it can be determined well by calculation and for this we must know the correct values of the various coefficients of local head losses in the screens, inlet, gate and in the outlet as well as losses due to a change in direction and section. The coefficients used for the calculation of local losses are given in the technical literature but more complicated cases necessitate the use of a scale model. Since we are concerned with a pressure system, we proceed in choosing the scale in accordance with the principles given in Sub-section 5.1.3. As the investigation of pressures and capacity of outlets is often combined with that of the function of the gate or valve placed within the outlet, and since we are also interested in the passage of air pockets through the outlet and transitional phenomena for low water levels in the reservoir, the model for these cases is usually made of perspex and the hydraulically rough prototype conduit is replaced on the model by a hydraulically smooth pipe. The value of the Reynolds number on the model must, therefore, be carefully checked whilst using the Froude law of similarity (*see* Sub-section 5.1.7). Alternatively, we can also use aerodynamic models (*see* Chapter 11).

To ensure the protection of the outlet against cavitation we usually increase the pressure throughout the outlet by decreasing the outflow area (naturally at the expense of the discharge capacity of the outlet). If the head loss at the outflow is

$$h_l = c \frac{v_2^2 - v_1^2}{2g}$$

where c is the coefficient, v_2 the outflow velocity and v_1 the velocity in the pipe, and further, if x is the reduction in the cross-sectional area of the pipe at its end $(x = (A_1 - A_2)/A_1)$, then the pressure head of water H above the axis of the outflow will be given by the equation

$$H = \frac{v_1^2}{2g} \left[\frac{1+c}{(1-x)^2} - c + \sum_1^n \xi \right] \tag{7.32}$$

$\sum_1^n \xi$ in Equation (7.32) gives the sum of all head loss coefficients, including friction, throughout the whole outlet, where $\xi_f = fl/D$. The cross-section near the outflow is reduced by a smooth transition, usually by lowering the ceiling and simultaneously widening the outlet and so facilitating easier energy dissipation. For a gradual change in section we may consider $c = 0.1$. In the case illustrated on Fig. 7.31 x was chosen as 15%, resulting in a reduction of the outlet capacity by 10%. If there is a valve or gate at the end of the outlet conduit it is advisable to reduce the cross-section directly at this gate. The resultant pressure line for an outlet with and without end reduction is shown in Fig. 7.31, from which the rise in pressure is evident, especially near the outflow. The longitudinal section of the outlet is given by the need of a smooth transition into the stilling basin and must be chosen so that the requirements of suitable pressures and energy dissipation are compatible.

If an increase in pressures is not ensured by the end contraction cavitation could occur at a bad weld or at the gate grooves (the velocity in the given case was nearly 30 m/s in prototype). Hydraulic calculations in the quoted example were fully confirmed by model tests on a model of scale 1:25 which was also used to investigate the flow in the outlet during the operation of the gates. Figure 7.32 shows the model of the outlet as used for experiments with high pressures (high water levels in the reservoir) and Fig. 7.33 shows the same model in a flume for studying its behaviour at low reservoir water levels.

According to results of measurements (Ball, 1959), at an absolute pressure of 20 m of water cavitation occurs at a wall surface irregularity 1.6 mm high with a velocity of flow $v = 21$ m/s, or a height of 3.2 mm and velocity $v = 17$ m/s, or a height of 6.4 mm and $v = 13.5$ m/s. At half pressure (10 m) the height of the projection causing cavitation also reduces to about half for each velocity.

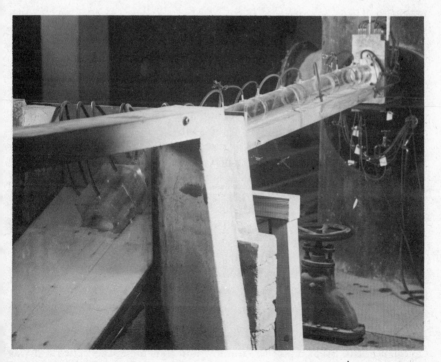

Fig. 7.32. Model of outlet operating under high upstream water levels. [Čábelka and Novák, 1964]

Fig. 7.33. Model of outlet operating under low upstream water levels. [Čábelka and Novák, 1964]

(d) *Outflow from the outlet*

The outflow from the bottom outlet can be directed either into its own stilling basin or into a stilling basin common with the dam spillway. If, in this case, the outlet terminates on the spillway surface, the task of model studies is to solve the junction of the outlet and the spillway in order to avoid cavitation. This may be achieved either by suitable baffles, or, if baffles are not needed for dissipation of the energy of the overfalling water, by aeration vents. The previously quoted study may serve as an example. Figure 7.31 contains detail 'a' where the part between the outlet and the spillway was not extended to a sharp end for construction reasons. For the operation of the outlet without an overfall there are no problems. During the spillway operation without the outlet the entire outlet beyond the gate is subjected to negative pressures which are sufficiently compensated for by aerating the pipe through the gate air vents. During the simultaneous operation of the outlet and the spillway negative pressures occurred on the model at the blunt junction, which would have meant cavitation in prototype when the overfall jet was high enough not to break up at the outflow and thus the space beneath it was not aerated. This space was therefore provided with a special aeration vent, which completely eliminated the danger. Further attention was paid on the model to pressures in the flume formed in the spillway downstream of the outlet outflow (Fig. 7.31, detail a).

7.4.2 Outlet gates and valves

Gates and valves in dam outlets may be classified in three ways; as regulating gates which must have a good hydraulic performance in all positions; as reserve gates installed for safety reasons and which are either fully open or fully shut; and lastly as emergency gates, with the aid of which the outlet is temporarily closed during maintenance, etc. According to their movement they are divided into normal or high-speed valves operated manually, electrically or hydraulically, and with regard to the magnitude of pressure, into low pressure, medium pressure and high pressure gates and valves. They may be placed according to the type and purpose at the inlet, inside or at the end of the conduit (near its outflow). The main types of regulating valves are the needle (Johnson), the tube, the hollow jet, the cone dispersion (Howell–Bunger) and the cylindrical valve, and the normal or reversed tainter gate. The non-regulating gates are usually the vertical lift gate, the butterfly gate (sometimes also used as a regulating gate) and ring follower gates; these are also used for regulating the flow, if the dam has a greater number of outlets (sometimes in several rows one above the other), and if the discharge is regulated by a full opening of the corresponding number of outlets, possibly at various pressure heads (e.g., Grand Coulee dam in USA).

Laboratory model studies of the characteristics, coefficients and pressure conditions for various positions of the valves were carried out in USA (Ball and Herbert, 1948; Elder and Daugherty, 1952), USSR (Kokaja, 1954) and a number of other countries. Figure 7.34 shows a scale model of a needle valve studied at the laboratory of the Brno Technical University Czechoslovakia (Kratochvíl, 1958). The discharge coefficient for a fully opened valve was $C_d = 0.65$, i.e. $\xi = 1/C_d^2 - 1 = 1.37$. In the inlet ring of the valve negative pressure occurred at a 100% opening for a pressure head $H > 20$ m. At this limit the cavitation number (*see* Sub-section 2.7.3) was

$$\sigma_c' = \frac{p - p_v}{\frac{1}{2}\rho v^2} = 3$$

Investigation of the relation between σ_c' and the percentage opening of the valve showed that $\sigma_c' < 3$ for an opening between 67 and 96%, i.e. the greatest danger of cavitation was in this range. On the basis of laboratory and prototype measurements Kratochvil established the relationship (Fig. 7.35) between the percentage opening of the gate or valve, expressed by the ratio A'/A (A' is the flow cross-section of the valve in a given

Fig. 7.34. Model of needle valve. [Kratochvil, 1958]

position and A is the pipe cross-sectional area) and the discharge coefficient C_d, ($C_d = Q/(A'\sqrt{(2gH)})$) for valves built into the conduit—region 'a'—(the left line represents hollow jet valves and the right line the dispersion cone type), or with a free discharge for all positions—region 'b'—(segment, cylindrical, etc. gates). The curves for 'a' end at $A'/A = 82\%$, because for the protection of the conduit (*see* above), even when the gate is fully opened, the flow area A' is smaller than the pipe cross-section A.

The aeration vent plays an important role in the correct functioning of outlet valves and gates. It serves to bring air to the point of negative pressures during partial or complete opening of the valve and thus to prevent cavitation, excessive flow pulsations and vibrations. According to the empirical formulae the diameter of the aeration vent is about $\frac{1}{3}$ to $\frac{1}{5}$ of that of the outlet pipe. Air velocity in the aeration pipe should not exceed

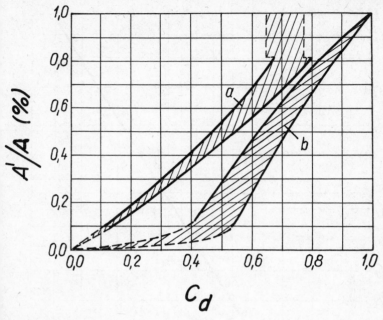

Fig. 7.35. [Kratochvil, 1958]

40 to 50 m/s. Novák and Wisner (1952) carried out a model study of the aeration of a ring follower gate and obtained the relationship (Fig. 7.36) of the dimensionless parameters p'/d_1' and $H'/(d_1'A_1')$, where $d_1' = d_1/D$ (D is the conduit diameter) $p' = p/D$ with p the negative pressure downstream of the gate (in m of water column), $H' = H/D$ and $A_1' = A'/A$. d_1 is the diameter of an orifice which, for discharge coefficient $C_d = 1$, has the same capacity as the aeration pipe with diameter d

$$\left(d_1^2 = \frac{d^2}{\sqrt{(1+\sum \xi^2)}} \right)$$

thus the value d_1 also includes the influence of the length and route of the aeration pipe. For the use of the graph in Fig. 7.35 we must determine from the model, or extrapolate from previous experience, the relationship between the critical value of A_1' which corresponds to the position of the gate at which the greatest negative pressure occurs on its downstream side and the head H' (usually $A_{1cr}' \approx 0.4$ to 0.6 for $H' = 20$ to 45; A_{1cr}' decreases with increasing head). Then for the chosen d', it is possible from the graph to ascertain the value p' and check whether it exceeds the permissible limit (recommended as about -8.0 m water column).

Haindl (1957), from measurements of the quantity of air drawn into the conduit by a hydraulic jump downstream of a partially opened vertical lift

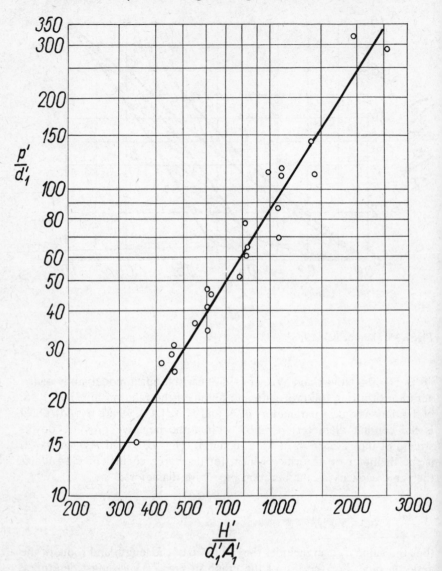

Fig. 7.36. [Novák and Wisner, 1952]

gate, recommends the calculation of the quantity of air q_a necessary for a 1 m opening of the gate from the equation

$$q_a = vC_cak\left(\frac{v}{\sqrt{(gC_ca)}} - 1\right)^{1.4} \tag{7.33}$$

where a is the height of the gate opening, C_c the coefficient of contraction to the depth upstream of the hydraulic jump y ($y = C_ca$ with

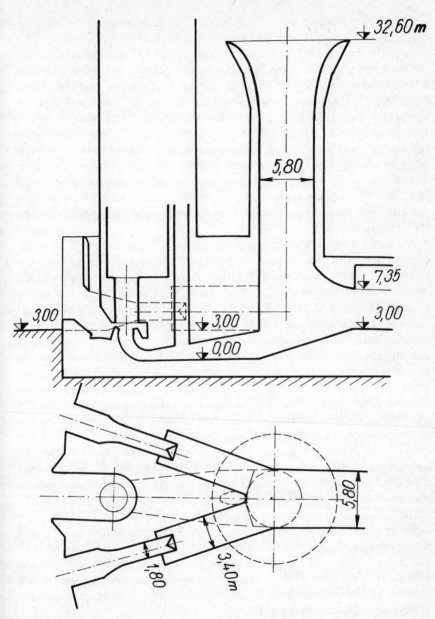

Fig. 7.37. [Haindl and Doležal, 1961]

$C_c = 0.64$ for a sharp-edged gate) and k is a constant. According to experimental results k is 0.012 but for safety may be increased to 0.02. Except for the value of coefficient k Equation (7.33) is in agreement with the Kalinske and Robertson equation for the quantity of air driven by the hydraulic jump into a pipe with circular section; there $k = 0.0066$. From Equation (7.33) it may be ascertained that q_a is greatest for a lift $a_1 = 0.09v^2/(gC_c)$. If this is greater than the height of the outlet it means that the maximum air consumption q_a occurs when the gate approaches full opening (at complete opening there is no reason for the hydraulic jump to occur). The cross-sectional area of the aeration pipe A' is then determined as $A' = bq_{a\,max}/v_a$, where v_a is the mean velocity of air in the vent, which is again determined so that the sum of head losses and the velocity head should be, at most, 10 m of water column or preferably less for reasons of safety.

A further very serious problem for research is the influence of structural elements in the conduits and outlets, and of the operation of the gate and its aeration on the fluctuation of hydrodynamic pressures acting on the walls of the outlet. The study carried out at the VÚV laboratory Prague (Haindl and Doležal, 1961) on a model ($M_l = 22.5$) of a shaft spillway, in the bend of which terminated two conduits leading from outlets controlled by valves with dispersion cones, and the draft tube of one turbine, can serve as an example (Fig. 7.37). It was found that the pressure fluctuation was greatest at the points of impact of the outlet jet from the valves on the walls of the conduit. Aeration of the valves decreased the mean value of these fluctuations by about 10% only and in the outflow conduit, where the walls were smooth, it was almost the same as for non-aerated valves. The frequency of oscillation on the model was about eight pulses per second. But when baffles were placed on the bed and ceiling of the conduit immediately beyond the point of impact of the flow from the valves, air consumption trebled and pressure fluctuations on the conduit wall upstream of them for an aerated valve decreased to about a third of the value for flow without baffles.

Elder (1961), using experiments on three models (ratio $1:1.5:6$) of flow downstream of a gate in a lock by-pass conduit, ascertained that both the frequency as well as the size of the pressure fluctuation followed the Froude law, i.e. that when operating the model according to the Froude law the results from all models (after recalculating them according to the scales) were practically identical.

7.4.3 Power station inlets

Similarly as with intakes of hydroelectric power stations with a free surface (Section 7.2) and also inlets into outlets of dams (Sub-section 7.4.1), the main task of experimental investigations of inlets of hydroelectric power stations operating under pressure is the development of a design where the inlet losses and the possibility of the occurrence of vortices and of the penetration of air or floating objects and sediments into the conduits are reduced to a minimum. Although considerable attention has in the past been paid to these problems, comparatively few satisfactory conclusions exist in particular from the investigation of inlets and outlets of pumped storage power stations where water flows alternately in both directions. It is important to know not only the value of total losses but also the share of partial losses caused by the individual elements of the inlet. Only then is it possible to correctly assess the influence of the various design alternatives and to determine to which part special attention should be paid.

These problems were dealt with by Gabriel and Grund (1965) in the laboratory at Bratislava on models of the Liptovska Mara and Ružín power stations, in Czechoslovakia (model scale 1:50). They investigated both the total losses and the partial losses caused by the shape of the inlet, the gate grooves, the screen frames and supports, and the screens for both directions of flow. The friction losses contained in the total losses were included in the losses caused by the inlet shape (their value is small and they would be difficult to measure). The conditions of similarity already discussed in Sub-section 5.1.3 (Fig. 5.1) were fulfilled.

The values of the coefficients of total and partial inlet losses were calculated from model measurements as follows:

(a) for turbine operation when water flows from the reservoir into the inlet of the turbine pressure conduit:

$$\xi_t = 2g\frac{\Delta h}{v^2} - 1 \tag{7.34}$$

(b) for pump operation when the water flows from the pressure pipe through the inflow into the reservoir:

$$\xi_p = 1 - 2g\frac{\Delta h}{v^2} \tag{7.34'}$$

where Δh is the difference between the water level in the reservoir at the inlet and the pressure head in the conduit (at the beginning of its prismatic part immediately beyond the inlet), and v is the mean velocity in the conduit. The authors determined the possible ranges of values of these coefficients: $0.026 < \xi_t < 0.500$ and $0.500 < \xi_p < 1.00$.

From a number of alternatives of inlets the most suitable was found to be the one shown by a solid line in Fig. 7.38. It has a low inlet sill, the inlet axis has a relatively small inclination (12°) and the whole inlet has plane surfaces. The broken lines show the previously investigated alternative with smooth streamlined lateral walls and ceiling. A comparison of

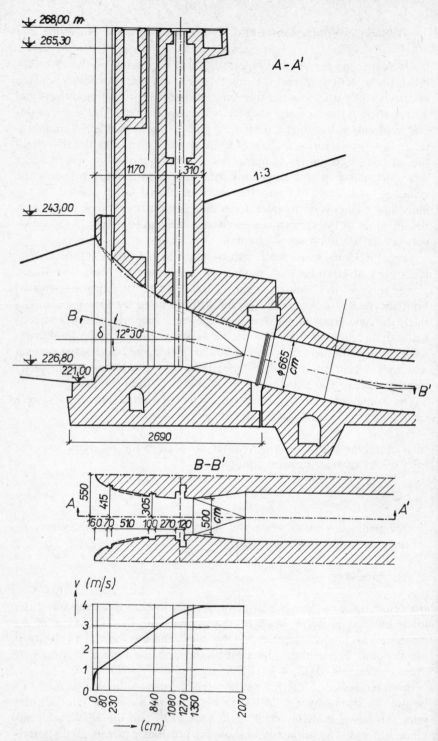

Fig. 7.38. Pumped storage power station inlet–outlet. [Gabriel and Grund, 1965]

Table 7.1 Losses in inlet during turbine operation

	Alternative I		Alternative II		Alternative III	
	ξ	%	ξ	%	ξ	%
Complete inlet	0.341	100	0.222	100	0.144	100
Shape of inlet	0.161	47.2	0.107	48.2	0.029	20.2
Grooves	0.103	30.3	0.037	16.7	0.037	25.7
Screen frame with screens	0.077	22.5	0.078	35.1	0.078	54.1
Screen frame only	0.042	12.2	–	–	–	–
Screen only	0.035	10.3	–	–	–	–

the head loss coefficient ξ for the entire inlet and its individual components for both flow directions is given in Tables 7.1 and 7.2 for the originally designed inlet (alternative I), the streamlined shape (alternative II), and the resultant plane-surface inlet shape (alternative III).

The results have shown that to reduce inlet losses it is possible to design inlets into pressure conduits of turbines with shapes resulting in slightly negative pressures and that the streamlined inlet surfaces between neighbouring grooves can be replaced by plane surfaces; this is also advantageous from the point of view of construction. At the bottom of Fig. 7.38 the smooth change in velocity in the inlet is illustrated.

During the above mentioned study, a vortex-free inlet for even the lowest operational water level in the reservoir was achieved by placing a suitably shaped concrete beam with a horizontal grille covering the screen slot above and in front of it (*see* Fig. 7.38).

The shape of the outlet part of turbine draft tubes, and particularly the outlet works, must also be designed to be suitable for both flow directions, i.e. both for turbine and pump operation.

Table 7.2 Losses in inlet during pump operation

	Alternative I		Alternative II		Alternative III	
	ξ	%	ξ	%	ξ	%
Complete inlet	0.725	100	0.660	100	0.660	100
Shape of inlet	0.725	100	0.660	100	0.660	100
Grooves	0.0	0	0.0	0	0.0	0
Screen frame with screens	0.0	0	0.0	0	0.0	0
Inlet proper	–	–	–	–	0.51	77.0
Region of reservoir	–	–	–	–	0.15	23.0

7.4.4 Culverts and inverted siphons

Culverts and inverted siphons are normally used to carry flows beneath canals, roads, railways, etc. They differ in their hydraulic regime in that in culverts water usually flows with a free surface, whereas in inverted siphons it is under pressure. Uncontrolled transition from free surface flow through a hydraulic jump to flow under pressure inside culverts and inverted siphons may cause problems, such as vibration, settling of structures, etc. Therefore models are used to study their design, particularly in order to preserve the same hydraulic regime for varying discharges.

Stabilization of the hydraulic jump in a culvert may be attained for example by a sudden expansion of the cross-section. In the case of inverted siphons a similar problem may be solved either by baffles on the bottom of the culvert beyond the inlet, or by splitting the overfall jet on the shaft crest and deviating the water curtain, which is formed on the opposite side of the shaft and which helps in the formation of a contraction at the inflow into the culvert (Fig. 7.39). In both cases it is advisable to provide a de-aeration chamber downstream of the hydraulic jump; the length of the zone of aerated water l may be determined from the following equation (Haindl, 1958):

$$l = 3 \frac{Q}{bv_b\sqrt{\dfrac{h}{y}}} \tag{7.35}$$

where h is the height of the contracted inlet to the culvert, y is the head of the free water surface in the de-aeration chamber (most frequently the height of the chamber), b is the width of the culvert, and v is the velocity of rise of air bubbles in standing water which may be considered to be about

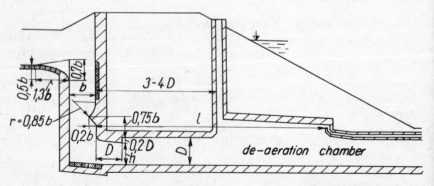

Fig. 7.39. Stabilization of a hydraulic jump in a culvert. [Haindl, 1958]

0.22m/s when the diameter of the bubbles is between 3 and 8 mm (according to Habermann, Morton and Muller).

It is advisable to design the de-aeration chamber for a mean annual discharge and for higher flows to provide in the culvert ceiling a small channel terminating in the de-aeration chamber, for drawing off the remaining entrained air.

7.5   Models of Energy Dissipators and Stilling Basins

7.5.1   Energy dissipation below overflow spillways

The passage of water from a dam spillway crest into the downstream reach involves a whole number of hydraulic phenomena, such as the overfall with the transition from subcritical into supercritical flow, the flow over the spillway, the hydraulic jump with a change back from super- to subcritical flow and the echoes of macroturbulence beyond the hydraulic jump, which are referred to as the hydraulic connection of the upstream and downstream reservoir of a hydraulic structure. The form of this connection and the share of its various phases in the dissipation of the excess energy of the overfall jet depends on the solution of the actual dam spillway.

At the classic type of overflow spillway, with its smooth streamlined surface and transition into the stilling basin, only a comparatively small part of the excess energy of the overfall jet, especially of a stronger one, is dissipated during its accelerated movement along the spillway surface. The major part of this energy, therefore, must be dissipated in the hydraulic jump and this requires an expensive stilling basin of considerable dimensions. To reduce the dimensions, forces acting on the stilling basin and construction costs, suitable alternatives are investigated, especially for higher dams. Their spillway surfaces are provided with baffles, ski jumps, etc., which facilitate intensive dissipation of the greater part of the energy of the overfall jet both before and during its impact into the lower water level. Only a residue of energy then remains to be dissipated in the hydraulic jump and the stilling basin can be considerably smaller and cheaper than for the classic type. If the overfall jet is thrown far enough from the toe of the dam and if at the same time, with the aid of a suitable spillway surface, it is split, then for a firm rock channel bed one can even omit a stilling basin altogether. The technically and economically most suitable design of the spillway with the most intensive energy dissipation can be best investigated on scale models using the Froude law of similarity.

At spillways with baffles or a ski jump there are *five distinct phases* in the passage of the discharge: the flow of the overfall jet along the spillway surface from the crest up to the spillway edge; the flight of the overfall jet through the air from the spillway edge to the downstream water surface; the impact of the jet into the downstream pool (stilling basin); the hydraulic jump in the downstream pool; and the transition from the hydraulic jump into the normal river flow.

(a) Energy dissipation on the spillway surface

In the *first phase*, in the accelerated movement of the jet along the spillway surface, energy losses occur due mainly to friction. In Bernoulli's equation

$$h_0 = h' + \frac{\alpha v'^2}{2g} + \Delta h_1 = h' + (1 + \xi') \frac{\alpha v'^2}{2g} = h' + \frac{\alpha v'^2}{2g\varphi'^2} \tag{7.36}$$

the losses Δh_1 up to the spillway edge are expressed as part of the velocity head of the mean velocity v' at the end of the spillway

$$\Delta h_1 = \xi' \frac{\alpha v'^2}{2g} \tag{7.37}$$

and the coefficient of losses ξ' by the velocity coefficient φ' (i.e. the ratio of the actual and theoretical velocity) as

$$(1 + \xi') = \frac{1}{\varphi'^2}$$

Skrebkov (1961) states that the velocity coefficient φ' of the overfall jet at the end of a smooth streamlined spillway decreases with the increasing relative height of the overfall S/H:

$$\varphi' = 1 - 0.0155 \frac{S}{H} \tag{7.38}$$

where S is the height of the spillway crest above the bottom of the stilling basin and H is the overfall head. This empirical relation is valid for $S/H < 30$.

The losses Δh_1 increase mainly with the relative length of the spillway surface l/h' where l is the length of the spillway surface in the direction of of flow and h' the thickness of the overfall jet at the spillway end, and also with the roughness of the surface, the Froude number and the degree of turbulence of the jet. The influence on the energy losses of aeration of the overfall jet moving along the spillway surface begins to show only at a large relative length of the surface, $l/h' > 100$ (*see* Sub-section 7.3.3). The energy losses of the overfall jet at the end of the spillway surface, or at the deflector or the ski jump edge, may be suitably characterized by the ratio of its actual and theoretical energy φ'^2. Then the difference $(1 - \varphi'^2)$

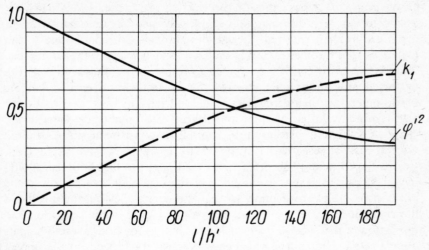

Fig. 7.40.

is the relative loss of the specific energy of the overfall jet occurring through the movement along the surface:

$$\kappa_1 = \frac{\Delta h_1}{h_0} = (1 - \varphi'^2) \tag{7.39}$$

where h_0 is the head at the end of the spillway surface.

Figure 7.40 shows the relationship between φ'^2 and κ_1 and the relative length of the spillway surface, l/h', which was established on models of overflow spillways of high dams with streamlined spillway surface and/or a ski jump, and where the surface was smooth (model—varnish, prototype—smooth concrete). The graph shows that for a relatively short spillway surface and for large specific discharges, which are common nowadays for high dams (i.e. small value of l/h'), the first phase of the overfall contributes towards energy dissipation only to a small degree. In practice it is usually not feasible to make use of the possibility of increasing energy losses by an increase in the roughness of the spillway surface mainly because of the danger of cavitation. For example for $l/h' = 60$, φ' decreases from 0.84 for a very smooth spillway to $\varphi' = 0.82$ for a model with a smooth concrete surface (prototype rough concrete) and to $\varphi' = 0.69$ for a model with glued 2 mm sand (coarse stone facing in prototype).

(b) *Energy dissipation in the free falling jet*
In the *second* phase, during the flight of the overfall jet through the air, from the edge of the spillway to the water surface of the downstream pool, losses occur through internal friction, air resistance and, above all,

by collision of various parts of the overfall jet and its water particles. The compact jets disintegrate peripherally and aerate intensively in depth during their free fall through the air. This is primarily due to the high degree of turbulence during the increasing velocity of the fall but can also be caused by the jets beginning to rotate, or by their collision. The dispersed and aerated jet stresses the downstream river bed (stilling basin) much less than a compact unaerated jet. This was used by Coyne (1951) for the design of spillway surfaces of a number of dams in the shape of a ski jump placed on the roof of the downstream power station. On the basis of research he proposed, for example, for the l'Aigle dam, spoon-shaped take-off surfaces for two ski jumps so that both jets should have a spiral movement in the air. For the Chastang dam he solved the position of the two ski jumps so that the overfall jets partially collided during their flight. However, at the l'Aigle dam the actual aeration and dispersion of the overfall jets was insufficient, as for great overfall heights a compact core remained which caused considerable scour at the impact point on the channel bed during floods even though the bed was formed of comparatively good rock. Nor was the collision of the overfall jets under a comparatively small angle on the Chastang dam sufficiently effective.

The disintegration and aeration of even very high overfall jets during their free fall through the air is considerably aided by baffles and sills placed on the spillway surface or, more suitably, on the take-off edge of the ski jump (Fig. 7.41). The junction of the spillway and baffles, etc.,

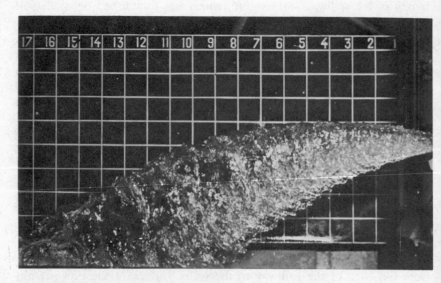

Fig. 7.41. Model of spillway jet. [Čábelka and Novák, 1964]

should be as smooth as possible to prevent cavitation. The baffles considerably increase the turbulence, the disintegration and the surface area of the overfall jet, and spread it over a considerably greater area. By a suitable design one can attempt to achieve a situation where even a very high overfall jet falls on the downstream water surface as a mixture of water and air without a compact core.

The complete disintegration and aeration of the overfall jet does not substantially increase the losses of energy during its fall; the decrease is only about 12% of its total energy as model research for a comparatively large range of the relative lengths of the free fall of the jet through the air, $l'/H' = 90$ to 1500, carried out by Hořeni (1956) has shown, but it contributes considerably to the dissipation of a great part of its energy at the point of impact into the downstream pool (*see* third phase of overfall). However, during the free fall of the overfall jet its energy losses can be substantially increased by the collision of two or more of its parts, or of the overfall jet with the outflow from the bottom outlets.

Treating this very complicated hydraulic phenomenon as a two-dimensional vectorial sum of the momentum of two water jets as if they were colliding solid bodies, Faktorovich (1952) derived an equation for the approximate calculation of the specific energy loss, κ_2 for the collision of two water jets under an angle β:

$$\kappa_2 = 1 - \frac{1 + \eta_q^2 \eta_v^2 + 2\eta_q \eta_v \cos \beta}{(1 + \eta_q)(1 + \eta_q \eta_v^2)} \tag{7.40}$$

In Equation (7.40)

$$\eta_q = \frac{q_{II}}{q_I}, \ \eta_v = \frac{v_{II}}{v_I}$$

where q_I and q_{II} are the specific discharges of two water jets I and II, and v_I and v_{II} their mean velocities at the point of collision. Thus during a collision of two equal jets under a right angle, i.e. for $\eta_q = \eta_v = 1$ and $\beta = 90°$ the specific energy loss is $\kappa_2 = 0.5$.

The collision of the jets causes their deformation, high turbulence and possibly also their disintegration and full aeration. Volumetric changes of the entrained air bubbles exposed to a sudden compression at the point of the jet collision also contribute to energy losses. The actual energy losses for the jet collision are thus greater than indicated by Equation (7.40).

Different designs of overflow spillways have been suggested utilizing the principle of jet collision for intensive energy dissipation. Faktorovich mentions several alternatives combining the flow on spillways with bottom outlets; Anufriev uses spillways combined with siphons, Roberts uses a spillway with a number of baffles and a take-off surface placed beneath them (used in 1943 for the Loscop and Vaalbank dams in South Africa), Skoupý suggests a deflector as shown on Fig. 7.42a, etc. By a combination

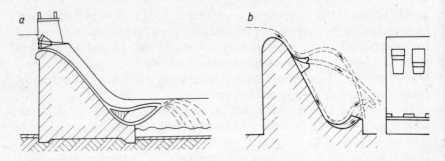

Fig. 7.42. Baffles and deflectors on a spillway. [Horský, 1961]

of baffles and deflectors placed at different positions on the spillway (*see* Fig. 7.42b) substantial energy dissipation can be achieved (Horský (1961)).

(c) *Energy dissipation at impact into the downstream pool*

In the *third phase* of the overfall, i.e. at the impact of the jet on the downstream water surface, energy losses occur through both collision of the masses of water and the compression of the air bubbles contained in the overfall jet at the point of impact where increased pressures occur. These losses increase with the intensity of disintegration and aeration of the overfall jet. The decrease in energy in this phase of the overfall is therefore manifest particularly in overfall jets which have been fully dispersed and intensively aerated before their contact with the downstream water surface. To take full advantage of this effect for energy dissipation there must be a sufficiently deep water cushion at the point of impact. The angle between the incoming jet and the stilling basin floor should not be smaller than 40° so that the jet ejection effect does not lower the water level near the toe of the dam too much thus reducing energy dissipation.

Assuming isothermal volumetric changes, the energy of the overfall jet used to compress a unit volume $V_0 = 1 \, \text{m}^3$ of air contained in the jet under normal atmospheric pressure $p_0 = 10^5 \, \text{N/m}^2$ to increased pressure H m (water column) at the point of impact can be calculated from the relation:

$$E = 2.3 p_0 V_0 \log \frac{p_0 + H\gamma}{p_0} = 238000 \log \frac{10 + H}{10} \, [\text{Nm}] \tag{7.41}$$

Beyond the point of impact in the region of lower pressures, compressed air bubbles expand in the flow and move upwards, perpendicular to the direction of flow, so increasing the turbulence. For example, on the model of the Slapy dam (Fig. 7.43) which has a ski-jump overfall with deflectors

Fig. 7.43. Model of the Slapy Dam on the River Vltava. [Čábelka and Novák, 1964]

placed on the take-off edge, it was found that for a head of about 50 m the diffused and aerated overfall jet exerted an average pressure $H =$ 25 m of water at the point of its impact into the downstream stilling basin. For one compression of 1 m^3 of air contained in the aerated jet at this pressure about 13×10^4 Nm of energy is required, which is about 25% of the energy of 1 m^3 of water falling from a height of 50 m (50×10^4 Nm). With a fifty percent aeration in the given case about 25% of the energy of the overfall jet is needed for one compression of air bubbles at the point of the impact on the downstream water surface. A number of bubbles, however, are exposed to several compressions in succession, so that the decrease in the jet energy is even greater.

(d) Energy dissipation in the first three phases

The energy loss of the overfall jet in all its first three phases $\Delta h_1 + \Delta h_2 + \Delta h_3$, i.e. from the spillway crest up to the point of its fall into the downstream pools, can be characterized as in the first phase by its velocity coefficient φ and the ratio of its actual and theoretical energy φ^2. The expression $(1 - \varphi^2)$ gives the relative loss of specific energy, κ_{1-3}, of the jet in the first three phases.

It is impossible to ascertain the value of the velocity coefficient φ at this point of the jet entry into the downstream pool by direct measurement of its parameters (depth h_1 and mean velocity v_1) because of the dispersion and aeration of the flow and because of pressure fluctuations. When studying the effect of various alternatives of spillway design on energy dissipation during the fall of the jet we must, therefore, make use of indirect measurements by applying the basic equation of the hydraulic jump (which is valid also for aerated supercritical flow). The problem is usually solved as a two-dimensional one in a hydraulic flume by measuring the depth of the flow downstream of the hydraulic jump h_2, i.e. the conjugate depth of the jump. From this and from the known specific discharge q on the model the supercritical depth h_1 of the hydraulic jump may be ascertained for each experiment from the relation

$$h_1 = \frac{h_2}{2}\left(-1 + \sqrt{\left(1 + \frac{8\beta q^2}{g h_2^3}\right)}\right) \tag{7.42}$$

From this fictitious depth h_1 of the flow of water (without air) into the hydraulic jump and from the specific discharge q the actual mean cross-sectional velocity of flow v_1 is then calculated (the velocity of air contained in the flow is identical with the velocity of water). By comparing it with the theoretical velocity of the overfall jet upstream of the hydraulic jump the corresponding value of the velocity coefficient, φ, of the jet and thus also the ratio of its real and theoretical energy can be found.

By systematic research on a number of models quantitative relationships have been determined, some of which are shown in Figs. 7.44, 7.45 and 7.46 and from which it is possible to draw the following general conclusions (Cábelka and Horský, 1961):

(1) The energy dissipation effect of nearly all the above mentioned factors decreases (the value of the velocity coefficient increases) with the increasing specific discharge q, i.e. with the increasing thickness of the overfall jet.

(2) For the classic type of overflow spillway with a smooth streamlined spillway surface, the values of the coefficient φ are considerably higher than for a streamlined spillway surface provided with baffles of various levels (Fig. 7.44a) or where the spillway has been terminated by a vertical surface (Fig. 7.44b). Even lower values of coefficient φ are attained by suitably designed baffles placed on the take-off edge of an interrupted streamlined spillway surface (Fig. 7.44c). The lowest values of coefficient φ are attained when the overfall jets collide in the air (Fig. 7.42)

(3) The height of the take-off edge of the spillway surface above the downstream water level and its detailed design, as well as the use of different types of baffles, influence the dissipation of energy of the jet, i.e.

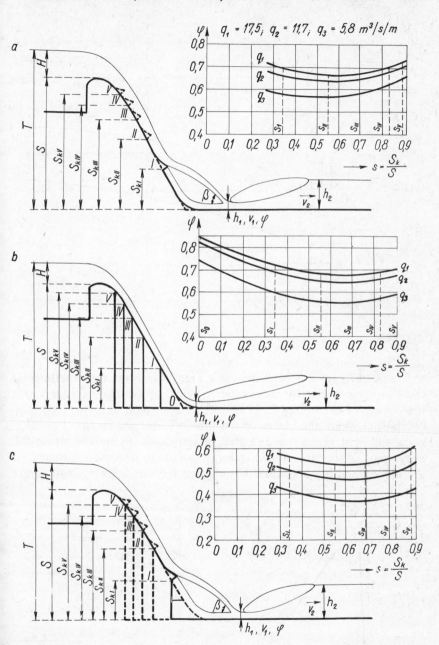

Fig. 7.44.

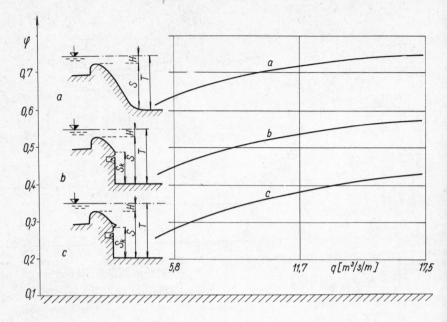

Fig. 7.45.

the value of its velocity coefficient (*see* Fig. 7.44). From the experimental results the most effective mean relative height of the take-off edge above the bottom of the stilling basin ($s = Sk/S$) is $s = 0.60$ (0.55 to 0.65). The overfall jet where the baffles or the take-off edge are in such a position gains sufficient velocity and degree of turbulence by moving along the upper part of the streamlined spillway surface to disperse effectively on the baffles, and has a sufficiently long free fall through the air to aerate

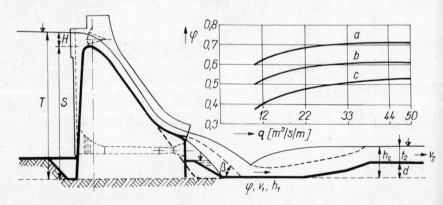

Fig. 7.46.

intensively and break up its core. Figure 7.45 compares φ for different specific discharges q for a relatively low spillway of a classic type (curve a) and for a take-off edge at the optimum relative height $s = 0.65$ without baffles (curve b) or with baffles of a suitable type and size (curve c).

(4) If, in the case of medium and high dams, the take-off edge of the spillway is at the optimum height ($s \simeq 0.6$) the overfall jet falls into the downstream pool far from the downstream toe of the dam. This is advantageous if the strongly exposed part of the bed at the point of jet impact is to be moved away from the dam (i.e. when no stilling basin is provided). If a stilling basin is used, it is advisable to adjust the height, shape and angle of the take-off surface of the jump so that the jet hits the downstream water surface near the toe of the dam. This considerably shortens the necessary length of the stilling basin with a slight increase in the value of coefficient φ. Thus, for example, for the ski jump above the power station at the Slapy dam (Fig. 7.43) the take-off surface with relative height $s = 0.45$ was chosen so that the overfall jet hit the horizontal bed of the stilling basin immediately downstream of the turbine draft tube outlets. The take-off edge of the ski jump placed above the outlet valves of the bottom outlets of the Orlik dam (Fig. 7.46) is still lower ($s = 0.3$). The figure also shows the increase of coefficient, φ, with specific discharge, q, for the classic type of spillway (a), for a ski jump without baffles (b) and for a jump with baffles (c).

(5) An extension of the path of the free fall of the overfall jet through the air achieved by a change in the inclination of the take-off surface of the jump has been found to have little effect in any position. The unfavourable effect of reducing the depth of the water cushion beneath the jet by increased ejection, for a jet angle β reduced to below 40°, also made itself felt.

The stilling basin bed at the point of incidence of the jet falling freely from the ski jump is subjected to a greater specific hydrodynamic pressure and pressure fluctuations than in the classic spillway type where the stilling basin is considerably larger. Nevertheless, if the take-off edge has suitable baffles the stilling basin is subjected only to about half the pressure than is the case if the baffles are omitted. At the same time this pressure is more evenly distributed over a larger surface and also has considerably lower fluctuations. The stilling basin is even less stressed for a spillway with a collision of jets in the air. In this case the stilling basin is subjected to roughly the same pressures as for a classic spillway. This is particularly advantageous for stilling basins on poor foundations.

Experimental results show that the amplitudes of the pressure fluctuations increase with the height of the spillway take-off edge above the stilling basin, because of the increasing vibration of the overfall jet flying freely through the air. On the other hand, by an increase of the tail-water depth the amplitude and the frequency of the pressure fluctuations decrease. The average frequency also decreases slightly with increasing specific discharge, i.e. with the increasing thickness of the overfall jet. The similarity of frequency of pressure fluctuations requires the same Strouhal number on the model as on its prototype.

Since the intensity of aeration and the disintegration of the overfall jets depend mainly on the absolute value of their velocity, due to the greater velocity of the jets in prototype, the velocity coefficient φ here will be somewhat smaller than on the model. Thus in reality the energy dissipation in the stilling basin is even more effective, which increases the safety of the hydraulic structure. This is not an uneconomic cumulation of safety, because the safety factors used in the hydraulic design of a stilling basin are low (*see* Sub-section 7.5.2) when compared with the safety factors generally used in technical practice.

7.5.2 Stilling basins below overflow spillways

The design of the stilling basin below overflow spillways of dams and at weirs is based on the theory of the hydraulic jump.

The equation for the conjugate depths h_1 and h_2 of the hydraulic jump in a rectangular channel may be written for $\beta = 1$ in the form (*see also* Equation (7.42)):

$$h_1 = \frac{h_2}{2} \left(\sqrt{(1 + 8Fr_2^2)} - 1 \right) \tag{7.42a}$$

or

$$h_2 = \frac{h_1}{2} \left(\sqrt{(1 + 8Fr_1^2)} - 1 \right) \tag{7.42b}$$

where

$$Fr = \frac{v}{\sqrt{(gh)}} = \frac{q}{\sqrt{(gh^{3/2})}} = \left(\frac{h_{cr}}{h} \right)^{3/2}$$

and the critical depth

$$h_{cr} = \frac{v_{cr}^2}{g} = \sqrt[3]{\frac{q^2}{g}}$$

The height of the hydraulic jump is given by the difference of the conjugate depths h_2 and h_1 as

$$h_2 - h_1 = \frac{h_1}{2} \left(-3 + \sqrt{(1 + 8Fr_1)} \right) \tag{7.43}$$

The length of the hydraulic jump l is often expressed as a multiple of the height

$$l = m(h_2 - h_1) \tag{7.44}$$

where Smetana gives $m = 6$.

According to research results by Bakhmetev and others, (Chertousov (1957)) m changes with the Froude number in the range from about 4.5 to 8.0, decreasing with increasing Fr. The limit for the validity of the formation of the normal hydraulic jump, confirmed several times from various view-points is $Fr_1^2 \geqslant 3$, i.e. ($h_2/h_1 \geqslant 2$); for lower values of Fr, the hydraulic jump occurs in the form of an undulatory wave. When dimensioning the stilling basin one must start from the requirement that the hydraulic jump should be contained in it with sufficient safety under all discharges and corresponding tail water depths. To ensure this and, at the same time, to stabilize the hydraulic jump at the toe of the spillway a depth h_2' of subcritical flow greater than h_2 (related to h_1 upstream of the hydraulic jump) is created in the stilling basin; $h_2' = \sigma h_2$, where $\sigma > 1$ is the depth safety factor creating a drowned jump. If the depth of the subcritical flow downstream of the stilling basin is h', then the depth of the stilling basin, h^+, is given by the equation (Fig. 7.47)

$$h^+ = h_2' - h' = \sigma h_2 - h' \tag{7.45}$$

and the length of the stilling basin

$$l_s = nl = nm(h_2 - h_1) = K(h_2 - h_1) \tag{7.46}$$

For the calculation of the stilling basin the specific discharge q and the depth of the downstream water h' are usually known. The depth of the supercritical flow h_1 can be obtained from Bernoulli's equation, connecting it with the upstream reservoir level:

$$T_0 = h_1 + \frac{\alpha_1 q^2}{2g\varphi^2 h_1^2} \tag{7.47}$$

The depth h_1 can be established from Equation (7.47) or from graphs prepared for various values of φ and $\sqrt{\alpha}q/T_0^{1.5}$. The calculation must

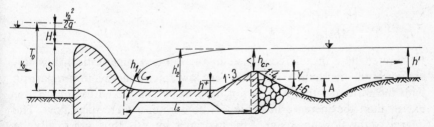

Fig. 7.47.

sometimes be repeated several times because the value of T_0 depends on the depth of the stilling basin h^+. The value of φ is chosen according to the height of the dam and according to the principles quoted in Subsection 7.5.1. This iteration may be replaced by the procedure established by Bashkirova which has been further developed by Boor et. al. (1968). After the calculation of h_1, h_2 may be determined from Equation (7.42b) and the dimensions of the stilling basin from Equations (7.45) and (7.46). Smetana (1933) recommends the values $\sigma = 1.2$ to 1.5 and $n = 0.8$ to 1.1; Chertousov (1957) uses $\sigma = 1.05$ to 1.10 $n = 0.7$ to 0.8.

Since this range of coefficients gives widely varying dimensions of the stilling basin for larger dimensions of the hydraulic jump, it is advisable, especially for more serious cases, to obtain more accurate and economic stilling basin dimensions through model studies. As a result of his investigations Novak (1956) recommends the choice of $K = nm$ in Equation (7.46) as follows:

$$K \approx 5.5 \quad \text{for} \quad 3 < \frac{h_2}{h_1} < 4; \quad K \approx 5.0 \quad \text{for} \quad 4 < \frac{h_2}{h_1} < 6;$$

$$K \approx 4.5 \quad \text{for} \quad 6 < \frac{h_2}{h_1} < 20; \quad K \approx 4.0 \quad \text{for} \quad \frac{h_2}{h_1} > 20;$$

i.e. K is a function of the Froude number. For σ he recommends, in agreement with Chertousov, the value $\sigma = 1.05$ to 1.10 as being sufficient. On the basis of a comparative study he further proved that an increase of the stilling basin above the minimum limit necessary to contain the hydraulic jump, and given by the above mentioned coefficients, does not achieve a corresponding decrease in scour and is therefore uneconomical.

The jump causes energy losses which occur due to the sudden change of the small supercritical depth h_1 to the greater subcritical depth h_2. This change is accompanied by the formation of the hydraulic jump roller above (or below) the basic flow, a strongly increased turbulence of the flow and intensive vortex formation between the main flow and the hydraulic jump roller.

Losses of specific energy in the hydraulic jump can be calculated from the equation

$$\Delta h_{4,5} = \frac{(h_2 - h_1)^3}{4 h_2 h_1} \tag{7.48}$$

In aerated flow the air contained in the aerated supercritical flow upstream of the hydraulic jump has a very low kinetic energy, in comparison with the water, so that it does not have to be considered to any greater extent than the increase in depth of the aerated supercritical flow. The energy of this flow upstream of the hydraulic jump is, thus, practically the same as of the unaerated flow of the same discharge and velocity.

Equations (7.42) and (7.48), therefore, are also valid for the aerated supercritical flow if h_1 is the fictitious depth of this flow without air. This was verified by model studies where small air bubbles were artificially introduced into the supercritical flow upstream of the jump. This had no effect on the energy dissipation in the jump as its height $(h_2 - h_1)$ remained constant for different degrees of aeration. But artificial aeration substantially shortened the length of the jump, this decrease being directly proportional to the air content. The air bubbles in the jump rise towards the surface and thus also influence the movement of water particles, so increasing turbulence and shortening the distance required for the transition from the aerated supercritical to the unaerated subcritical flow and for the dissipation of excess kinetic energy. This explains the shortening of the hydraulic jump observed on models of spillways with ski jumps or baffles permitting a full aeration of the overfall jet upstream of the jump. Since the validity of the Froude law of similarity for the hydraulic jump with aerated water roller has been proved for a large range of scales it is valid also for the dissipation of energy of the aerated flow by the hydraulic jump.

Equation (7.48) was derived for $\alpha_1 = \alpha_2 = 1.0$. Immediately downstream of the jump, however, $\alpha_2 > 1.0$, due to the macroturbulence of the flow, which disappears only at a certain additional distance, l_1, downstream, where it may already be assumed that $\alpha = 1.0$. Equation (7.48) thus expresses the losses of specific energy of flow occurring not only in the actual hydraulic jump of length l_j but also in the transitional section of length, l_1, beyond it, i.e. in both of the last phases four and five (*see also* Sub-section 7.5.5.). For energy losses in the outflow from a hydraulic jump Kadyrov (1958) recommends the equation

$$\Delta h_5 = 0.25 h_{cr} \qquad (7.49)$$

where h_{cr} is the critical depth of flow.

The slope of the sill of the stilling basin considerably influences the dimensions and shape of the downstream scour. After a comprehensive analysis of the scour, Novak (1955) recommends 1 : 3 as the most suitable slope (the optimum slope is also a function of the downstream water depth, which is mostly variable). The horizontal part of the sill should be as short as possible, its length being given only by structural requirements, because it does not contribute towards a reduction in scour. For a stepped stilling basin sill the scour is somewhat smaller than a simple sloping sill, but the differences decrease with the duration of flow, the downstream water depth and the slope of the sill. It is, therefore, more suitable to use a simple sill, in particular where sediments or ice pass, as they can damage the steps in the stilling basin. And lastly it is advantageous to slightly raise the top of the sill by a height y above the bed of the downstream channel (combined sill). However, as the depth above the sill must not approach the critical depth, the limit was determined experimentally as $y \leqslant \frac{2}{3} h_{cr}$.

Closely beyond the stilling basin sill where the excavation necessary for its construction has to be filled in, it is advisable to protect the sill by rough rip-rap placed at a slope of $1:4$ to $1:6$ below the river bed (Fig. 7.47). If no suitable stone is available the sill may be protected by concrete cubes or prisms placed in one or several rows.

The stilling basin sill also influences the entire energy balance and Equation (7.45) represents a considerably simplified estimate of water level, because in reality the water level above the sill is higher than in the downstream channel.

The above considerations apply to the basic, classic type of stilling basin. In order to economize still further on costs of stilling basins, research is being carried out in almost all hydraulic laboratories to improve energy dissipation; only some of the results may be generalized. The different types used include divergent stilling basins, sloping aprons, 'bucket' basins and various stilling basins with baffles and sills (US Bureau of Reclamation, 1965). The choice of the basin is strongly influenced by the relationship between the conjugate and tailwater depths.

For the dissipation of energy below an overflow spillway it is also possible to use a stilling basin with a surface regime hydraulic jump in which the flow at the beginning of the stilling basin is directed upwards from a take-off surface whose edge is usually submerged below the tail water surface. A lower roller of the hydraulic jump with reverse flow near the bottom is formed in the basin. The studies of the hydraulic jump with a surface regime and of its application on a stilling basin design were carried out particularly in the USSR, e.g., by Sabanejev, Bjeljashevskij, Chertousov, Kumin, Skladnev, etc. Their results have been summarized and supplemented by Rybníkář (1957). Figure 7.48 shows three typical regimes of a surface hydraulic jump caused by a variation in downstream depth for a constant discharge Q over a weir spillway:

Type A—simple surface hydraulic jump;
Type B—surface hydraulic jump with adjoining wave;
Type C—surface hydraulic jump with backwater wave.

In type A the greatest velocities occur only on the surface and this is suitable for a smooth transfer of floating objects e.g. ice, over the weir (*see* Fig. 7.5b). The water level below the weir, however, is disturbed for a considerable length, which requires a stronger bank reinforcement. Beyond the ski jump on the bottom there is a roller with considerably slower reverse flow than on the surface of the hydraulic jump, so that the weir is not threatened by scour. By raising the tail water level the first wave is increased and the flow below the weir passes into a surface

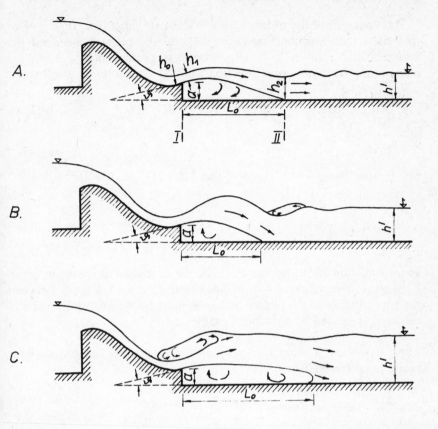

Fig. 7.48.

hydraulic jump of type B; a smaller surface roller downstream of the first wave contributes considerably towards the quietening of the surface, so that it does not transmit as intensive a wave formation as is the case in type A to the river channel downstream of the weir. On the other hand, the bed downstream of the first wave is subjected to greater loads than in the preceding case. Type C occurs if, during a further increase in the tail water depth t, a continuous covering roller begins to form on the overfall jet above the ski jump. At the same time the height of the first and the following wave decreases considerably. The bed downstream of the first wave is considerably less stressed than in type B. The disadvantage is that floating debris may collect in the covering roller above the ski jump (see Fig. 7.5c). Nevertheless the surface hydraulic jump of type C is the most suitable solution, especially with regard to energy dissipation and scour formation, and the river bed need not be as strongly reinforced as for weirs with the classic hydraulic jump with bottom flow.

The thickness of the overfall jet above the ski jump is h_1 (Fig. 7.48A) and since the streamlines are curved here, the pressure head on the surface of the spillway is $h_0 > h_1$. From a theoretical analysis using the momentum theorem between section I and II after solution we obtain

$$\frac{h_2}{h_1} = 2\sqrt{\frac{B}{3}} \cos\left(60° - \frac{\beta}{3}\right) \tag{7.50}$$

where

$$\beta = \cos^{-1}\frac{C}{2\left(\dfrac{B}{3}\right)^{3/2}} \qquad B = \psi^2 + 2\psi\phi + \phi + 2Fr_1^2 \qquad C = 2Fr_1^2$$

$$\psi = \frac{a}{h_1} \qquad \phi = \frac{h_0}{h_1} \qquad Fr_1 = \frac{v_1}{\sqrt{(gh_1)}}$$

From Equation (7.50) we can calculate the necessary downstream depth h_2. The relative values $\phi = h_0/h_1$ are determined for the limits between the various types of the surface hydraulic jump by the following empirical relations suggested by Skladnev (1956):

Limit I between a submerged bottom hydraulic jump and surface hydraulic jump (type A)

$$\phi_1 = \frac{16 - \psi}{10} - \frac{1.75}{Fr_1^{0.4}} + 1 \tag{7.51}$$

Limit II between the surface hydraulic jump type A and B

$$\phi_{II} = 0.2Fr_1\sqrt{\psi} + 1 \tag{7.52}$$

Limit III between the surface hydraulic jump type B and C

$$\phi_{III} = 0.8Fr_1 + 0.02Fr_1^2 + 0.5 \qquad \text{for} \qquad Fr_1 < 5$$
$$\phi_{III} = 0.8Fr_1 + 1 \qquad \text{for} \qquad Fr_1 > 5 \tag{7.53}$$

If the tail water depth is lower than the necessary depth h_2 computed from Equation (7.50), so that a surface hydraulic jump of type C (submerged wave) does not occur, a deepened stilling basin must be used with the bed at a depth $h_2 = \sigma(a + z)$ below the downstream water level, corresponding to discharge Q over the weir which is decisive for the dimensioning of the stilling basin (σ is again the degree of submergence of the jump). Figure 7.49 shows the weir with a ski jump and stilling basin with Rybníkář's graph simplifying the calculation of the height of the take-off edge a and the dimensions of the stilling basin. The length of the stilling basin corresponds to the length of the bottom rollers of the surface

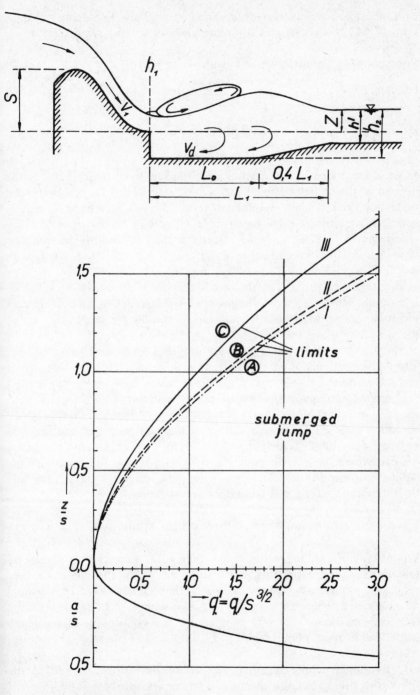

Fig. 7.49. [After Rybníkář, 1957]

hydraulic jump which were determined empirically by Skladnev (Equations (7.44') and (7.54) and Bjeljashevskij (1953) (Equation (7.55)):

For type A $\quad L = m(h_2 - h_1)\quad$ with $\quad m = 6$ to 7 $\hspace{2cm}$ (7.44')

For type B $\quad L = (h_2 - h_1)3.1\left(1 + \dfrac{0.65}{Fr_1^2 - 2}\right)$ $\hspace{2cm}$ (7.54)

For type C $\quad L = 5h_2 - 2.5\,\dfrac{q}{S + a}$ $\hspace{2cm}$ (7.55)

In these equations h_2 is the actual depth of the downstream water to the bottom of the stilling basin. If the stilling basin bed is formed by rock it need not be artificially reinforced at all. In other cases it is usually sufficient to reinforce it by stone rubble with the mean size $d = 0.03 v_d^2$ (m) (Bjeljashevskij, 1953). v_d is the velocity at the bed towards the weir; for type A and B of the surface hydraulic jump $v_d \simeq v_1/2$; for type C with $\sigma = 1.0$ $v_d \simeq v_1/3$ and for $\sigma = 1.25$ $v_d \simeq v_1/4$.

The take off surface of the small ski jump is usually designed as horizontal. However, some studies have confirmed that a small upward inclination of up to $10°$ is advantageous, especially for small heights a of the ski jump above the bed.

The classic type of stilling basin serves also for a comparison of various alternative methods of energy dissipation. Even though some other types are successful the classic type, if correctly designed, is often the cheapest and achieves energy dissipation by purely hydraulic means (just as does the type with the surface jump), without the use of baffles and sills, which are often exposed to considerable velocities and pressures and must be very carefully built. Their use must, therefore, be considered separately for every case, bearing in mind the frequency of the functioning of the stilling basin, and in important cases the most suitable solution may only be determined after a full laboratory investigation.

7.5.3 Energy dissipation below chute spillways

When designing stilling basins below chutes it is necessary first to ascertain if interference or translatory waves occur on the chute, as they require a more costly energy dissipator than steady flow. They should be eliminated wherever possible (*see* Sub-section 7.3.3b). One of the following methods is usually adopted for the connection of the chute to the downstream pool (Haindl and Lískovec, 1973):

(a) The sloping chute is usually joined to the horizontal bed of the reinforced stilling basin by means of a streamlined surface in the shape of a parabola meeting the horizontal plane either at an obtuse angle or

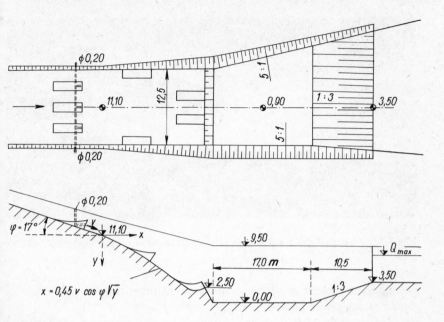

Fig. 7.50.

smoothly with the aid of a cylindrical transition surface. This solution is suitable and economic only for small chutes. For chutes with great velocities and great specific discharges this design results in stilling basins that are too large. It may also be unsuitable for cases where local conditions permit the omission of a stilling basin.

(b) On the streamlined surface above the stilling basin, baffles of suitable shape and dimensions are placed to disperse and aerate the flow and to intensify its energy dissipation. This solution is suitable for smaller specific discharges and reduces stilling basin dimensions and pressures acting on it.

(c) The streamlined surface above the stilling basin has suitably placed baffles above the downstream water surface, and above the stilling basin bed (i.e. below the downstream water surface) it terminates in a ski jump with cylindrical surface. The ski jump directs the water stream upwards into the air to clash there with the jets from the spillway surface. This produces intensive energy dissipation and the stilling basin can then be small and where foundations are good its concrete reinforcement may be omitted completely. Figure 7.50 is an example of such a solution adopted for the termination of the chute of the lateral spillway of the Velká Domáša dam in Czechoslovakia. The outflow from the stilling basin was relatively calm and evenly distributed along its entire width. This was particularly important since, as a result of local conditions, the stilling

Fig. 7.51. Model of chute stilling basin. [Čábelka and Novák, 1964]

basin in plan had an unsymmetrical divergent shape. Figure 7.51 shows a model of the chute and stilling basin in operation.

(d) The streamlined surface at the end of the chute terminates above the tail water level in a ski jump (possibly with baffles on the take-off edge) to disperse and aerate the jet from the chute whilst directing it to a point sufficiently removed from the dam, thus reducing local erosion or stilling basin size to a minimum. This is particularly important for short chutes with high specific discharges where aeration of the flow on the chute hardly occurs.

The dissipation of energy at the end of the chutes with ski jumps is similar to that of outlets from conduits (*see* Sub-section 7.5.4). The difference lies in the fact that when designing a chute spillway there is greater freedom in choosing its route, chutes usually have considerably smaller specific discharges, and the water is more aerated. The design of the ski jump at the end of the chute is primarily influenced by the design discharge and local conditions. Such ski jumps hardly ever change the direction of the jet, because when designing the chute there is usually sufficient freedom in the choice of direction of its final part. Sometimes, however, it is impossible to carry out the necessary change of direction of the chute so that the axis of its end corresponds to the axis of the downstream channel at the point of impact of the deflected jet. Then it is necessary to deflect the jet in the required direction with the aid of suitable baffles, placed on the take-off edge of the jump (e.g. the chute of the Alto Rabagao dam in Portugal, Kobarid in Jugoslavia and Hrinova in Czechoslovakia).

(e) In some cases a combination of chute spillway with the bottom outlets has been found suitable. It is then advisable to place the regulating gates of the bottom outlets, which are usually cone dispersion valves, below the ski jump of the chute and use a joint stilling basin.

7.5.4 Energy dissipation at bottom outlets and outlet tunnels

(a) *Bottom outlets*

Usually water flows from the bottom outlets of dams in a concentrated stream of great velocity. The outlet may terminate below or above the downstream water level and there may be an outlet valve at the end (*see* Sub-section 7.4.2). When searching for the most effective and most economic method of energy dissipation of the outflow jets research and design follows two main trends: the jets are either artificially dispersed and aerated whilst they move over a sufficiently long distance through the air to reduce the value of the velocity coefficient, φ, or they are artificially increased in width, i.e. specific discharge q is reduced at the point of contact with the bottom of the stilling basin.

In the first method the objective is achieved by suitably designed baffles placed downstream of the outlet gates (e.g., vertical lift or segment gates) or through the function of the outlet valves themselves (e.g., Howell–Bunger or hollow jet valves). Increased aeration and disintegration of the outflow jet may also be achieved by artificially causing its rotation or directing it to clash with another outlet or with the overfall jet.

In the second method the jets flowing from relatively narrow outlets are forced to spread into a considerably wider stilling basin. This substantial reduction of the specific discharge results in shallower and shorter stilling basins. To spread the outflow jet in older dams massive blocks or sills were used which were quickly damaged by abrasion and cavitation erosion, gradually lost their effect and required increased maintenance costs. A better method is the distribution of the jet by guide walls into symmetrical low streams dispersed over the entire width of the stilling basin, e.g., the solution adopted at the Cimljanskaja dam, USSR. This method approaches the hydraulically most effective solution where the dissipation of the excess energy of the outflow jet is left to the water mass itself. But there is the danger that even with metal facing of the concrete guide walls and blocks these could be quickly damaged by the flow and that maintenance could be expensive.

Therefore, it is more advantageous to depress and widen the end of the outlet and to simultaneously direct the outflow jet to the stilling basin bed. This is demonstrated on Fig. 7.52 showing both the original and the modified design of a bottom outlet with stilling basin. In the case of two outlets the widening of the outlet end may be asymmetrical to ensure the best performance of the stilling basin in case of flow from one outlet only.

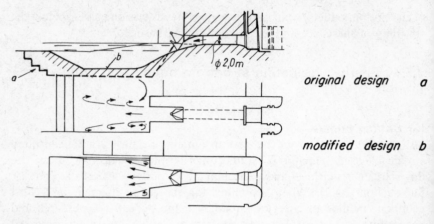

Fig. 7.52.

Figure 7.53 shows this particular case on the model (scale 1:25) of a dam on the Hnilec river in Czechoslovakia.

(b) Outlet tunnels

The outlet tunnels of shaft or side channel dam spillways most frequently have a circular cross-section and water in them often flows at supercritical velocities with a free water surface. The tunnel should be without bends to avoid separation of the flow, occurrence of spiral flow and non-uniform velocity distribution at the outflow. The concentrated supercritical flow from the outlet should be distributed evenly across the entire width of the stilling basin, which is usually divergent in plan. Figure 7.54 shows some examples of suitable stilling basin designs as established by scale model studies.

At shaft spillways passing large discharges under a great head it is often not possible to use the above mentioned stilling basins at the end of the outlet tunnels. In such cases a deflector can be constructed, which throws off the outflow jet so that it hits the river bed at a point sufficiently distant from the dam and disperses, aerates and spreads it as far as possible over the entire width of the river. The deflector sometimes also serves to change the direction of the water flowing from the tunnel. This possibility considerably simplifies the optimum layout of the entire hydraulic structure, but results in a more complicated solution of the shape of the deflector, greater loading and greater danger of cavitation. On the other hand, with a deflector designed in this way it is easier to achieve effective aeration of the deflected jet and the necessary dispersion.

The US Bureau of Reclamation (1965) recommends a deflector which may be modified according to local conditions (Fig. 7.55). Figure 7.56

Fig. 7.53. Model of a dam with outlets and energy dissipation. [Čábelka and Novák, 1964]

illustrates a deflector with a 'pool' and lowered take-off edge, used for the outlet from the spillway of the Infiernillo dam in Mexico. The USBR type (Fig. 7.55) is suitable particularly for gated spillways where the outflow is controlled so that only discharges which the deflector throws off safely over the necessary distance pass over the spillway. The deflector with the

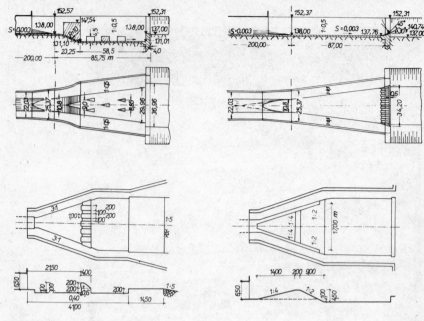

Fig. 7.54.

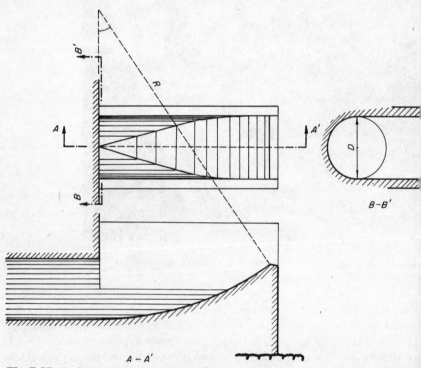

Fig. 7.55. Deflector at a tunnel outlet. [After US Bureau of Reclamation, 1965]

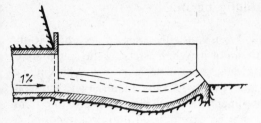

Fig. 7.56.

lowered take-off edge (Fig. 7.56) or an unsymmetrical deflector with the take-off edge of varying height or without one lateral guide wall, is suitable for free spillways, with slow increase (or decrease) of overfall discharges. For low discharges the pool in the deflector forms a stilling basin from which the water flows out harmlessly over the edge into the river without causing dangerous scour directly downstream. On the other hand, during large discharges the surface of the deflector safely throws the outlet jet over the necessary distance.

To prevent negative pressures and cavitation at the end of the deflector, its edge should be bevelled at least an angle of 35° with the direction of its surface. The angle under which the jet leaves the jump determines the distance of its impact on the downstream water surface, the ratio of the horizontal and vertical velocity components at impact and thus also the loading of the river bed. This angle also influences the length of the jet passage through the air, and thus its disintegration and aeration, as well as the ejection effect of the jet. Suitable take-off angles lie in the range 15° to 35° from the horizontal. For angles smaller than 15° it is usually not possible to throw off the outlet jet over the necessary distance and, furthermore, the downstream water level is greatly reduced by ejection. It is unnecessary to increase the take-off angle over 35° since this does not increase the length of the flight of the jet through the air and thus its dispersion and aeration. It is also unsuitable because it increases the depth of scour of the river bed at the point of jet impact. For an effective throwing off of the outlet jet it is necessary that the radius of the curvature of the surface of the deflector be greater than four times the greatest depth of water at the end of the outlet tunnel. For a good operation of the deflector the downstream water level is also very important. The maximum downstream water level should not reach a level greater than half the height of the outlet tunnel at its end upstream of the deflector.

Deflectors downstream of the outflow from spillway outlet tunnels may be designed on the basis of hydraulic research in such a way as to fulfil various requirements and suit local conditions. If correctly designed they represent a reliable and economic method of energy dissipation.

7.5.5 Local erosion at stilling basins

The effectiveness of the stilling basin is usually assessed according to the local scour in the bed downstream of it. When assessing the suitability of various alternative solutions a qualitative investigation is sufficient, i.e. the bed is simulated on the model by any movable material and the scour compared after repeated experiments of equal duration, e.g. one hour. Here the size of the scour cannot be extrapolated into prototype.

In practice, however, it is important to estimate the size of the scour at the stilling basin, i.e. a quantitative result is required. For this purpose we must ascertain why scour occurs beyond the hydraulic jump and the stilling basin. The reasons are as follows:

(1) A vortex with a horizontal axis scouring the bed and shifting sediment towards the basin sill occurs downstream of a stilling basin which is deeper than the river channel.

(2) The total energy dissipation in the hydraulic jump, expressed by Equation (7.48), occurs not only in the jump proper, but for some distance downstream, where due to the uneven velocity distribution and increased turbulence beyond the hydraulic jump the energy line is considerably higher than would correspond to the normal subcritical flow and only slowly approaches this level. This means that the Coriolis number α for the flow is appreciably greater than one. If we denote the real value of the Coriolis number beyond the hydraulic jump as α', and the value for the normal flow as α, the increased energy beyond the hydraulic jump is expressed by the equation

$$\Delta h_5 = (\alpha' - \alpha) \frac{v_2^2}{2g} \tag{7.49a}$$

and the efficiency of the actual hydraulic jump from the point of view of energy dissipation for $\alpha = 1$, taking into account Equation (7.42), can be expressed as

$$\frac{\Delta h_4}{\Delta h_{4,5}} = 1 - \frac{\Delta h_5}{\Delta h_{4,5}} = 1 - 4(\alpha' - 1) \frac{\sqrt{(1 + 8Fr_1^2)} + 1}{(\sqrt{(1 + 8Fr_1^2)} - 3)^3} \tag{7.56}$$

If we plot α' and $\Delta h_4/\Delta h_{4,5}$ against Fr_1^2 we obtain, according to USSR experimental results, the graphs on Fig. 7.57. These show that α' grows with Fr_1^2 and further that the efficiency of energy dissipation in the hydraulic jump proper drops with the Froude number and for low Froude numbers up to 50% of the energy remains to be dissipated. Thus the flow of water with high turbulence and great velocity near the bed has an appreciably higher transport capacity than the normal flow.

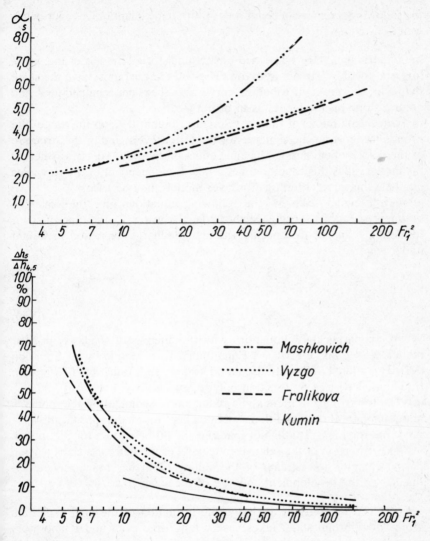

Fig. 7.57.

The actual value of the resulting scour, especially for a variable discharge, may only be ascertained with the aid of laboratory research taking into account the respective laws of similarity. This problem has been studied particularly in Switzerland (Eggenberger, Müller, Meyer-Peter, Jaeger) in Italy (Scimemi, Ghetti), in the USSR (Pikalov, Mircchulava), the Netherlands (Breusers), Czechoslovakia (Novák, 1955, 1956; Grund, 1962) etc. The theoretical and experimental studies permit the following summary of conditions for attaining quantitative scour below weirs on models:

(a) Experiments must be carried out on undistorted models of the structure and the downstream reservoir. The bed material must have the same shape of the grain distribution curve and the same compactness and natural slope on the model as in prototype.

(b) Under conditions of fully developed turbulent flow on the model the Froude law ensures the similarity of the water levels, and of the structure of the velocity field and its dynamic effect on the bed. To assess whether the model fulfils this condition, i.e. if flow is independent of the Reynolds number, the same criteria as for river models may be used.

(c) For a model scale M_l the following equations give the scales of sediment size d, its specific weight under the water γ'_s, the time of scour formation t and of the specific sediment discharge expressed in weight under water g'_s:

$$M_d M_{\gamma_{s'}} = M_i \tag{7.57}$$

$$M_t = M_l^{1/2} M_{\gamma_{s'}} \tag{7.58}$$

$$M_{g_{s'}} = M_l^{3/2} \tag{7.59}$$

When comparing these equations with the analysis of similarity in river models we see that for $M_{S_e} = 1$ Equation (7.57) is identical with Equation (VI), Equation (7.58) with Equation (6.56') and Equation (7.59) with Equation (VII) (see Sub-section 6.2.5).

(d) The lower limit of permissible reduction of sediment on the model is about 0.5 mm. If this condition cannot be kept for model specific gravity = 2.65, i.e. for $M_{\gamma_{s'}} = 1$, a lighter material should be chosen for the model.

(e) The distortion of the relative roughness of the bed for a short section of the channel downstream of the stilling basin has practically no influence on the development and size of the scour.

For a certain constant discharge the formation of the final maximum scour (equilibrium state) takes a very long time even under laboratory conditions, but the largest part of the scour in the region immediately downstream of the stilling basin, up to the greatest scour depth, forms in a comparatively short period of time. This is why Novak (1956) proposed the computation of the maximum final scour from the course of its development in time. If we denote A_1 the depth of scour measured on the model in time t_1, then the scour A in time t is given by:

$$\frac{A}{A_1} = a - be^{-c(t/t_1 + d)} \tag{7.60}$$

where a, b, c and d are constants dependent on the type of stilling basin used (simple basin with sloping sill, basin with stepped sill, stilling basin with baffles, etc.) which may be determined from model results. For the classic type of stilling basin with sloping sill and for $t_1 = 1$ hour, Novak recommends $a = 1.65$, $b = 1.0$, $c = 0.23$ m and $d = 1.0$. For the final depth of the scour A_f at $t = \infty$, Equation (7.60) is simplified to

$$A_f = aA_1 \tag{7.60'}$$

i.e. in this type of stilling basin the final scour is 1.65 times greater than the scour formed after an experiment of one hour (for constant discharge). The fact that Equation (7.60) is independent of sediment size is because it applies to the development of scour in time $t > t_1$, i.e. at a stage when the decisive factor for the development of scour is the rotating and pulsating vortex in the bed downstream of the stilling basin in contrast to the initial stage, when the scour, especially for a horizontal apron without a sill, is influenced above all by increased turbulence and uneven velocity distribution.

A number of researchers (Schoklitsch, Veronese, Jaeger, Patrashev, Eggenberger; *see* Novak, 1955) tried to establish equations for the determination of the final depth of the scour below an overfall without stilling basin. Novak (1964) suggested the use of some of these equations for the calculation of the final depth of the scour beyond the stilling basin for constant specific discharge q, by multiplying them by a coefficient c, which is slightly dependent on the degree of submergence σ of the hydraulic jump. Thus for example when using Jaeger's equation for A_f at a classic stilling basin we obtain the equation

$$A_f = c\left[6H^{0.25}q^{0.5}\left(\frac{h'}{d_{90}}\right)^{1/3} - h'\right] \tag{7.61}$$

where $c = 0.45$ to 0.65 for $\sigma = 1.0$ to 1.6.
H is the difference between the upstream and downstream water levels (m),
h' is the downstream depth (m),
q is specific discharge (m²/s),
d_{90} is 90% grain size of sediment forming the river bed (mm).
This means that the stilling basin reduces the scour in the river bed to only about half of that formed below an overfall without a stilling basin, but naturally the scour would be close to the structure in the latter case.

During laboratory investigations on stilling basins and scour in hydraulic flumes we usually work with clean water without the supply of sediments from the upstream reservoir. The influence of this sediment discharge on scour formation was further studied by Novak (1961) with the following conclusions:

(a) The passage of sediments through a hydraulic structure greatly influences the formation of downstream scour which decreases, as compared with scour for flow of water without sediments, with increasing sediment size and discharge.

(b) The scour attains its final value always in a finite time (and not asymptotically as expressed by Equation (7.60) for the discharge of water without sediment); this time is the shorter, the greater the sediment discharge.

(c) Measurements of velocity distribution and turbulence in the cross-section above the stilling basin sill did not differ significantly from the results for the flow of water without sediment. From this it follows that the reduction of scour downstream of stilling basins with passage of sediment through a hydraulic structure is almost exclusively achieved by the fact that, in a certain finite and comparatively short time, a state of equilibrium is achieved between the amount of sediment carried away from the scour hole and that transported from the upstream reservoir.

(d) If during flood discharges the passage of sediment is preserved in prototype on a structure, its stilling basin may be economically designed by using lower values of constants in the empirical equations, as these are valid for the discharge of water without sediments, given a suitable stilling basin end sill and sufficient bank protection.

7.6 Models of Spillway Gates

7.6.1 Shape of gates

The shape of the movable parts of hydraulic structures such as spillway and weir gates and outlet or by-pass gates, must be solved with the hydraulic structure as a whole in mind and be suitably adapted to the flow of water. This concerns not only all the surfaces of gates over which water flows, but also their supports, lateral plates, seals, etc.

The surfaces of movable weir and dam spillway gates are best designed in streamlined shapes, (*see* Sub-section 7.3.1) so that no unfavourable negative pressures occur on them. However, for technical and economical reasons, the surfaces of steel gates cannot be produced with a smooth change of curvature following the shape of the lower envelope of a free overfalling jet (according to which the spillway surface is solved). They are usually shaped so as to be made up (in the cross-section) from two or three circular segments of various radii adhering as much as possible to the required shape. With a suitable choice of radii and length of circular arches favourable hydraulic loading without local negative pressures is achieved (*see* Sub-section 7.6.2). The lower surface of vertical lift gates must be suitably shaped to prevent the occurrence of negative pressures with all their unfavourable consequences, i.e. increase of the vertical lifting force, possibility of cavitation and vibration of gates, etc. It is advisable, therefore, to construct the lower sealing surface of the lift gates in such a way that at every point and in all gate positions it is subjected to positive (upward) pressures. When determining a hydraulically suitable shape for this surface we set out, as in the solution of the streamline spillway surface, from the shapes of the surface of a jet flowing under pressure below a horizontal sharp edge of a plate placed in a hydraulic flume with a horizontal bed. The shape of the outlet curves depends on the ratio h/a (where h is the head of the water level above the bed upstream of the plate and a is the height of the outlet orifice), and possibly on the ratio h_0/a ($h_0 = h + v_0^2/2g$, where v_0 is the approach velocity). Apart from this the shape of the outlet jet also depends on the slope and shape of the plate. For similarity, according to the Froude law, 'a' should be greater than 60 mm.

The outlet jet surface curves illustrated in Fig. 7.58A have been determined experimentally by Smetana (1953) for a vertical plane plate (lifting gate, *see* Fig. 7.58B) and for a height of the outlet orifice, $a = 1.0$ (e.g. 1.0 m); they are the so-called 'unit' shapes of outlet curves. The unit theoretical outlet curve, which was determined on the assumption of a two-dimensional potential flow of an ideal fluid, forms the lower limit of the real 'unit' outlet curves, measured with viscous fluid (water). These real unit outlet curves (Fig. 7.58A) may be characterized as follows:

(a) The unit curve S_1, which is valid for all values of the ratio $h/a \geqslant 3.3$ indicates a smaller contraction of the jet than the theoretical curve T_1.
(b) The unit outlet curves N_1 are valid for the values of $h/a < 3.3$. Their shape varies with the value of the ratio h/a and the jet has a smaller contraction than for the case denoted by the curve S_1. Figure 7.58A shows the experimentally determined curves for the ratio $h/a = 1.6$ $(N_1)_{1.6}$, 1.4 $(N_1)_{1.4}$ and for the ratio $h/a = 1.2$ $(N_1)_{1.2}$; the ratio $h/a = 1$ $(N_1)_1$ signifies the free surface touching the edge of the plate.
(c) The contraction of the real unit outlet jet is also influenced by the velocity of approach v_0, so that the greater the velocity, the smaller the contraction.

The shape of the outlet jet surface for a height of the outlet orifice 'a' different from one, is geometrically similar to the appropriate unit curve $(T_1, S_1, (N_1)_x, x = h/a)$ (*see* Fig. 7.58C).

The suitable shape of the outlet surface for the lower part of a vertical lift gate is determined by the value of 'a' and h/a which gives the greatest contraction of the outlet jet. This guarantees that for each opening of the gate during operation positive pressures only will act on its entire lower (seating) surface (Fig. 7.58D) thus considerably decreasing the lifting forces necessary for the movement of the gate and excluding the risk of vibration and cavitation. In this way one can determine the hydraulically effective shapes of the lower surfaces of lifting gates of comparatively

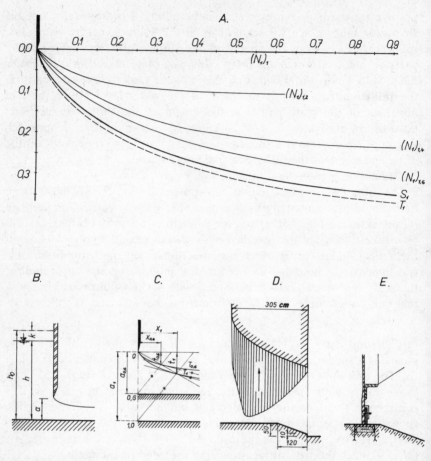

Fig. 7.58. Outflow jet from under a gate. [After Smetana, 1953]

small length (span) where the water pressure does not result in a deflection, which in turn could cause leakage when the gates are closed against a fixed sill. If deflection of the gate must be taken into consideration the seating surface should be parallel with the plane of the deformation and as narrow as possible. A suitable design is a metal plate fitted with an adjustable rubber seal (Fig. 7.58E).

Apart from overflow and outflow surfaces of movable gates it is advisable also to design all other parts of gates round which the water flows, i.e. side plates, seals, supporting structures, bearings, suspensions, wheels, arms of the segments, flaps on top of gates, on the basis of model studies. Their shapes and positions must be solved so that the overfall or outlet jet is smoothly guided and does not hit or damage any part of the gate (*see* Fig. 7.59).

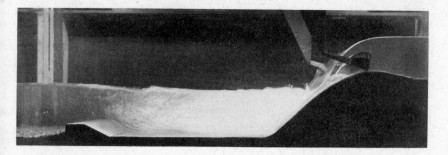

Fig. 7.59. Model of a gate and stilling basin.

The same holds good for the design of slots and grooves in the guide walls of piers on spillways and at intakes. At these grooves, serious damage, caused by unsuitable design and flow of water at great velocities, may occur. Furthermore, the grooves cause an increase in the loss coefficient of the inlets and a decrease in the spillway discharge capacity. This problem has been dealt with systematically and in detail, e.g., by the US Bureau of Reclamation (Ball, 1959), where investigations were carried out on hydraulic and aerodynamic models; in some cases the results were verified by prototype measurements. The pressure conditions have been expressed as $(h_x - h_0)/k$, where h_x is the pressure head at the respective point in the region of the grooves, h_0 is the pressure head related to the level of the lower edge of the raised gate, and k is the velocity head of the mean flow velocity in the outlet orifice. Figure 7.60 shows four of a series of tested designs of vertical lift gate grooves. On the basis of this study it is possible for the required values of the shape

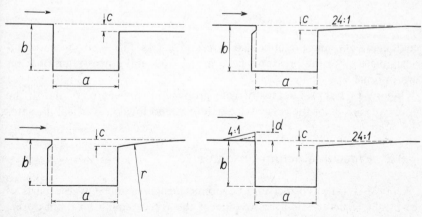

Fig. 7.60. [Ball, 1959]

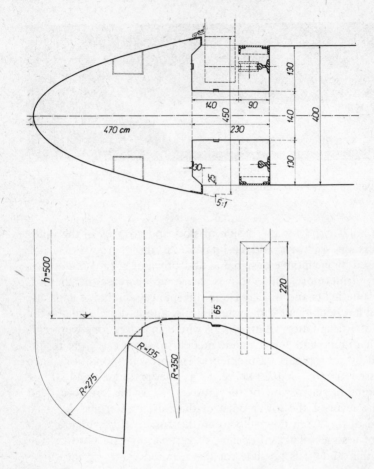

Fig. 7.61.

coefficient a/b, and possibly also of c and d (*see* Fig. 7.60), to choose a design such that the pressures both in the slots and downstream of them are optimal.

Figure 7.61 shows details of gate grooves in spillway piers and of the spillway surface of the Štěchovice dam, Czechoslovakia (vertical lift gates 5×20 m²).

7.6.2 Pressures acting on gates

The basis for the correct and economic design of the movable parts of hydraulic structures is a knowledge of the forces acting on them during operation. The hydrodynamic pressure is usually the main force; subsidiary forces acting on these structures are caused by waves, ice, impact of floating bodies, vibration, etc. Hydraulic pressures caused by stationary water or by a steady uniform flow of water parallel with the surface of the gate can be determined by the laws of hydrostatics.

Pressures caused by steady nonuniform curvilinear flow along the gate surfaces, e.g., in the case of an overflow or outflow, can be determined by various methods based on the potential flow theory, by finite element methods and analogues, and lastly by direct measurements on scale models which give the most reliable results. The models are operated according to the Froude law of similarity and pressures are most frequently measured by piezometers.

In good designs the distribution of the hydrodynamic pressure is smooth, the pressure is usually positive and its fluctuations caused by turbulence comparatively low. The measured pressure head may be extrapolated according to the length scale to geometrically similar structures. Figure 7.62 gives as an example the unit pressures (for $H = 1.0$) acting on a weir flap gate in its various positions, measured on a scale model with the aid of twenty piezometers. The curvature of the covering plate of the flap is given by a single radius of $2.25H$. Pressures were measured in ten flap positions for a constant upstream water level and for

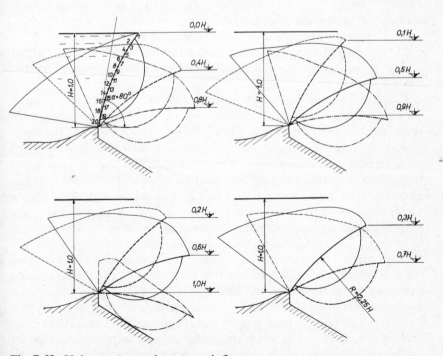

Fig. 7.62. Unit pressures acting on a weir flap gate.

various downstream water levels (in Fig. 7.62 the influence of downstream water level is ignored).

If the surfaces of gates are unsuitable hydraulically, separation of flow from the surface, variable negative pressures and substantial pressure fluctuations may occur. This may lead to vibrations of the gates and even their failure. Variable pressures may also be caused by unsteady flow, e.g., by waves. The investigation of hydraulic pressures acting on the gates is then more difficult as neither computational methods nor measurement by piezometers are suitable and it is necessary to use pressure gauges, possibly dynamometers of various types, and to record their output. However, it is difficult to determine the total hydrodynamic load acting on the gates and its changes with time in this way. For this purpose special dynamometers connected to the suspension mechanism of the gate and to an oscillograph are normally used.

Experimental investigations of hydrodynamic pressures acting on gates of various types have been carried out by many hydraulic laboratories and in particular great attention has been paid to various designs of automatic (hydraulically operated) gates.

7.6.3 Vibration of gates

Vibration of gates is a very dangerous phenomenon as it can cause metal fatigue and, ultimately, failure of the gates endangering the whole structure. It increases seepage under and settling of the structure as well as uplift reducing stability and safety. Vibration of gates can occur either with an overfall of water or during the outflow under pressure (undershot gates).

Every overfall jet has a tendency to vibration when freely falling a sufficient distance over a horizontal spillway edge and remaining unbroken to the point of contact with the downstream level (with the space beneath it shut off from the surrounding air). Vibration has been observed most frequently in the case of a comparatively thin sheet of water falling over a partly lowered flap (gate) attached to the top of a higher gate, which often starts vibrating as well if in resonance with the vibrating jet. However, vibration also occurs at overfalls over partly lowered gates, particularly if they are hydraulically unsuitable in shape, and it may also occur in the case of thicker overfall jets.

The vibration of gates can be explained as self-induced vibration where the gate with its hydraulic load, the free overfalling jet and the air cushion beneath it participate. The vibrating overfall jet causes compression and easing of the pressure in the air cushion beneath the jet, which is transferred as positive and negative pressure waves to the (flap) gate, causing or maintaining its vibration, particularly if the frequency of the jet vibrations is the same as, or in resonance with, the frequency of the gate, the vibration of which in turn supports the vibration of the overfall jet. The increase in the amplitude of vibrations of the gate is dampened by the viscous friction of the water mass surrounding the vibrating structure, by the friction in the bearings and by energy dissipation.

Vibration may be prevented by the use of streamlined spillway surfaces and by aeration of the space beneath the overfall jet, but above all by the use of baffles on the spillway surface separating the continuous overfall jet into a number of jets of varying thickness and shape, and thus also with different frequencies, so that the factors causing vibration of the gate cancel each other out.

To aerate the space beneath the overfall jet an aeration vent is usually used. This may be dimensioned with the aid of Hickox's (1942) experimental study and his empirical equation

$$q_a = \frac{(CH)^{3.64} g^{0.5}}{p^{1.14}} \tag{7.62}$$

where q_a is the quantity of air (m³/s) per metre width of the overfall; H is the overfall head (m); p is the negative pressure beneath the overfall jet (metres of water), the value of which is given by the head loss for the flow of air through the vent (chosen at about 0.05–0.5 m); and C is the constant dependent on the ratio of discharge under the gate and the flow over it (for a simple overfall $C = 0.077$).

The total discharge of air through the aeration vent diameter D with an overfall width B is then

$$Q_a = q_a B = \frac{C' \pi D^2}{4} \sqrt{(2gp\gamma_2/\gamma_1)} \tag{7.63}$$

where $C' = 1/\sqrt{(1 + \sum \xi)}$ includes all head loss coefficients for the air flowing through the pipe and γ_2/γ_1 is the ratio of the specific weight of water and air at the assumed temperature (about 830 for a temperature of 20°C). From these equations it is then possible to calculate the diameter D of the aeration vent

$$D = C'' \frac{H^{1.82} B^{0.5}}{p^{0.82}} \qquad C'' = \frac{2C^{1.82}}{\sqrt{(C'\pi)} \sqrt[4]{(2\gamma_2/\gamma_1)}} \tag{7.64}$$

For a simple overfall $C'' \simeq 0.00406$ when expressing D, H, p and B in metres.

Equations (7.63) and (7.64) are not dimensionally correct (B would have to be dimensionless) and do not take into consideration the length of contact of the overfall jet with air, which may be expressed by the difference, T, between the upstream water level and the point of impact of the overfall jet. These shortcomings (for a simple overfall without outflow under the gate) are eliminated by the studies of Wisner and

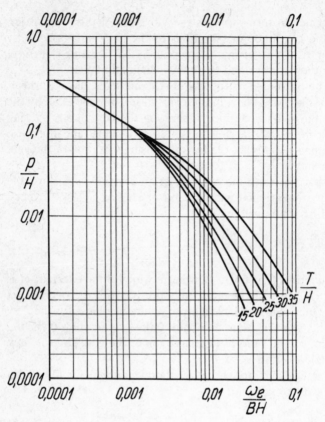

Fig. 7.63. [Wisner and Mitric, 1961]

Mitric (1961) who, on the basis of measurements in the laboratory and in prototype, determined the relationship given in Fig. 7.63, where ω_e is the equivalent area of an orifice diameter d, which for discharge coefficient $C_d = 1$ has the same capacity as the aeration vent diameter D, i.e.

$$D = 2\sqrt{\left(\frac{\omega_e}{\pi C'}\right)}$$ (7.65)

From the graph in Fig. 7.63 ω_e/BH may be ascertained for a chosen ratio p/H and the given ratio T/H, and from Equation (7.65) D may be found. For $p/H > 0.1$ the results according to Equation (7.64) and (7.65) are practically identical.

Measures for the prevention of gate vibration are best verified by research either directly on the prototype structure itself or on scale models. Modelling of hydrodynamic phenomena during gate vibration is carried out according to the Froude law of similarity, because when the model is sufficiently large the flow of thicker jets with a free surface and a high Reynolds number is not noticeably influenced by the viscosity of water or surface tension. During the vibration of the gate, however, apart from the forces caused by the flow of water there are also other forces present, such as inertia, the elastic forces of the gate and forces damping the vibration. For the dynamic similarity of these forces other laws than the Froude law are valid (Kolkman, 1976). For the similarity of hydroelastic forces the ratio of the specific mass of the structure ρ_k and water ρ on the model and in prototype must be constant

$$\frac{\rho_{k_p}}{\rho_p} = \frac{\rho_{k_m}}{\rho_m} = \text{const.} \tag{7.66}$$

For the forces of elasticity, as far as they influence the vibration, the Mach (Cauchy) law of similarity is valid, according to which the scale of forces is given by the relationship

$$M_p = M_E M_l^2 \tag{7.67}$$

and the scale of time by the relationship

$$M_t = M_E^{-1/2} M_l \tag{7.68}$$

where M_E is the scale of the modulus of elasticity of the gate material.

For the damping forces the Reynolds law of similarity ($M_p = 1$ and $M_t = M_l^2$) is valid, because their greatest part can be attributed to viscous friction of water surrounding the vibrating gate, which in turn is proportional to the velocity of its vibration. Since according to the Froude law the time scale of vibration is given by $M_t = M_l^{1/2}$, it is possible to fulfil this and Equation (7.68) simultaneously only if

$$M_E = M_l. \tag{7.69}$$

For usable model scales, however, few materials exist which would fulfil this condition. Trovidure can be used to reproduce steel ($M_l \simeq 60$) and concrete ($M_l \simeq 6$), but Equation (7.66) cannot be fulfilled simultaneously for experiments in water as $M_{\rho_k} \simeq 5.5$ instead of 1.

Since, when using the Froude law, it is not possible to comply simultaneously even with the Reynolds law, during model research the influence of the various forces must be successively investigated so that by a suitable experimental arrangement (e.g., adding mass to the model structure), or by suitable measuring methods, certain influences during measurements are either excluded or kept constant and accounted for.

References

Anwar, H. O. (1968). Prevention of vortices at intakes, *Water Power*, **2**, No. 10, pp. 393–401.

Arsenishvili, K. J. (1961). *Translatory Waves on Hydraulic Structures,* (in Russian), Sakartvelo, Tbilisi.

Ball, J. W. (1959). Hydraulic characteristics of gate slots, *Proc. ASCE, J. Hydraul. Div.* **85,** No. HY10, pp. 81–140.

Ball, J. W. and Herbert, D. J. (1948). The Development of High Head Outlet Valves. *Proc. 2nd General Meeting IAHR, Stockholm,* **II,** Paper 14, pp. 237–261.

Bjeljashevskij, N. N. (1953). *Surface Jump Stilling Basins,* (in Russian), Izd. Akademii Nauk ukrajinskoj SSR, Kijev.

Blau, H. (1970). Die Berechnung flachkroniger Einläufe von Schachtüberfällen, *Wasserwirtschaft-Wassertechnik,* No. 6, pp. 209–212.

Bollrich, G. (1965). Berechnung und Gestaltung der Einläufe von Schachtüberfällen, *Wasserwirtschaft-Wassertechnik,* No. 3, pp. 92–97.

Boor, B., Kunštátský, J. and Patočka, C. (1968). *Hydraulics for Engineering Structures,* (in Czech), SNTL, Prague.

Bradley, J. N. (1952), *Discharge Coefficients for Irregular Overfall Spillways,* Engineering monographs No. 9, Bureau of Reclamation, Denver, Colorado.

Bradley, J. and Peterka, A. (1957). The hydraulic design of stilling basins, *Proc. ASCE, J. Hydraul. Div.* **83,** No. HY5, 129 pp.

British Hydromechanics Research Association. (1975). *Proceedings of International Symposium on the Design and Operation of Siphons and Siphon Spillways,* BHRA Fluid Engineering, Cranfield.

Brkich, A. (1953). Rid vertical pumps intake design of guess with model tests. *Power,* **97,** No. 2, pp. 90–91; 192–194.

Cábelka, J. (1950). Hydro-electric station design. Modernisation of a Czech power plant. *The Electrician,* London, pp. 1881–1886.

Cábelka, J. (1950a). The suitable layout of a low-head hydro-electric plant built next to weirs, *Proc. 4th World Power Conference, London,* Sec. H2, Paper No. 4, pp. 1–14.

Cábelka, J. (1954). Contribution of hydraulic research to the design of stilling basins at large dams, (in Slovak), *Vodohospodársky časopis SAV,* No. 2, pp. 139–182.

Cábelka, J. (1955). Hydraulics of barrage gates, (in Slovak), *Oceliarsky sborník SAV,* Bratislava, pp. 257–291.

Cábelka, J. (1955a). Losses of mechanical energy of the overfall jet on the spillway section of a dam, *Proc. 6th General Meeting IAHR, The Hague,* **3,** Paper C27, 10 pp.

Cábelka, J. (1971). The contribution of hydraulic research towards the solution of shaft spillways, (in Czech), *Vodní hospodářství,* No. 5.

Cábelka, J. and Horský, T. (1961). Contribution a l'étude de l'amortissement de l'énergie d'un courant d'eau sur les deversoirs de hauts barrages et de la charge du radier, *Proc. 9th General Meeting IAHR, Dubrovnik,* pp. 244–257.

Cábelka, J. and Novák, P. (1964). *Hydraulic Research 1—Research on Models,* (in Czech), SNTL, Prague.

Cábelka, J. and Spánek, F. (1954). Hydraulic studies of the Slapy dam, (in Czech), *Vodní hospodářství,* Nos 4 and 5, pp. 113–122; 141–151.

Cebertowicz, R. (1958). *Hydraulic Construction in the Light of Model Investigations,* (in Polish), Państwowe Wydawnictwo naukowe, Warsaw.

Chertousov, M. D. (1957). *Hydraulics*, (in Russian), Gosenergoizdat, Moscow.

Chow, Ven Te. (1959). *Open Channel Hydraulics*, McGraw-Hill, New York.

Coyne, A. (1951). Observations sur les deversoirs en saut de ski, *4th Congres de Grands Barrages, New Delhi*, **2**, Paper R89, pp. 737–756.

Creager, W. P., Justin, J. D. and Hinds, J. (1945). *Engineering for Dams*, John Wiley and Sons, New York.

Crow, D. A., King, R. and Prosser, M. J. (1978). *Hydraulic Model Studies of the Rising Sector Gate: Hydrodynamic Loads and Vibration Studies. Thames Barrier Design*. ICE, London.

Davis, C. V. (1969). *Handbook of Applied Hydraulics*, 3rd Edn., McGraw-Hill New York.

Denny, D. T. and Young, G. A. J. (1957). The prevention of vortices and swirl at intakes, *Proc. 7th General Meeting IAHR, Lisbon*, **I**, Paper C1, 18 pp.

Ehrenberger, R. (1930). Eine neue Geschwindigkeitsformel für künstliche Gerinne mit starken Neigungen und Berechnung des Wassers, *Wasserwirtschaft*, **23**, No. 28, pp. 573–575, **23**, No. 29, pp. 595–598.

Elder, R. A. (1961). Model-prototype turbulence scaling. *Proc. 9th Congress IAHR, Dubrovnik*, pp. 24–31.

Elder, R. A. and Daugherty, C. B. (1952). Characteristics of fixed dispersion cone valves, *Proc. ASCE*, **78**, No. 153, pp. 341–349.

Elevatorski, E. A. (1959). *Hydraulic Energy Dissipators*, McGraw-Hill, New York.

Faktorovich, M. E. (1952). Energy dissipation at jet collision, (in Russian), *Gidrotechnicheskoje strojitelstvo*, No. 8, pp. 43–44.

Fraser, W. H. (1953). Hydraulic problems encountered in intake structures of vertical wet-pit pumps and methods leading to their solution, *Trans. ASME*, **75**, No. 4, pp. 643–652.

Gabriel, P. and Grund, I. (1965). *Intakes of Pump Storage Power Stations*, (in Slovak), Práce a štúdie No. 31, VÚV Bratislava.

Gallay, M. and Vincent, J. (1960). Hydraulic research of the lay-out of the Wolfsthal barrage, (in Slovak), *Vodní hospodářství*, No. 1, pp. 23–27.

Galperin, R. S., Oskolkov, A. G., Semenkov, V. M. and Tsendrov, G. N. (1977). *Cavitation at Hydraulic Structures*, (in Russian), Energija, Moscow.

Gardel, A. (1949). Les évacuateurs de crues en deversoirs circulaires, *Bulletin Technique de la Suisse Romande*, No. 27, pp. 341–349.

Govinda Rao, N. S. and Rajaratnam, N. (1961). On the inception of airentrainment in open channel flows, *Proc. 9th Congress IAHR, Dubrovnik*, pp. 9–12.

Grund, I. (1962). *Similarity in Model Studies of Local Erosion at Hydraulic Structures*, (in Slovak), Práce a štúdie No. 15, VÚV Bratislava.

Haindl, K. (1957). The design of aeration vents, (in Czech), *Strojírenství* No. 11, pp. 827–830.

Haindl, K. (1958). *Theory of the Hydraulic Jump in Pipelines and its Application in Engineering Practice*, (in Czech), Práce a štúdie No. 98, VÚV Prague.

Haindl, K. (1963). Outflow from culverts and tunnels, (in Czech), *Vodní hospodářství*, No. 2, pp. 43–48.

Haindl, K. and Doležal, L. (1961). Turbulent pressure fluctuations in a complex hydraulic structure, *Proc. 9th Congress IAHR, Dubrovnik*, pp. 56–65.

Haindl, K., Doležal, L. and Král, J. (1962). Contribution to the hydraulics of a shaft spillway, (in Czech), *Vodohospodársky časopis SAV*, Nos 3 and 4, pp. 288–315, 370–381.

Haindl, K. and Lískovec, L. (1973). *Supercritical Flow in Hydraulic Engineering*, (in Czech), Práce a štúdie No. 132, VÚV, Prague.

Halbronn, G., Duraud, K. and Cohen de Lara, G. (1953). Air entrainment in steeply sloping flumes, *Proc. 5th General Meeting IAHR*, Minneapolis.

Hall, L. S. (1942). Open channel flow at high velocities, *Proc. ASCE*, pp. 1100–1140.

Hardwick, J. D. (1974). Flow-induced vibration of vertical lift gate, *Proc. ASCE, J. Hydraul. Div.*, **100**, No HY5, pp. 631–644.

Hickox, G. H. (1942). Aeration of spillways. Trans. ASCE, **109**, Paper No. 2215, p. 537.

Hino, M. (1961). On the Mechanism of Self-Aerated Flow on Steep Slope Channels, *Proc. 9th Congress, IAHR, Dubrovnik*, pp. 123–132.

Hoření, P. (1956). *Disintegration of a Free Jet in Air*, (in Czech), Práce a štúdie No. 93, VÚV, Prague.

Horský, T. (1961). L'amortissement de l'énergie méchanique par collision des lames deversantes, *Proc. 9th Congress IAHR, Dubrovnik*, pp. 1122–1127.

Hrbek, J. (1961). The vertical loading of lift gates, (in Czech), *Rozpravy ČSAV—řada TV*, No. 1, Nakl. ČSAV, Prague.

Ippen, A. T. (1949). Mechanics of supercritical flow, *Proc. ASCE*, **75**, No. 9, pp. 1290–1317.

Jain, A. K., Ranga Raju, K. G. and Garde, R. J. (1978). Vortex formation at vertical pipe intakes, *Proc. ASCE, J. Hydraul. Div.*, **104**, HY10, pp. 1429-1445.

Jambor, F. (1959). Mögliche Erhöhung und Entwicklung der festen Wehrsohle, *Die Bautechnik*, No. 6, 8, pp. 221–228, 297–300.

Jermář, F. (1956). *Hydrostatic and Automatic Gates*, (in Czech), SNTL, Prague.

Jevjevich V. and Levin, L. (1953). Entrainment of air in flowing water and technical problems connected with it. *Proc. 5th General Meeting IAHR, Minneapolis*, pp. 439–454.

Kadyrov, A. A. (1958). Energy dissipation in the roller of the hydraulic jump and downstream of it, (in Russian), *Izvestija AN-UzSSR, serija TN*, No. 1.

Kokaja, N. V. (1954). Hydraulic characteristics of cone-disperser valves, (in Russian), *Gidrotechnicheskoje stroitelstvo*, No. 4, pp. 26–28.

Kolkman, P. A. (1970). Models with Elastic Similarity for the Investigation of Hydraulic Structures, Publication No. 49, Delft Hydraulics Laboratory, Delft.

Kolkman, P. A. (1976). Flow Induced Gate Vibrations, Publication No. 164, Delft Hydraulics Laboratory, Delft.

Komora, J. (1962). The utilisation of jet collision in air for the dissipation of energy downstream of a chute, (in Slovak), *Vodohospodársky časopis SAV*, No. 4, pp. 382–401.

Komora, J. (1962a). Study of flow in side-channel spillways, (in Slovak), *Vodohospodársky časopis SAV*, No. 2, pp. 193–206.

Kratochvil, S. (1948). *Hydraulics of High Dam Spillways*, (in Czech). SNTL, Prague.

Kratochvil, S. (1958). Hydraulic characteristics of needle and segment valves, (in Czech), *Vodohospodársky časopis SAV*, No. 4, pp. 283–296.

Kunštátský, J. (1956). *Hydraulic Computations of Culverts and Bridges*, (in Czech), SNTL, Prague.

Laco, V. (1963). *Hydraulics of Low Dams*, (in Slovak), Práce a štúdie No. 23, VÚV, Bratislava.

Linsley, R. K. and Franzini, J. B. (1972). *Water Resources Engineering*, 2nd Edn, McGraw-Hill, New York.

Lískovec, L. (1961). *Study of Bottom Outlets of Dams*, (in Czech), Práce a štúdie No. 102, VÚV, Prague.

Lískovec, L. and Weigl, M. (1958). *Contribution to the Computation of Discharge over Overfall Spillways and the Position of Crest Gates*, (in Czech), Základním výzkumem k rozvoji vodního hospodářství, ČSAV, Prague.

Maitre, R. and Obolensky, S. (1954). Etude de quelques caractèristiques de l'écoulement, *La Houille Blanche*, No. 4, pp. 481–511.

Martins, N. (1959). L'aération dans les évacuateurs en puits, *Proc. 8th Congress IAHR, Montreal*, Paper 4D, 15 pp.

Mojs, P. P. (1970). *Shaft Overfalls*, Energija, Moscow.

Mosonyi, E. (1963, 1965). *Water Power Development I and II*, 2nd English Edn, Hungarian Academy of Sciences, Budapest.

Naudascher, E. (1959). Beitrag zur Untersuchung der schwingungserregenden Kräfte an gleichzeitig über-und unterströmten Wehrverschlüssen, *Technische Mitteilungen Krupp*, **17**, No. 5, pp. 230–275.

Naudascher, E. and Locher, F. A. (1974). Flow-induced forces on protruding walls, *Proc. ASCE, J. Hydraul. Div.*, **100**, No. HY2, pp. 295–313.

Nichiporovich, A. A. (1934). Results of investigations of the chute at the Girel-donskoj hydroelectric power station, (in Russian), *Gidrotechnicheskoje stroitelstvo*, No. 5.

Novak, P. (1955). Study of stilling basins with special regard to their end sill, *Proc. 6th Congress IAHR, The Hague*, Paper C15, 14 pp.

Novak, P. (1956). *Study of Stilling Basins and Scour*, (in Czech), Práce a štúdie No. 91, VÚV, Prague.

Novak, P. (1961). Influence of bed-load passage on scour and turbulence downstream of a stilling basin, *Proc. 9th Congress IAHR, Dubrovnik*, pp. 66–75.

Novak, P. (1964). Einige Bemerkungen zur Bestimmung der maximalen Kolke unter Wehren, *ISCH Conference, ISCH Studii de Hidraulica VI*, Bucarest.

Novak, P. and Wisner, P. (1952). The Bicaz Dam Roumania—Bottom Outlets, (in Czech), *Technical Report*, VÚV, Prague.

Peterka, A. J. (1956). *Spillway Tests Confirm Model–Prototype Conformance*, Engineering monographs, US Bureau of Reclamation, Denver.

Peterka, A. J. (1964). *Hydraulic Design of Stilling Basins and Energy Dissipators*, US Bureau of Reclamation, Washington.

Poliakovskij, V. I and Perelman, R. G. (1959). *Vortex Modelling in Fluids with a Free Surface*, (in Russian), Gosenergoizdat, Moscow.

Poskitt, F. F. and Elsawy, E. M. (1976). Air regulated siphon spillways at Spelga Dam, *J. Inst. Water Engrs Sci.*, **30**, No. 4, pp. 177–190.

Rohan, K. (1954). Flow of water in tunnels and long culverts, (in Slovak), *Vodohospodársky časopis SAV*, No. 1, pp. 68–79.

Rohan, K. (1968). *Drain Vortex in Hydraulic Engineering*, (in Slovak), Vydavatelstvo SAV, Bratislava.

Rolle, N. L. (1953). Coefficients of discharge of cone dispersion valve, (in Russian), *Gidrotechnicheskoje stroitelstvo*, No. 4, pp. 35–38.

Rozanov, N. P. (1940). *Spillways with Negative Pressures*, (in Russian), Gosstrojizdat, Moscow.

Rybníkář, J. (1957). Dissipation of energy in a surface jump, *Vodní hospodářství*, No. 4, pp. 97–101.

Scimemi, E. (1937). Il profilo delle dighe sfioranti, *L'Energie Elettrica*.

Sikora, A. (1962). Passage of ice floes over barrages, (in Slovak), *Vodohospodársky časopis SAV*, No. 1, pp. 66–81.

Sikora, A. (1965). Aeration of Shaft Spillways, (in Slovak), Práce a štúdie No. 35, VÚVH, Bratislava.

Skladnev, M. F. (1956). Limits of surface and bottom hydraulic jumps, (in Russian). *Izv. VNIIG*, **53**, Leningrad.

Skrebkov, G. P. (1961). Numerical values of velocity coefficients, (in Russian) *Energetika*, No. 12.

Slisskij, S. M. (1953). *Ejection Downstream of Hydroelectric Power Stations*, (in Russian), Gossenergoizdat, Moscow.

Smetana, J. (1933, 1934). Experimental study of hydraulic jump, (in Czech), *Zpravy veřejné služby technické*, Prague, pp. 314–327.

Smetana, J. (1945). Study of spillway surface of high dams, (in Czech), *Rozpravy ČSAV*, Prague, **54**, No. 22.

Smetana, J. (1953). *Outflow Jet from under a Gate* (in Czech), Nakl. ČSAV, Prague.

Štoll, C. (1937). Stilling basin design, (in Czech), *Technický obzor*, No. 16, pp. 257–263.

Straub, L. G. and Anderson, S. G. (1958). Experiments on self-aerated flow in open channels, *Proc. ASCE, J. Hydraul. Div.* **84**, No. HY7, Paper 1890, 35 pp.

Strauss, V. (1960). Computation of the ejection effect of outlet works, (in Slovak), *Vodohospodársky časopis SAV*, No. 2, pp. 160–183.

Symposium (1947). Cavitation in Hydraulic Structures, *Trans. ASCE*, **112**, p. 73.

US Bureau of Reclamation. (1948). *Studies of Crests for Overfall Dams. Bulletin 3. Part VI—Hydraulic Investigations*, Boulder Canyon Project Final Reports, Bureau of Reclamation, Denver, Colorado.

US Bureau of Reclamation. (1960). *Why Close Tolerances are Necessary under High Velocity Flow*. Hydraulic Laboratory Report, No. 473, Denver.

US Bureau of Reclamation. (1965). *Design of Small Dams*, Third Printing, US Dept. of Interior, Washington D.C.

Vedernikov, V. V. (1946). Properties of flow of water in open channels, (in Russian), *Doklady Ak. Nauk SSSR*, **52**, No. 3.

Wagner, W. E. (1956). Morning-glory shaft spillways. Determination of pressure—controlled profiles, *Trans. ASCE*, **121**, Paper 2802, pp. 345–383.

Wijdicks, J. (1972). *Hydraulic Aspects of the Design of Pump Installations*, Delft Hydraulics Laboratory, Delft.

Wisner, P. and Mitric, A. (1961). Studies of air entrainment on spillways, (in Roumanian), *Hidrotehnica*, No. 9.

Zchiesche, O. (1954). *Die Berechnung von Streichwehren auf Grund von Modellversuchen mit geraden und schräg gestellten Streichwehren*, Berlin. Ph.D. Thesis.

8 Models of Navigation Structures and Inland Waterways

8.1 General

Hydraulic problems encountered in inland navigation and often solved by scale models include:

(a) River regulation for navigation; hydraulic phenomena occurring during navigation on inland waterways and their effect on the banks and beds of rivers; determination of suitable location, direction and shape of bridge piers on navigable waterways, etc.

(b) Optimum location of navigation installations as part of the general layout of hydraulic structures; approaches and entry to locks, ship lifts, railways and ports situated outside navigable rivers, and intersection of a canal and navigable river.

(c) Translation waves in the upper and lower reaches of the canals and in forebays, arising from lockage, use of gates and operation of hydroelectric power plants, and measures against the unfavourable effect of these waves on navigation.

(d) Design of locks of various types and dimensions for the safe passage of vessels in the shortest possible time. This includes, e.g.: the design of hydraulically and structurally effective shapes; dimensions and arrangement of filling and emptying systems; determination of the course, time and coefficients of filling and emptying and of forces acting on the ships; design of lock gates and culvert valves.

(e) Passage of ice and floods through navigation locks.

(f) Design of ship lifts, railways and inclined flumes permitting ships to overcome high heads quickly and safely and with the minimum use of water.

In the experimental solution of these problems mostly three-dimensional geometrically similar models are used (*see* Chapters 6 and 7). Hydraulic phenomena are modelled according to Froude's law of similarity observing the necessary limiting conditions (*see* Section 2.10). Thus models must be big enough for the forces of surface tension to be negligible and for the turbulent flow regime to be preserved as in prototype. In models of locks with culverts for filling or emptying, the conditions for modelling of pressure systems must also be fulfilled (*see* Sub-sections 5.1.4 to 5.1.8).

8.2 Models of Inland Waterways as Part of River Training

8.2.1 Siting of locks

When making rivers navigable by building barrages, locks are usually placed close to the weirs. However, usually hydroelectric power is being utilized simultaneously with the plants also sited near the weirs. Sometimes both the lock and the power station are built on a canal leading from the upstream reservoir. The separate parts of a complex hydraulic structure influence each other mostly unfavourably and scale models are used to find the best possible technical, economical and operational solution by investigating the effect of various alternatives on the flow regime, movement of ice and sediment, and river morphology. For more complicated projects aerodynamic models are often used in the first instance (*see* Section 11.2). The solutions found are then the subject of detailed research on a hydraulic model. Such a procedure is usually faster and cheaper than using a hydraulic model only.

The following is an example of the effective placing of locks suitable for smaller regulated rivers based on detailed model studies (Čábelka, 1949). Locks on navigable rivers are usually placed close to one side of the weir with the power station on the other side (Fig. 8.1a), the upper and lower forebays being separated from the river by full dividing walls. In operation this solution has been found to have many drawbacks. For larger discharges transverse flow, contraction, large eddies and extensive erosion occur at the leading edge of the full dividing wall (Fig. 8.2). These unfavourable features increase with the width of the upstream lock approach, the proximity of the leading edge of the dividing wall to the weir and the velocity of flow. Furthermore, both the lock approaches, particularly the lower one, tend to silt up with fine sediment. Another unfavourable feature is that the part of the river in which the weir has been built must be trained in a comparatively long, straight line (*see* Fig. 8.1a) which is unsuitable both hydraulically and morphologically.

A much better solution is to train navigable rivers in a smooth curve with the weir at its vertex. The best position for the lock is then next to the weir on the convex (inner) bank of the bend so that the straight inlets from the river into the upper and lower lock approaches terminate at the nearest upstream and downstream concave bank of the trained river (Fig. 8.3). The lock and its approaches are separated from the weir and

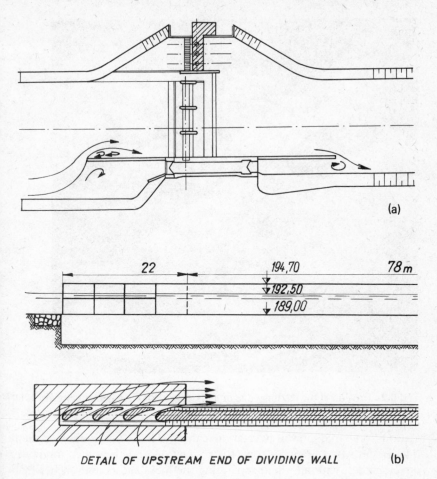

(a)

(b)

DETAIL OF UPSTREAM END OF DIVIDING WALL

Fig. 8.1.

the river channel by a small island, which is usually raised above flood level.

If the simultaneous use of navigation and water power is contemplated, then on rivers with little ice movement the power station is best placed close beside the weir on the opposite side to the lock, i.e. on the concave side of the river bend (*see* Fig. 7.4). Transverse flow in the bend prevents sedimentation at the concave banks containing the inlets and outlets of the power station and the entries to both lock approaches. This solution (Fig. 8.3) is also suitable from the operational point of view as the separate parts of the hydraulic structure hardly influence each other. A similar solution may also be used when placing locks next to power

Fig. 8.2. Erosion at the leading edge of a dividing wall [Čábelka and Novák, 1964]

stations on large power–navigation canals. There the canal is usually divided into two branches, one for navigation and the other for power development, with an island separating the lock and its approaches from the power station.

On large rivers, with heavy ice and possibly also sediment transport, (e.g., Danube, Rhine) it is more advantageous from the operational point of view to place the barrage in the streamline of the river. Depending on local conditions it is sometimes better to place the power station and navigation lock side by side, usually on the convex bank at the weir (e.g.,

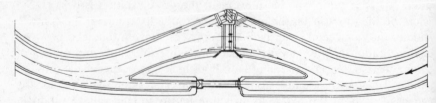

Fig. 8.3.

Jochenstein on the Danube), or to divide the power station into two smaller structures on both sides of the barrage and place the lock into the convex bank of the river bend (*see* Figs. 7.1 and 7.2) to protect the inlets into the power station and the entries into the upper lock approaches against the direct pressure of ice.

8.2.2 Lock approaches on navigable rivers

A satisfactory design of the upstream lock approach situated close to a barrage can often be achieved only by model research as it must take into account the movement of barges, which, at limited speed and therefore usually also with reduced manoeuvrability, enter in the downstream direction with a decelerating motion or leave the lock more quickly in the upstream direction with an accelerating motion. The first instance is substantially less suitable for rudder-steered ships than the second, because the relative velocity of the vessel with regard to the surrounding flow, on which the reaction of the rudder and the control of the boat depends, is considerably lower.

A number of investigators have dealt with the problem of improving the flow conditions in the entry to the upper approaches of the lock, at barrages on the Danube, the Rhone and Rhine and elsewhere. On the basis of results of studies on a model scale 1:45, the scoured and collapsed dividing wall of the upstream lock approach at a weir on the Elbe was reconstructed so that its front part was extended upstream by a beam supported by a number of thin curved concrete piers (Fig. 8.1b). These piers effectively distribute the flow from above the lock inlet into the river channel above the weir, thus reducing the transverse component of velocity and increasing the safety of passing vessels. They also guide the water along the dividing wall directly into the first weir section next to the lock, eliminating the lateral contraction of flow at the head of the dividing wall and the large scour of the bed that used to occur here. This design has proved satisfactory in operation and has therefore also been used in other cases. More recent experience has shown that it is more effective to terminate the piers below the water surface of the upstream reservoir with a full smooth guide wall above them.

8.2.3 Entrances to ports and canals

Inland ports located outside navigable channels are connected to them by comparatively narrow entrances or short canals. The width of the entrance should be as small as possible so that it does not silt up, but sufficiently wide for ships to pass each other safely. It is advantageous for the inlet or the canal to be joined as smoothly as possible to the river bend in its concave bank. The angle between the axis of the inlet and the streamline in the river should not exceed 30° (the greater the flow velocity in the river, the smaller this angle should be). The flow conditions in the area of the entrance to the ports should be studied on models for a wide range of river discharges.

8.2.4 Model barges

On models of navigable waterways where the manoeuvrability of model barges is being examined various methods of their remote control are used. Figure 8.4 shows the manoeuvre of a push-tow and cargo ship on a model of a river crossing (Delft Hydraulics Laboratory). A high degree of accuracy in the determination of the position of the model ship in motion has been attained by the development of an optical direction-finding system using laser beams. The motion of the ship models may be radio controlled with all quantities measured during the test (position, propeller speed, rudder angle) recorded and processed by a computer; indeed in the latest models the computer controls the steering and propulsion of the

Fig. 8.4. Control of model boats. [Courtesy Delft Hydraulics Laboratory]

model vessel, or models with an autopilot reacting to deviations from a track are being used.

The scale of the ship model must be such as to preserve a minimum value of the Reynolds number when using Froude's law of similarity, which, for the body of the vessel related to its length, is $Re = 5 \times 10^6$ (for artificial turbulence $Re = 3 \times 10^6$); for the rudder of the vessel $Re = 1.5 \times 10^6$ and for the propeller $Re = 7 \times 10^4$ to 3×10^5. In the study of mobility of self-propelled vessels we are concerned with their unsteady movement. Therefore, apart from the geometric similarity, the similarity of distribution of mass, of the location of the centre of gravity, of the propeller revolutions and of the speed of rudder manoeuvres must also be preserved. Based on experience, investigations of mobility of self-propelled vessels are carried out on models reduced, at the most, to a scale of 1:15. At a ratio of depth of water to the draft of the vessel smaller than 1.3 its mobility sharply drops. These and other aspects of navigability of constrained waterways are studied on scale models and in the field (Delft Hydraulics Laboratory, 1978).

8.3 Translatory Waves and Measures against their Effect on Inland Navigation

8.3.1 Subject and aims of research and criteria of similarity

The safety of navigation on rivers and on canals is unfavourably influenced by oscillatory waves due to wind and the movement of ships, and by translatory waves caused by changes in discharge, i.e. filling or emptying of locks, movement of gates and operation of power plants. These wave phenomena must be investigated in detail when designing the height of the banks and their protection and stability, and when determining the optimum operation of hydraulic structures. Slow movements of gates result in smooth translatory waves in the upper and lower reservoirs, whilst sudden changes in discharge caused by the very fast opening or closing of turbines or gates result in surges which are dangerous to the vessels in the waterway. Positive surge can flow over the sides of fully loaded vessels or drive them against obstacles, e.g., an oncoming ship, whilst the negative wave in the downstream reservoir reduces the depth of flow and may cause fully loaded vessels to run aground on the uneven bed. All types of waves strain the bodies of the vessels. A sudden change in the slope of the water surface further upsets the equilibrium of forces acting both on moving ships and on vessels moored at the banks.

The unfavourable effects of translatory waves on the safety of vessels can be reduced by various constructional and operational measures (*see* Sub-section 8.3.2).

The mainly numerical methods of solution of unsteady flow in open channels, i.e. of surges and translatory smooth waves, are based on experimentally verified theory (*see also* Chapter 6). These methods have all been developed for open channels with a dominant longitudinal dimension. In hydraulic structures on large lowland rivers, where locks and power plants are usually placed on either side of the barrage and where the reservoirs are relatively wide as compared with other sections of the river channel, far more complicated conditions of unsteady flow prevail. Waves caused by a change in the flow through the power plant spread radially and when passing through the reservoir are subject to spatial deformation. Such a complicated case of unsteady flow cannot be mathematically expressed and handled by known methods of computation, which give only approximate results. The problem of the rise, dimensions, velocity of propagation and deformation of surges and of their effective damping is, therefore, best studied on scale models.

For model studies of surges in long reservoirs and channels it is often economically suitable to use a shortened river model, i.e. a distorted model with the same scale for depth and width and a reduced longitudinal scale, instead of geometrically similar models. When deriving the laws of similarity for modelling unsteady flow, it has been shown in Sub-section 6.2.1 that the criteria derived for steady nonuniform flow also represent the necessary condition for modelling unsteady flow (i.e. flood waves, surges and waves of oscillation) if the Strouhal criterion $M_t = M_l/M_h^{1/2}$ is also taken into account (Equations (6.32) to (6.38)).

For a geometrically similar model where $M_h = M_b = M_l$, $C_p = C_m (M_C = 1)$. For a shortened model the ratio of Chezy's coefficients (from $M_v = M_h^{1/2} = M_C M_R^{1/2} M_r^{1/2} M_l^{-1/2}$) will be given by

$$M_C = \frac{M_l^{1/2}}{M_R^{1/2}} \tag{8.1}$$

Also as $M_b = M_h \neq M_l (M_b < M_l)$ the channel cross-section is not distorted and $M_R = M_h (= M_b)$. Thus

$$M_C = \frac{M_l^{1/2}}{M_h^{1/2}} = \frac{M_l^{1/2}}{M_b^{1/2}} \tag{8.2}$$

From Equation (8.2) it follows that $M_C > 1$ (as $M_b < M_l$) and $C_p > C_m$. The friction coefficient of the model λ_m is thus bigger than the coefficient λ_p for prototype ($C = \sqrt{(2g/\lambda)}$).

It is also possible to use a combination of a geometrically similar and shortened model when studying the wave motion downstream of a barrage during the emptying of a navigation lock.

Combined and shortened models can, however, be used only when studying waves moving in one direction. For the investigation of more complicated cases including wave refraction the model must be geometrically similar throughout.

The effect of surface tension on the rise and propagation of translatory waves is negligible if the wave velocity is greater than 0.5 m/s. For a velocity 0.3 m/s the retarding influence of surface tension is about 5%.

8.3.2 Translatory waves and measures to contain them

Many hydraulic laboratories have studied the formation, spread and reduction of surges caused by a sudden closure of hydraulic power plants. These studies have been carried out both on scale models and on completed hydraulic structures where the effectiveness of various structural and operational measures to decrease the unfavourable effect of surges on vessels and navigation was investigated.

The unfavourable effect of the breakdown of a power plant is best eliminated immediately at the point of occurrence or as close to it as possible. Thus possibilities for a reduction of surges should be looked for in the (a) electrical, (b) mechanical, and (c) civil engineering part of the plant, or (d) by a suitable layout of the entire hydraulic structure. Usually a combination of several measures is found to be operationally and economically most suitable.

The following approximate relation is valid:

$$Q = Q_c + Q_b + Q_t + Q_e \tag{8.3}$$

where Q is the total flow through the turbines of the power plant before shutdown; Q_c is the change of discharge causing a still permissible wave in the channel; Q_b is the flow capacity of the turbine by-passes; Q_t is the flow which it is possible to pass through the turbines after the hydroelectric plant has fallen out of the grid; Q_e is the change in discharge achievable by measures in the electrical part of the plant.

The various methods of decreasing surge waves are briefly discussed below (Čábelka, 1976):

(a) In the *electrical* part of the plant the unfavourable effects of the breakdown can be reduced to a permissible level by a speedy switch-over of the output of the generators to a (water) resistance, which can be done in about two seconds. A wave will still form in the canal and it is neither necessary nor effective to design the resistances for the full output of the generators (80 or 85% of output is usually considered). Since the fall-out may occur at various performances of the plant, the problem of smooth synchronization of the resistances with the variable outputs of the generators remains. Although water resistances are an economically suitable solution for surge reduction, they are not regarded as the only independent device, since so far their operational safety is only guaranteed in conjunction with some other measure.

(b) In the *mechanical* part of the plant the unfavourable effect of its fall-out from the grid may be reduced by a harmless passing of part of the discharge through the turbines, which is possible through automatic severance of the linkage of the guide and rotating vanes of Kaplan turbines, by throttling the outflow from the turbines by valves or gates in their draft tubes, or by discharging water through by-pass valves connected to the spiral casing of the turbines.

In the first case, a brief separation and reassembly of the optimum linkage between the guide and rotating vanes of the Kaplan turbines causes a considerable drop in their efficiency and thus output, and is characterized by a change in flow with time. During the first three seconds after the drop-out a sudden reduction in discharge through the turbines by about 30% takes place. This causes surges which cannot be eliminated through manipulation, but which are considerably lower than in the case of a sudden stoppage of the entire flow through the turbines. After the first three seconds the turbines slowly stop and the gradual reduction of the flow does not cause any further waves endangering navigation.

In the second case, the reduction of the surge is attained by closing the draft tubes together with a short-term severance of the linkage of the turbine vanes. Again it is not possible to prevent a sudden drop in the flow through the turbines by about 30% at the beginning of the operation, resulting in a harmless wave. The fact that the closing of the turbines is considerably slower than in the first case is an advantage.

In the third case, the joining of by-pass valves to the spiral casing of the turbines causes reduction of their efficiency by about 1 to 2%. The effect of the by-passes on the reduction of the surge wave is somewhat more favourable than in the preceding cases, but the operation is more complicated.

All the three above-mentioned devices have been used at a number of hydroelectric power stations.

(c) In the *civil engineering* part of the plant suitable by-passes and outlets may be used for the reduction of surges. This is the most common method in use so far. The function of special outlets in the sub-structure of the power plant can be replaced by the weir gates adjacent to the power plant. The governing mechanisms of the by-pass valves or the weir gates are connected to the automatic regulators of the power station turbines, so that they can pass the greater part of the flow through the power station turbines as quickly as possible before the stoppage. Between the onset of the closure of the turbines and the opening of the valves and gates a certain delay necessarily occurs due to purely operational or mechanical causes. This delay must be as short as possible (usually it is 2–3 seconds) and at the same time the flow through the gates must increase smoothly and at the same rate as the flow through the turbines decreases. If these principles preserving continuity of flow through the hydraulic structure (important, e.g., at cascades of power stations with a common canal) are not kept, this may cause even more unfavourable conditions for vessels and navigation, and also for the stability of the channel, than would the sudden breakdown of the plant itself.

When designing the outlets and valves that are to reduce the surge waves, it is necessary on the basis of detailed hydraulic studies to choose a suitable type and to investigate their capacity, the rate at which they can be operated and the possibilities of the automatic synchronization of their opening with the closing of the turbines of the power station. On the model a suitable location for the outlets and their effective incorporation into the layout of the hydraulic structure must also be studied, and all factors which may influence the choice of the final design taken into consideration, i.e., flow regime in the upstream and downstream reservoir, its effect on vessels and navigation, winter regime, channel stability, flexibility of operation, automation, cost, etc. The proposed design should also be assessed, whenever relevant, for its suitability for passing part of flood discharges and possibly ice floes from the intake into the outlet of the power station. For stability of the outlet canal and safety of vessels and navigation in it, a small specific discharge in the outlets, if possible placed symmetrically along the entire length of the power station, is most suitable. For operational reasons outlets with flow under pressure are better than free-flowing spillways.

Equation (8.3) shows that the by-passes of hydroelectric plants need not be designed for the full capacity of the turbines. On the basis of research in France for hydraulic structures on the Rhone and Rhine and in Czechoslovakia for plants on the Váh and Danube and elsewhere, the capacity of the by-passes is usually designed as 40% to 80% of the corresponding maximum discharge through the turbines; the actual value depends on local conditions and on whether other measures for reduction of the surges are also being used;

(d) By a *suitable design of the hydraulic structure as a whole*, i.e. a special inlet and outlet canal shape in the close vicinity of the power plant, waves caused by fast closure or opening of the turbines may also be effectively reduced. Depending on local conditions these measures may be highly effective.

When combining several of the above-mentioned measures the use of resistance, of gates in the turbine draft tubes and of by-passes from the spiral casing of turbines is usually omitted because these measures have so far not been sufficiently tested and verified to guarantee the desired effect. A combination of the remaining three possibilities is normally used.

The use of barrage gates for the control of surges was investigated in Czechoslovakia on a three-dimensional model (scale $M_l = 60$) of the

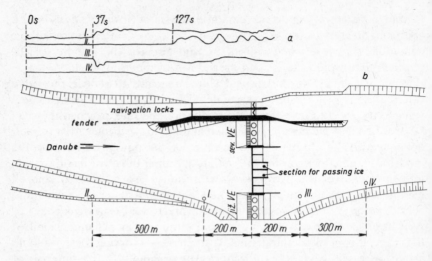

Fig. 8.5. Surge waves at the Bratislava-Wolfsthal barrage. [Sikora, 1961]

planned hydraulic structure on the Danube (Bratislava-Wolfsthal; Sikora, 1961; Fig. 8.5). This included a hydroelectric power station with six turbines divided into a northern and a southern part, a barrage with six gate sections each 24 m wide, and two navigation locks with dimensions of 230×24 m and with forebays situated near the left bank (Fig. 8.5b). The number of turbines thus equalled the number of barrage sections, which were equipped with double segment gates. The flow through the turbines on the model was regulated by cylindrical valves. The surge waves caused by a sudden change in flow through the turbines were measured on the model by four gauges. Three characteristic discharges were tested: minimum, mean and maximum flow for navigation (1000, 2024 and 5850 m³/s prototype); and various combinations of flow through the turbines. The surge waves were investigated both with and without considering the simultaneous automatic opening of the lower part of the double segment gates, each of which belonged to one turbine. The highest wave occurred at a mean flow, $Q = 2024$ m³/s, when all three turbines of the fully loaded southern power station suddenly dropped out of operation (sudden stoppage of flow $\Delta Q = 1230$ m³/s). This caused a positive wave in the upper reservoir of maximum height 72 cm (Fig. 8.6a) and celerity 5.5 to 6.1 m/s, which reached a height of 150 cm (prototype) at the concave bank of the river bend above the structure. In the lower reservoir a negative wave of the same height occurred. When the lower parts of the corresponding double segment gates of the barrage opened automatically with a rate of rise of 1 cm/s in prototype at the same time as the turbines dropped out, surges hardly occurred. Instead, only low, smooth waves about 10 to 15 cm high which are not dangerous to shipping, formed in the upstream and downstream reservoir. To achieve the same result by using the top segments a much higher lowering speed would be necessary; only rates higher than 10 to 15 cm/s were effective.

Similar research was carried out for the hydraulic structure at Birsfelden on the Rhine (Wittmann and Bleines, 1953), where the large spatial deformation of surge waves, caused by a sudden drop-out of all four turbines, was reduced by the simultaneous rapid lowering of the gates of the four weir sections. In such cases stereophotogrammetry is used to advantage for the recording of the immediate shapes and heights of the waves.

Even more important is the study of measures for the reduction of surges at *power stations situated on derivation and navigation canals.* A typical example is the detailed research of this problem carried out in Czechoslovakia for the Gabčíkovo structure on the Danube (Gabriel *et. al.,* 1967). The Gabčíkovo power station consists of a reservoir from which water is passed through a canal to the power station and locks. The downstream canal terminates in the Danube. The upstream canal is about 18 km long and the downstream canal about 7 km. The power station, which has a maximum output of 700 MW, has 9 Kaplan turbines with a total capacity of about 4800 m³/s.

Three models were used for this study: a hydraulic model scales 1:1000/70, an aerodynamic model scales 1:1000/500 and a large hydraulic model of scale 1:70. Whilst the first two models served mainly for the investigation of the optimum layout of the structure, the large hydraulic model was designed above all to determine the optimum operation of various parts of the structure and of their effect on vessels and navigation. The programmed control of the models of turbines and gates of the by-passes aided this investigation (Fig. 8.6).

The study of the layout, which involved the testing of twelve alternatives, has shown that to mitigate the waves in the region of the inlet to the upper lock approaches it is advisable to widen the adjoining section of the inlet canal to about 650 m. The locks were placed at the left-hand bank with the upstream approaches separated from the power station inlet canal by a concrete dividing wall whose first quarter was designed as a throughflow wall. Downstream of the power plant it was not necessary to extend the outlet canal width and thus it was possible to separate it from the downstream lock approach by an island. The final design is shown in Fig. 8.7a.

The study of the waves in the canals has shown that for a complete shutdown of the power plant without any wave reduction measures, the surge in the upstream unextended section of the inlet attains a height of about 1.20 m, whereas in the case of the widened canal the resulting wave height was only 0.60 m. In the outlet section the maximum negative wave height was 1.25 m. The most noticeable reduction in height of the surges

Fig. 8.6. Model of the Gabčíkovo canal barrage on the Danube. [Gabriel, *et al.*, 1967]

was achieved on the model by severing the turbine linkage. The height of the waves in the inlet and outlet canals was then only about 25 to 30 cms. For these reasons the use of by-passes in the substructure of the power station was proposed only as a reserve measure.

The gates of the by-passes are automatically linked with the turbine regulators—always one by-pass with one turbine. In the case of a break-down in the severance of the turbine linkage the gates of the by-passes begin to open about two and a half seconds after fall-out, when the flow through the turbines has already been suddenly reduced by about 20% of the original value. The rate of opening of the by-passes is automatically controlled so that the time of operation agrees with the time of closing the turbines.

The maximum capacity of the by-passes is one-third of the discharge capacity of the turbines, i.e. $Q = 1600 \, \text{m}^3/\text{s}$. These by-passes reduce the height of the surges in the inlet canal by roughly one-third and in the outlet canal to about 0.90 m; even these values are not dangerous to navigation. The most suitable type of by-passes in this case were culverts flowing under pressure and placed in the turbine blocks distributed across the entire width of the power plant.

Figure 8.7b shows the discharge through the turbines Q_T after break-down in the case of severed linkage, Fig. 8.7c the discharge with only the by-passes functioning (Q_W) and Fig. 8.7d a combination of separated turbine linkage and by-passes.

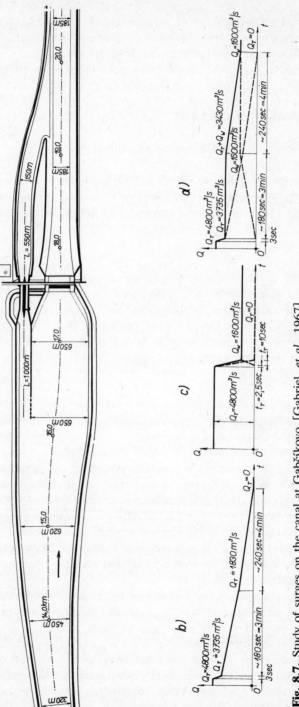

Fig. 8.7. Study of surges on the canal at Gabčíkovo. [Gabriel, et al., 1967]

The height and celerity of surge waves on rivers and canals used both for power production and navigation, and measures for the reduction of the waves have also been investigated in several cases on completed structures to verify the results of model studies or of computations.

8.4 Models of Locks

8.4.1 Subject and aims of research

The transport capacity of canals and navigable rivers with a series of locks is usually considerably lower than that of free waterways (without locks). The theoretical capacity of a lock per year in both directions is given by:

$$K' = 365 \times 24 \frac{2M}{t_n} \ (t) \tag{8.4}$$

where M is the tonnage of a typical vessel or train of barges making optimum use of the lock dimensions on the waterway of a certain classification, and t_n is the total time (hrs) of one cycle of passing through the lock in both directions (following closely after each other).

The practical transport capacity of a lock per year for both directions is given by the expression:

$$K = r \times K' \ (t) \tag{8.5}$$

where $r = r_1 \times r_2 \times r_3 \ldots r_n < 1$ is the total reduction coefficient expressing various influences, which in practice limit the theoretical annual capacity determined for optimum conditions.

This transport capacity of a lock depends above all on the value t_n, which should be as small as possible. To reduce this time, which from the point of view of navigation is lost time, its individual phases, i.e. the opening and closing of the lock gates, the entry of the ships into the lock, exit from it and finally the time of filling and emptying the lock must be as short as possible. When shortening the separate phases of the process of the vessel passing through the lock, neither its safety nor the functioning of the lock must be endangered, and economic factors must also be considered.

The time necessary for the opening or closing of the lock gates depends on their dimensions (weight), type and construction. In the case of modern locks this time is usually so short already (about one to two minutes) that a further reduction is not realistic. The next phase, i.e. entry of the vessel into the lock and exit from it, is considerably longer. It may be reduced by the introduction of push-towing and by a suitable design of the size and shape of the lock approaches and of the lock filling and emptying systems. The closer to the lock gates the vessels can wait for locking, the shorter will be the time of their entry into the lock. A suitable design of the lock approaches is often investigated on scale models.

However, the most important hydraulic problem in the design of locks is a reduction in the time needed for filling and emptying without endangering the safety of the ships; this time depends on the dimensions of the lock, water level difference, the type, dimensions and general arrangement of the filling and emptying system, and lastly on the flow regime in the lock during filling and emptying.

The head H (water level difference) of locks may be:

very low	$H < 5.0$ m,
low	$5.0 < H < 10.0$ m,
medium	10.0 m $< H < 15.0$,
high	$H > 15.0$.

Locks may be classified as follows according to their method of filling and emptying (*see* Fig. 8.8):

(a) Very low-head locks filled and emptied through sluices in the gates (Fig. 8.8A);

(b) Very low and low-head locks with direct filling (emptying) using upstream (downstream) gates;

(c) Low and medium-head locks filled or emptied through short culverts in the lateral walls of the gates (Fig. 8.8B), or in the lock bottom or the sill beneath the gates (Fig. 8.8C);

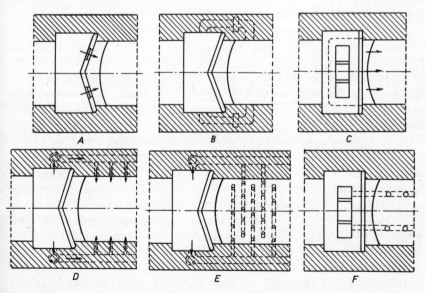

Fig. 8.8.

(d) Medium or high-head locks filled and emptied through long culverts in the lateral walls (Fig. 8.8D), or the bottom of the lock to which they are linked by manifold openings (Fig. 8.8E,F);

(e) Locks with combined filling or emptying, i.e. with filling/emptying through long culverts and gates;

(f) High-head locks (also locks with large dimensions) filled and emptied through a complicated system of culverts with outlets in the bottom of the lock designed for approximately equal flow through all openings;

(g) High-head locks with thrift basins (possibly combined locks) filled and emptied usually by a complicated system of culverts, connected to the upstream and downstream reservoirs and to the thrift basins.

Scale models are used to investigate the hydraulic phenomena and their effect on the vessels in the lock for all these types with the aim of attaining the speediest and safest passage.

Hydraulic research on locks started immediately on the inception of hydraulic laboratories at the beginning of this century, and this problem has remained of constant interest due to the continuously increasing dimensions and heads of locks and requirements of water transport. This is also supported by the fact that the discussion of this problem is frequently included in the programme of international congresses (PIANC and IAHR).

Models of locks are geometrically reduced models of hydraulic structures where the Froude law of similarity is applied. In studies of locks with culverts and complicated filling and emptying systems the limiting conditions for the scale must be upheld (*see* Chapters 2 and 5).

The criterion for the assessment of the maximum permissible rate and suitable system of filling and emptying a lock is the magnitude of the horizontal forces acting on the vessel passing through or waiting in the lock approaches. These forces, which are overcome by tying the vessel to the walls of the lock or to bollards on the guide walls of the lock approaches, must not exceed a certain empirically determined value dependent primarily on the displacement of the fully loaded vessel, W. The longitudinal components P_L of the horizontal forces transferred from the vessel by the pull of the lashings to the lateral walls of the lock are most dangerous for the passing vessel and also for the lock gates. The transverse components P_T of these forces are usually considerably smaller than the longitudinal components P_L and also less dangerous, since they are transferred from the vessel by pressure to the lateral lock walls. The longitudinal and transverse components of these horizontal forces are measured directly on models of vessels built to the same scale as the model of the lock.

The permissible (limiting) value of the longitudinal component of the horizontal forces $P_{L_{\text{lim}}}$ is given by some authors as a simple linear relation

$$P_{L_{\text{lim}}} = \frac{W}{600} \tag{8.6}$$

On the basis of analysis and from measurements in prototype, a non-linear relationship is more suitable. The empirical expressions of Michajlov (1966):

$$P_{L_{\text{lim}}} = 0.03\sqrt[5]{W^3} \tag{8.7}$$

or Semanov:

$$P_{L_{\text{lim}}} = 0.3\sqrt[3]{W} \tag{8.8}$$

give a more acceptable value for $W > 3000t$. The limiting value of the transverse component of the horizontal forces acting on the model vessel should not exceed 50% of the longitudinal component $P_{L_{\text{lim}}}$.

If the forces measured on the model are greater than the computed limiting value, then either the filling (emptying) systems of the lock must be suitably altered, or the rate of filling of the lock especially in the initial phase must be slowed down. The results of model studies of locks have been verified in a number of cases by direct measurements after construction was completed; generally a very good agreement with model results was found.

8.4.2 Methods used in model investigations

Experimental studies of locks may be divided into three groups:

(a) study of locks with unsteady flow;
(b) study of locks under steady flow conditions;
(c) study of horizontal forces acting on vessels passing through the lock.

(a) Investigation of locks with *unsteady flow* concentrates on the mode and time of filling (emptying) the lock, the value of the coefficient of filling (emptying) and on alternate solutions of filling (emptying) systems. It is necessary to measure the change of the water level in the lock and of the position of the gates in the filling (emptying) culverts as well as the time of filling (emptying). The water level in the lock should be measured at several points placed so as to record the longitudinal slope of the water level and the amplitude of the waves moving along the lock and measurements should be repeated at least twice. From these data the expressions $h = f(t)$ and $a = f(t)$ (Fig. 8.9) are plotted, where h is the difference between the levels in the lock and the upstream (downstream) reservoir, a is the cross-section of the flow under the gates of the filling (emptying)

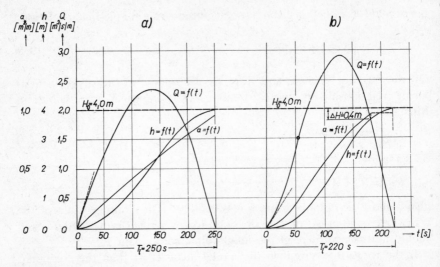

Fig. 8.9.

devices, t is the time from the start of the gate opening and H_0 is the initial head of the lock.

The total time T of filling (emptying) is also obtained from these measurements.

From the above results and the area of the water surface in the lock, the discharge $Q = f(t)$ is then computed (Fig. 8.9). For vessel safety the slope of the rising branch $\Delta Q/\Delta t$ and the maximum discharge are particularly important; in the case of large locks Q_{max} may reach $450 \, \text{m}^3/\text{s}$ (prototype). To prevent too great a fluctuation in the surface of the upstream (downstream) water level on the model, the upstream (downstream) reservoir is provided with a long spillway edge capable of passing the maximum flow through the model ('constant head-tank').

From the values of Q_t and a_t the velocity $v = f(t)$ may be obtained. Finally it is possible to calculate the value of the discharge coefficient C_{d_t} for unsteady flow (i.e. during filling or emptying of the lock) from the equation $Q_t = C_{d_t} a_t \sqrt{(2gh_t)}$. For the full relationship $C_d = f(t)$ it is advisable to calculate about ten values of the coefficient C_d for the corresponding values of h, Q and a. It is also useful to compute the mean value of the coefficient for the whole time of filling (emptying).

(b) The study of a lock under *steady flow* conditions is used mainly for the determination of the discharge coefficients and the effectiveness of energy dissipation for individual phases of filling and emptying. During measurement it is necessary to maintain on the model not only a constant discharge but also the corresponding water levels in the lock (deduced from the unsteady flow experiments (Fig. 8.9)).

The coefficients of discharge, C_d are again determined from the relationship $Q = C_d a \sqrt{(2gh)}$ for various values of partial and complete opening of the gates. When studying energy dissipation, which is important particularly in the case of locks filled and emptied through lock gates or short conduits, it is necessary to investigate the velocity distribution and the shape of the water surface in important sections downstream of the energy dissipator (stilling basin) situated in the lock (usually below the upper gates) or beyond it (below the downstream gates). The energy dissipator must be designed in such a way that the forces acting on a vessel do not·exceed the permitted limit and that the bed beyond the stilling basin is not eroded.

(c) *The horizontal forces acting on the vessel during the filling or emptying of the lock* are investigated experimentally on models of vessels both inside the lock and in its (downstream) approach by measuring the reactive effects of water on the vessel and the changes of these forces with time during filling or emptying the lock, $P = f(t)$. The magnitude and usually also the direction of the horizontal forces acting on the vessel change during the filling (emptying) of the lock and the vessel is pulled alternately to the upstream and downstream gates. This is caused by the dynamic effect of waves passing from one end of the lock to the other. The waves arise at the point of filling (emptying) by sudden changes in the discharge. The forces exerted by direct and reflected waves on the passing vessel are stronger than the resistance of the vessel to flow and the pull of the vessel caused by the slope of the water level. Whilst the dynamic forces due to the wave action change their direction in the course of filling (emptying) the two other forces, flow resistance and gravity component, do not, and as their directions of action in locks with concentrated filling are usually opposite each other, they may be eliminated to a considerable extent by a suitable design of the filling (emptying) system. Equally the magnitude of the transverse forces acting on the vessel, and dependent above all on how the flow of water is directed into and out of the lock, may be reduced to a minimum.

The dynamometers for the measurement of horizontal forces are usually connected to recorders with a time base where the opening of gates and the water levels in the lock and the approaches are simultaneously recorded. To eliminate forces of inertia and friction the dynamometers must prevent substantial movement of the model vessels, which must be stabilized at a chosen point. The horizontal plane in which the forces are measured lies either in the variable level of the deck of the vessel or is at a constant level above the upstream water surface. In the latter method, which has been used almost exclusively until recently, the horizontal forces acting on the vessel are transmitted by two vertical masts to two rings placed in the horizontal measuring plane. The masts, which are fixed to the bow and stern of the vessel, pass without resistance through the rings to which dynamometers of various types are fixed.

The simplest and at the same time a very sensitive measuring device is a float dynamometer where the sockets (rings) of the vertical masts are fixed to a light frame hanging above the model of the lock on long threads. From each socket three threads pass through the frame, two in opposite transverse directions perpendicular to the axis of the lock and one longitudinally along (and extending) the axis of the vessel. The threads passing over sensitive pulleys vertically along the outer walls of the lock are attached at their lower end to equal (large and heavy) floats submerged in containers filled with water to the same level.

Float dynamometers, first used by Krey and Winkel, work on the principle of the difference of displacement of the opposite floats. A deviation of the vessel and floats from the normal equilibrium position, which is proportional to the acting horizontal force, is recorded in three components; one longitudinal and two transverse (at the stern and bow of the vessel). The disadvantage of the float dynamometers is that during measuring they permit comparatively large movements of the vessel and thus also the application of the forces of inertia, which may distort the forces measured.

From this point of view it is more suitable to fit a mechanical (spring) dynamometer to each of the two sockets through which the masts of the vessel pass, for which the movement of the vessel is considerably limited. Figure 8.10 shows a dynamometer of this type constructed at VÚV Prague (Čábelka, 1949a), consisting of two light metal carriages with wheels placed at an angle of 45° (to prevent sliding friction), moving on horizontal rails. The lower carriage (d) of the dynamometer moves longitudinally on rails (e) parallel with the axis of the lock. Its normal position is fixed by two springs (f), fitted to the carriage and to the frame. The longitudinal carriage has horizontal rails (g) perpendicular to the axis of the lock, along which the upper carriage (h) moves transversely. Its position is given by two springs (i) fixed to the transverse and longitudinal carriages. The upper transverse carriage has a socket (c), through which the vertical mast (b) of the model of vessel (a) passes with the help of sensitive bearings. Thus the vessel can rise and fall in the lock almost without resistance and the horizontal forces can be transferred from it to the dynamometers. The deviation of the dynamometers from the normal position, which is proportional to the acting forces, is transmitted by threads to the registering pens on a rotating drum (k) placed beside the model. It is also possible to measure very small deviations of this dynamometer accurately with stronger springs either by dial indicators or electrically, for example with the aid of potentiometers, and to record the results in the former case on film and in the latter case with the aid of an oscillograph.

A hydraulic dynamometer permitting only negligible movement of the ship and almost excluding the forces of inertia is also sometimes used.

Fig. 8.10. Dynamometer for the measurement of forces on model barges. [Čábelka, 1949]

The complete exclusion of inertia is achieved by the use of strain gauges stabilizing the vessel almost at one point.

The common disadvantage of all dynamometers placed on a horizontal measuring plane above the model of the lock are the moments caused by the long arm of the mast, especially at the beginning of the filling of the lock, when the water level is at its lowest and when the greatest horizontal forces usually act on the vessel. It is therefore more advantageous to place the dynamometers directly on the level of the deck of the vessel as illustrated in Fig. 8.11 (Mäsiar (1958)).

The spring dynamometers used are hollow cylinders closed at one end with a coiled spring and piston. A rod firmly connected with the piston passes through the centre of the spring and the cylinder lid. At one end the rod has a wheel with ball bearings mounted so that it can transmit forces in various directions. On the other end of the rod there is a small plane surface in contact with the tip of an indicator showing the compression of the dynamometer spring. The sensitivity of the spring can be adjusted according to need. The cylinders and indicators are fitted in a horizontal position on the deck of the model vessel. Three dynamometers are fitted at both the bow and stern; two placed in the axis of the vessel (one at the bow, the other at the stern) measure the longitudinal forces

Fig. 8.11. Dynamometer for the measurement of forces on model barges. [Mäsiar, 1958]

and the two pairs of dynamometers placed facing each other measure the transverse forces. On the inside wall of the model of the lock vertical strips are fitted over which the wheels fixed to the end of the dynamometer rods move. The disadvantage of this type of dynamometer is that the results must be recorded on film; should it be sufficient to record only the maximum values of the acting forces, the indicators can be adjusted so that this value is read directly.

One more device for measuring horizontal forces consisting of a set of three dynamometers at the bow and stern of the model vessel is worth mentioning. The recording points of each set touch perpendicular rods which are not firmly connected to the vessel, but rest on it and follow its rise or fall. Both rods pass freely through long vertical sockets on a fixed frame placed above the model of the lock.

8.4.3 Examples of research on scale models of locks

The following few examples of model studies concentrate on different types and methods of lock filling and emptying. The main conclusions that can be generalized and used in design are mentioned. Research has shown that as far as the safety of vessels is concerned the speed of emptying may be about double that of filling.

(a) *Filling (emptying) locks through gate ports*

The filling (emptying) through ports in the lock gates (usually mitre or sliding gates) is used mainly for locks with very low heads; outflow is, wherever possible, below the level of the downstream water. The ports in the gates are closed by sluices controlled by mechanisms usually fixed directly on the gates themselves. This solution complicates the construction of the gates, increases their weight and causes frequent breakdowns. It is therefore used only exceptionally, usually as a supplement to other methods of filling (emptying) the lock to speed up the process. An example is the study of filling and emptying through mitre gate ports (two in each gate leaf) of locks on the river Trent, Great Britain, dimensions 57.0×9.0 m and heads from 2.5 to 3.5 m (Novák, 1947).

Forces acting on a 200 tonne barge were investigated on lock models of scale 1:24 for various heads, combinations and rates of sluice gate opening and with the barge at different positions in the lock. Since the resultant forces in the original filling arrangement were considerably higher than their permissible value, two methods of directing the flow of water from the openings in the gates into the lock and of dissipating their energy were investigated: in the first alternative the flow from the sluices entered the lock through culverts in the lock sill with the outflow jets directed against each other; in the second the flow from the sluices was dispersed by suitably shaped grilles, with three large longitudinal openings in the centre and two vertical ones near the edges, and placed only 15 cm in front of the inner face of the gates, so as not to hinder navigation when the gates open. The forces acting on the barge were reduced to up to one fourth of their original value. In the first alternative the time of filling was somewhat extended, whereas in the second this time remained the same as for filling through ports without the grilles. Model study results were verified in prototype with very good agreement (the difference in the time of filling and emptying was less than 2%).

(b) *Direct filling (emptying) with lock gates used as filling (emptying) devices*

This method of filling (emptying) locks with gates fulfilling two functions, i.e. closing and filling (emptying) the lock, is suitable for locks with low and very low heads.

For direct filling, flap gates of various types, segment gates and lastly vertical lift gates may be used. The latter release the flow through an opening, usually under the gate, and after complete opening are lowered so that sufficient navigation depth remains above them. Water flowing into the lock should not entrain air, as this encourages strong wave formation which is dangerous to vessels. If air entrainment cannot be prevented a deaeration zone should be incorporated at the upstream end of the lock and separated from the lock proper by a vertical wall with outlets, the dimensions and function of which should be verified by model studies.

Lift gates may be used for direct emptying. This solution is suitable particularly where the head of the lock is large enough to enable the vessels to pass under the completely raised gates without resorting to high portals. To empty locks with low heads usually short culverts passing round the downstream gates and possibly also ports in the downstream gates are used.

For direct filling and emptying of locks with very small heads two sector gates with vertical axis are also used which turn into recesses in the lateral walls of the lock when open (Douma, *et al.*, 1969).

One typical example of direct filling of locks with *very small heads* by using tilting flap gates is the design developed in Czechoslovakia by Čábelka (1949). Its suitability has been verified by research on model scales 1:20 and by more than twenty years of operational use on a lock with dimensions 12.0×85.0 m. Because of the simplicity of construction, reliability of function, hydraulic effectiveness, smooth and speedy filling, low forces acting on the passing vessel and economy of construction and operation, similar gates were used for the direct filling of a number of locks with a head of up to $H_0 = 5.50$ m, constructed in recent years on the Elbe and Vltava. Two types of tilting gates were designed for these locks on the basis of studies on models of scale 1:25; one type for a lock width 12.0 m (Fig. 8.12) and the other for a lock of double width (Čábelka and Kubec, 1969).

Fig. 8.12. Tilting gate for direct lock filling. [Čábelka and Kubec, 1969]

In both cases the gate has a horizontal axis of rotation situated closely beneath the centre of pressure of the resultant upstream hydrostatic force. This pressure therefore keeps the gate in a closed position without making use of its moving mechanism. During the filling of the lock the gate tilts with its upper end upstream, initially at very low speed; at the same time below its bottom end the filling slot is gradually opened and water flows through this from the upper reservoir into the lock without any dangerous filling wave being formed. The stilling basin below the gate has baffles which aid the energy dissipation of the stream and direct it against the bows of the vessel to decrease its pull towards the upstream gate. The filling of the lock is therefore carried out smoothly and forces acting on the vessel do not exceed the limit values.

Just before the completion of filling the rate at which the gate is turning increases considerably so that the lock fills more quickly (possibly even using a slight overfall over the top of the gate), thus reducing the time needed for complete opening and equalization of water levels. After the gate has been tilted completely into a horizontal position there is sufficient depth above it for the ship to pass.

The dimensions and construction of both types of tilting gates are standardized for all heads up to 5.50 m so that the gates of locks of equal width are interchangeable and can quickly be replaced in case of breakdowns, repairs or maintenance. Both types of gates have a unilateral hydraulic mechanism permitting the use and regulation of various speeds of rotation.

Tilting gates may also be used as flood gates during high flow in the river or to pass ice floes and to remove ice from the lock itself.

Limitation of the use of these types of tilting gates for direct filling of locks to a head of 5.50 m results from the requirement that the lower end of the gates must be submerged below the lowest water level of the lock to prevent air entrainment. The use of these gates for direct filling of locks with a head higher than 5.5 m would be possible in principle, but would require a special energy dissipator and deaeration space downstream of the gates, separated from the lock proper by a vertical grill wall, similar to those used with vertical lift and segment gates for direct filling.

Complete model studies with both types of gates were carried out for heads from 2.50 m to 5.50 m in steps of 0.5 m. Figure 8.9a illustrates the results for one of the locks on the Elbe, with dimensions 85.0 m × 12.0 m and head $H = 4.0$ m. It shows the case of continuous tilting of the gate at steady speed during the entire filling of the lock, so that at the moment when filling is complete the upper edge of the gate, turned through an angle of 33°, is just submerged below the equalized water levels. The function $Q = f(t)$ is concave throughout, so that the maximum increase in flow $\Delta Q/\Delta t$ occurs at the beginning of the filling of the lock when the depth of water in it is still at its lowest and when, therefore, the dynamic effect of the direct filling wave moving in the initial phase from the upstream to the downstream gate causes a longitudinal force on the vessel (displacement W):

$$P = \frac{W}{g(A_l - A_s)} \left(\frac{\Delta Q}{\Delta t}\right) \tag{8.9}$$

where A_l is the transverse cross-sectional area of water in the lock and A_s is the cross-sectional area of the submerged part of the ship. With the described manipulation of filling during which the longitudinal component of the horizontal force acting on the ship has not exceeded $P_{L_{lim}}$ the time of filling in prototype was $T_l = 250$ s.

Further research was oriented towards a substantial shortening of time T_l whilst preserving the same level of vessel safety. First a gradual increase of the rate of tilting of the gates during filling was investigated. This manipulation did not give satisfactory results. Therefore, the lower end of the gate was re-designed and a console introduced on the vertical wall beneath the gate as in Fig. 8.13. This reduced both the flow area a and the coefficients of lock filling at its beginning and it was possible to increase the rate of uniform turning of the gates throughout the filling process. The results obtained are illustrated in Fig. 8.9b.

It is evident from this that the functions $a = f(t)$ and $Q = f(t)$ at the beginning of filling are convex and that therefore the greatest value $(\Delta Q/\Delta t)_{max}$ occurs at the inflexion point of curve $Q = f(t)$ in about one quarter of the total time of filling, when the water level has already risen by about $0.1H_0$. During this faster uniform tilting the top of the gate reaches the water level of the upstream water before the water levels are equalized. If the gate were to stop in this position, when the filling opening beneath the gate attains the area a_{max}, the lock would fill in a time $T_l = 220$ s. If, after attaining this position, the gate is tilted further at a considerably greater angular velocity, the time is reduced by about 10% ($T_l \approx 200$ s). (The small overflow over the upper edge of the gate does not endanger the safety of the vessel.)

Apart from the described types of tilting gates for direct filling a number of further types have been designed and tested in various laboratories, e.g., gates designed by GHH, Krupp and Man companies in Germany.

Locks with *small heads* of up to about 10 m can be filled through a vertical duct in the upstream sill, the flow through which is closed by the lower part of tilting, segment or lift gates (with a filling shield). The filling conduit extends through the full width of the lock for even filling.

Figure 8.14 shows a model scale 1:20 of a lock with dimensions 12.0×85.0 m and head 10.5 m; the inlet into the filling conduit is closed by the lower end of the gate that may be tilted downstream (Čábelka, 1949b). The gate tilts downstream through an angle of 45° during the

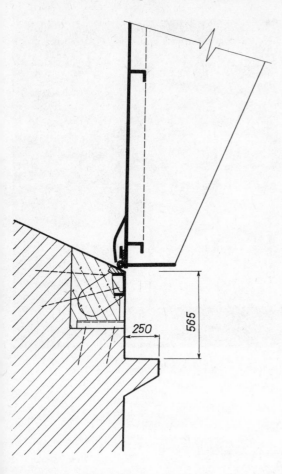

250

565

Fig. 8.13.

initial filling phase and this operation must be carried out very slowly to prevent a high, steep filling wave in the lock. When the lock is nearly full the second phase begins when the gate is turned at a considerably higher speed and the completion of filling may again be speeded up by a small overflow over the top of the tilted gate. After the gate has turned into a horizontal position there is sufficient depth above it for navigation.

The results with two speeds of gate rotation are shown in Fig. 8.15. During the faster filling (full line) a high wave moves along the entire length of the lock from the upstream to the downstream gate, and back again after reflection, causing considerable longitudinal forces. When the gate is turned slowly (Fig. 8.15 broken line) these forces are reduced to permissible values.

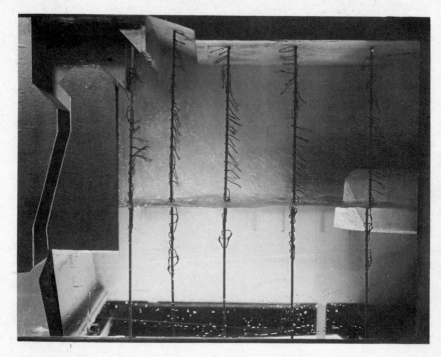

Fig. 8.14. Tilting gate and filling of a model lock. [Čábelka, 1949]

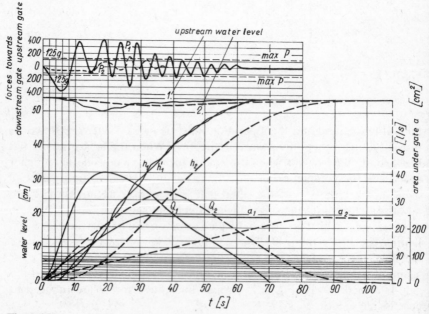

Fig. 8.15.

Air entrained through the conduit into the lock deteriorates flow conditions in it and considerably increases the forces acting on the passing vessel. This is why only those types of upstream gate where the longitudinal seal between the lower edge and the lock sill can be made airtight, e.g. various types of tilting gates, are suitable for this system of lock filling. At vertical lift gates where it is impossible to prevent air entrainment, it is again necessary to create a special space for energy dissipation and deaeration in the lock.

(c) *Filling (emptying) locks through short culverts round the gates*

Locks with low and medium heads may also be filled (emptied) through short culverts in the lateral walls or the gate sills which are provided with separate sluice gates or valves. The filling (emptying) is carried out by a concentrated inlet (outlet) of water at the upstream (downstream) gates. The basic hydrodynamic problems usually investigated on models are, therefore, very similar to those of the preceding type of lock with direct filling. They are more complicated insofar as the jets from opposite sides of the lock must not only be effectively dissipated but also suitably directed and evenly distributed over the full width of the lock so that the transverse forces acting on vessels do not exceed the permissible limit. Longitudinal waves causing longitudinal forces may be reduced to permissible values by a gradual opening of the culvert gates.

Model studies on this type of filling (emptying), have been carried out in a number of laboratories but only the results of some studies carried out for locks with short culverts and special design features will be mentioned.

The dimensions of the lock at Kamýk on the Vltava, Czechoslovakia, are only 6.5×35.0 m, but the head is comparatively large i.e. a maximum of 15.5 m. The lock is filled through one short conduit only, leading from the upstream reservoir to the inlet openings and stilling basin at the bottom of the upstream wall. It is emptied directly under the downstream lifting gates.

On the basis of model studies at a scale of $1:15$ (Fig. 8.16) the filling system has been designed with five equal inlet openings, which are regularly and symmetrically distributed along the width of the lock and have a total flow area equal to 1.05 times that of the filling conduit. Between the inlets directing the jets towards the bottom of the stilling basin there are dividing walls guiding the flow in a direction parallel to the axis of the lock. A comparatively even distribution of the water flowing through the inlets into the lock throughout its width was made possible by a bend in the filling conduit just upstream of the inlet openings; the effect of the centrifugal force which increased the flow through the first inlet openings close to the concave bend of the filling conduit practically equalized the influence of increased pressure at the

Fig. 8.16. Model of Kamýk lock on the River Vltava. [Čábelka and Novák, 1964]

end of the conduit which tended to increase the flow in the last inlet openings. Acceptable longitudinal forces were attained by slow and steady opening of the conduit gate (in prototype over three and a half minutes), and by a suitable design of the inlet stilling basin which has two rows of baffles directing the flow upwards against the bow of the ship.

When emptying the lock it is necessary to raise the downstream gates slowly (2 mm/s) until the lock is almost emptied (a lift of gates of about 44 cm); the further lifting of the gates to the full height is completed at a considerably greater speed of about 6 cm/s (prototype values). If another vessel is waiting in the downstream lock approach, the initial gate raising speed during emptying must be reduced by about one half, so as not to exceed the permissible values of forces acting on the moored waiting vessel.

For the locks of the proposed barrage Bratislava-Wolfsthal (two locks next to each other), with head of about 12 m and dimensions of 24× 230 m, model studies at a scale of 1:35 were carried out (Mäsiar, 1962), comparing three different methods of filling and emptying: through two long culverts, with outlets along the entire length of the lock; direct filling beneath the upstream lift gates and emptying through ports in the downstream mitre gates, similar to locks on the Austrian section of the Danube at Jochenstein and Ybbs-Persenbeug (PIANC Congress 1969); concentrated filling of the lock at its upstream end and emptying by short conduits. The third method was found to be economically, hydraulically

Fig. 8.17. Model of Danube lock. [Mäsiar, 1962]

and operationally the most suitable and was therefore recommended for construction. In the accepted solution each lock has a short filling culvert connected to the upstream reservoir directly above the barrage and a short emptying conduit leading into the downstream reservoir. These filling and emptying culverts at each lock are interconnected beneath it in a deepened stilling basin connected with the lock by longitudinal openings. Since the locks are placed upstream of the barrage, the stilling basin with filling (emptying) openings is placed close to the downstream mitre gates (Fig. 8.17).

A great advantage of the accepted method of filling and emptying is the fact that the filling (emptying) culverts are not connected to the upstream (downstream) lock approaches where a comparatively strong flow and wave formation during filling (emptying) might endanger the safety of waiting vessels and, in any case, slow down their entry.

(d) Filling (emptying) of locks by long culverts

Locks with medium and high heads are most frequently filled and emptied by two long culverts along the entire length of the lock and connected with it by filling (emptying) ports (manifold). The long conduits are placed either in the lateral walls level with the bottom of the lock or beneath the bottom. In narrower locks they are directly connected to the lock by outflow ports. In wider locks with high heads it is more effective to lead lateral canals from the long culverts beneath the bottom of the lock, which are alternately connected to one or the other longitudinal culvert. Only these lateral canals are directly linked by ports with the lock.

The main conclusions of some studies that may be generalized and used for the design of similar locks are listed below (Čábelka, 1949a).

The lock at Štěchovice on the Vltava which has a length of 118.4 m between the upstream and downstream mitre gates, a width of 12.0 m, a minimum water depth of 3.0 m and a maximum head of 20.1 m can be used by 1000 tonne vessels with a tug boat. The lock is divided by central mitre gates into two parts of length 40.0 and 73.0 m respectively, for the passage of smaller vessels. The lock closely adjoins the dam on the other side of which the power station is situated (Fig. 8.18). Two long conduits in the lateral walls of the lock and linked to it by a total of forty inlet orifices are used for filling and emptying. On each conduit there are three sluice gates next to the lock gates.

The model of the whole hydraulic structure at a scale of 1:50 (Fig. 8.18) was used to study the function of the lock in the context of the entire structure, whilst a model of part of the conduit, scale 1:10, served for detailed investigations of the conduit and its gate and for different

Fig. 8.18. Model of lock at Štěchovice on the River Vltava. [Čábelka, 1949]

phases of filling or emptying of the lock. A model of the whole lock of scale 1:20, incorporated provisions for maintaining a constant upstream water level at various heights within the range of the reservoir levels. A model of a 650 tonne vessel which could also operate in the longer part of the subdivided lock was also used. The most suitable shape of inlet into both conduits, position and rate of opening of the conduit gates and shape, dimensions and position of the filling ports and energy dissipation in the stilling basin downstream of the lock were investigated.

Discharges through the individual filling ports and the relation between these discharges and the pressures and hydraulic gradient in the conduit were also studied. For this purpose the longer part of the lock was divided by vertical partitions into separate compartments, always with only one inlet orifice. The water flowing into the separate compartments was measured by rectangular notches under steady flow conditions (Fig. 8.19). For each measurement the water level was kept at the same level in all compartments, corresponding to the position of the water level in the lock for the given phase of its filling, the required level being obtained by vertically moving the outflow notches. Several sets of measurements were carried out with four different partial openings of the conduit gates and with a fully opened conduit. Discharge through the outlet orifices during the emptying of the lock was measured in such a way that water was supplied simultaneously into the separate compartments from hoses, and the individual discharges were regulated until the water level in all compartments was the same and then measured.

Fig. 8.19.

From the model studies the following general conclusions can be drawn:

(1) The inertia of the water in the conduit influences the discharge through individual outlet ports. At the beginning of filling this is shown by the fact that the water does not begin to flow out of the conduit into the lock through all the orifices simultaneously, but starts gradually from the upstream end. This results in a small and, on the whole, harmless wave in the lock advancing to its downstream gate. In the first phase, during rising flow velocity in the conduit, filling is slowed down due to inertia, whereas in the second phase, during decreasing flow velocity, it speeds up and 'overrunning' of the water level in the lock above that of the upstream reservoir occurs, which shortens the filling time by about 10%.

(2) The pressure line after water has started to move in the conduit gradually increases in the downstream direction. This increases the excess pressure, given by the difference between this head and the water level in the lock. The greatest excess pressure occurs at maximum discharge Q_{max} through the conduit. Thus water flows more quickly in the ports at the end of the conduit than in those at the centre or at the beginning of the lock. If equal inlets are uniformly distributed along the whole length of the lock, then its filling is uneven, as the greater part of the inflow is through the last ports near the closed downstream conduit sluices. This phenomenon is also supported by the fact that losses in the individual inlets are not the same, but gradually decrease in the direction towards the downstream end of the conduit, but in the last inlets they again increase considerably. This uneven inflow gives rise to currents in the lock and a slope of the water level from the downstream to the upstream gate; further, especially during a fast opening of the upstream conduit gates, a filling wave occurs, which is particularly dangerous to the vessel. During very fast opening of the upstream sluice gates it may even happen that several of the first ports draw water as an ejector from the lock into the conduits, considerably worsening hydraulic conditions in the lock and increasing the forces acting on the vessel. This depends, however, not only on the speed at which the conduit sluices are opened, but also on the ratio of the cross-sectional areas of the ports and conduits. This is the more noticeable the further this ratio exceeds its limiting value of 1.3 to 1.4. If this ratio does not attain the limiting value, water it is not drawn from the lock into the conduits even when the sluices are opened very quickly. At the limiting value of the ratio the coefficient of filling of the lock attains its maximum, and the time of filling its minimum value.

(3) The even distribution of inflow throughout the entire length of the lock from the conduits of constant section and roughness may be obtained in two ways: if the area of all ports is constant then their spacing must be

variable, i.e. greater at the end of the conduit and smaller at the beginning. If, however, the constant spacing of the ports is to be preserved, their area must decrease towards the end of the conduit in proportion to the increase in outlet velocity, i.e. with the square root of the difference of excess pressure between the neighbouring outlets.

(4) Such a distribution or dimensioning of the ports for a conduit with constant cross-section and roughness is suitable both for lock filling and emptying as here again the highest pressures (velocities) occur at the last ports.

(5) If the lock were emptied through the downstream gate, or possibly by a longitudinal conduit in which the direction of flow is the opposite of that used during filling, an even distribution of flow from the conduit into the lock along its entire length during filling and possibly from the lock into the conduit during emptying, might be obtained by a change in the cross-sectional area of the conduit, or a change in the roughness of its walls while keeping a constant cross-section. This change must be such, however, that the difference in the pressure head at the first and last outlet orifice is zero. Then spacing of the outlet posts as well as their area may be equal.

(6) If it is not possible to distribute the inlets along the lock in a way suitable for all cases, e.g., because of the division of the lock into two parts by central gates, the time and mode of opening the conduit sluices has to be determined to give an initially small and smoothly increasing rate of change in discharge $\Delta Q/\Delta t$, and thus fairly evenly distributed flow into the lock and acceptable longitudinal forces acting on the vessel.

(7) During the emptying of the lock the longitudinal forces acting on the vessel are considerably smaller than those acting on it during filling, because in the first decisive phase of emptying the water depth in the lock is high and the first wave occurring during opening of the downstream conduit sluices is considerably smaller than during filling. It follows that it is possible to empty the lock much more quickly than to fill it (by a speedier opening of the conduit sluices or an increase in the conduit cross-section).

(8) The transverse forces acting on the vessel are considerably smaller than the longitudinal forces both during filling and emptying. This is achieved by placing the outlets from the longitudinal conduits to alternate with each other rather than placing them opposite each other. During the filling of the lock the water level in its axis is somewhat lower than near the side walls so that the vessel floats comparatively calmly. The transverse forces are also reduced by the fact that the ceiling of the outlets is lowered and in turn their side walls flared, so that the thin outflowing jet is directed towards the bottom of the lock, does not impinge on the sides of the vessel and its energy is more easily dissipated.

(9) Air entrained into the conduit by the flowing water acts unfavourably

on flow conditions in it and in the outlet orifices, extends the filling of the lock and considerably increases wave formation on the surface, and thus also the forces acting on the vessel, sometimes even doubling them. Entrainment of air into the conduit during filling can be prevented either by placing the upstream sluice gates into the side wall conduits, i.e. below the downstream water level and/or by an airtight closure of the shafts of the provisional bulkheads in the conduits immediately downstream of the sluices.

(10) For energy dissipation of the outflowing water during the emptying of the lock the longitudinal conduits should extend below the downstream end of the lock and be provided with evenly distributed outlets ending opposite each other in a stilling basin. For each outlet to pass approximately the same discharge, the area of the orifices is gradually reduced in size in the downstream direction, e.g., for the same width the height of the outlet is gradually reduced. This results in an effective and economic design of the stilling basin and downstream lock approach.

The results of research carried out in various laboratories all over the world on locks filled and emptied by means of long conduits placed either in their walls or in the bottom agree with the above conclusions. According to PIANC (1969) this method of filling and emptying a lock represents a solution suitable for medium heads.

(e) Filling (emptying) of locks with high heads or of large dimensions

Locks with high heads or large dimensions usually have a fairly complicated system of filling or emptying to guarantee a speedy, smooth and safe passage of vessels or of whole, sometimes very large, groups of vessels.

Research has shown the suitability of *combined filling* (possibly also emptying) of locks, e.g., filling by long conduits is combined with direct filling through the gates. The hydraulic suitability of the combination of these two methods of filling of large locks rests on the fact that, to a considerable degree, the initial filling waves of both methods act against each other; when filling through long conduits the wave originates at the downstream gate whereas in direct filling the wave is formed at the upstream gate of the lock. To limit the unfavourable effects of flow and filling waves as much as possible, experimental investigations are carried out to determine the necessary lag in the beginning of opening of the upstream gate in relation to the beginning of opening of the filling inlets on the long conduits and the optimum speed of opening in both cases. While preserving the necessary safety of passing vessels the time of combined filling of locks may be reduced to about half of that of filling through long conduits alone.

For locks of large dimensions and heads, speedy, smooth and safe filling and emptying is achieved by a complicated system, which is symmetrical about the centre and longitudinal axis of the lock and linked with the lock proper by inlet *openings in the bottom*. The inlet openings are spaced in such a way that the inflow of water into the lock is evenly distributed over its area and this is so even if one of the conduits is put out of operation. The efficiency of filling large locks is the better the greater the part of the bottom surface taken up by the filling zone. To guarantee safety for vessels waiting in the lock approaches and to shorten the distance and time necessary for them to enter the lock, filling and emptying conduits are usually terminated outside their forebays. Rapid and safe filling with a complicated hydrodynamically balanced system has been attained on the basis of research, e.g., by French laboratories, for a number of hydraulic structures on the Rhine and the Rhone: at Saint Pierre with a head $H = 26.0$ m the water surface rises at a speed of 4.90 m/min; at Chateauneuf with a head of 19.20 m, 4.20 m/min, etc.

High rates of filling of high locks, i.e. a rise in water level faster than 5 m/min, already cause cavitation problems, especially at the gates of the filling conduits. High locks of large dimensions with complicated filling (emptying) systems, designed on the basis of research, were built in the USA, e.g., at the McNary dam on the Columbia River (head 28 m, filling time 16 min), at the Wilson dam on the Tennessee River and at the John Day dam on the Columbia River (heads 32 to 34.5 m; Richardson, 1969), etc.

Locks with high heads on canals with a shortage of water are usually designed as *thrift* locks with reservoirs or as combined locks. The filling and emptying system of these locks is usually complicated, with inlet openings in the bottom. The filling (emptying) conduits are connected not only to the upstream and downstream reservoir but also to the various thrift reservoirs situated beside the lock. Recently extensive research of locks with thrift reservoirs has been carried out by the laboratories in Germany (Technische Hochschule, Karlsruhe) where locks of this type are under construction on the Rhine–Main–Danube Canal.

8.5 Models of Ship Lifts and Inclined Flumes

8.5.1 Subject and aims of research

Very high heads in inland waterways are overcome by the use of ship lifts, inclined flumes and railways. The vessels are transported in flumes filled with water and only exceptionally on platforms without water. In the ship lifts the flume and the vessel are moved mechanically, usually in a vertical direction, between the upstream and downstream reservoirs. During this operation the flume is balanced by floats, pistons or counterweights.

Apart from ship lifts with a flume moving in a vertical direction a number of designs for ship lifts exist where the flume, filled with water, is moved by rotation or variously combined movement. The flumes of ship railways are fitted to undercarriages moving on inclined rails connecting the upstream and downstream reservoirs.

In the types of ship lifts whose flumes move only in a vertical direction in air, no hydraulic problems normally arise requiring solution by means of hydraulic research. On the other hand, in the case of ship lifts and inclines where the flume moves along an inclined, circular or other path parallel with the axis of the flume or perpendicular to it, and where it is lowered into the water, two problems are usually solved with the aid of hydraulic research: the fluctuations in water levels and forces acting on the vessel in the flume, and the effects of the entrance of the flume into the reservoir.

The vertical element of the movement of the flume and its changes do not affect the safety of the vessel. The horizontal element of the movement, especially its changes during starting and stopping of the flume, cause fluctuations of the water level and waves in it, and thus also forces acting on the moored vessel. Whereas during lateral movement of the flume (perpendicular to its axis) the fluctuations of the water level and the acting forces are relatively small, they may attain great values during the longitudinal movement (in the direction of its axis) which must be investigated by computation or model research. The forces acting on the vessel in the flume are of a similar character to those acting on a vessel during the filling and emptying of a lock and are compensated for by mooring the vessel to the lateral walls of the flume. During model studies these forces are again measured with the aid of dynamometers, which are more easily placed in the flume than in a lock, since the change in elevation of the vessel with regard to the flume is negligible.

Another set of problems that can be solved by model studies arises when the flume enters the water, involving the study of the impact and dynamic effects on the bottom of the flume, the possibility of it 'slipping' due to the great speeds at which the flume lands on the surface, investigations on waves occurring in the landing chamber as the flume enters, and lastly, research on the spreading of these waves in the downstream reservoir.

Since the modelled hydraulic phenomena depend on gravity, the Froude criterion of similarity is used. The models must be large enough to avoid viscous and surface tension scale effects.

8.5.2 Inclined ship lifts

So far comparatively few studies have been undertaken dealing with the solution of the hydraulic problems of inclined lifts. One of them is the research by Vasiljev (1959), carried out on the model of an incline reduced to a scale of 1:50. The flume in prototype was 110.0 m long, 18.0 m wide and 3.65 m deep (for vessels with a displacement of 3330 tonne). The inclination of the path of the flume was small, only about 3°.

Vasiljev first dealt with the movement of water in the flume without a vessel during steadily accelerating or decelerating movement. For the movement of water in the flume he established a partial differential equation giving the maximum rise in the water level, y_{max}, at the head of the flume by the expression

$$y_{max} = l \frac{a_x}{g + a_y} \qquad (8.10)$$

where l is the length of the flume, a_x and a_y are the horizontal and vertical components of acceleration and g is the gravitational acceleration. Similar results were obtained by de Ries (1962) who dealt with the problem of ship inclines in connection with the construction of a sloping ship lift near Ronquiere in Belgium.

In further studies Vasiljev investigated the forces acting on the vessel. The decisive force is the horizontal resultant P acting on the vessel in the direction of its axis and which must be transferred to the flume by various devices. Vasiljev assumes that force P consists of the force of inertia and hydrostatic forces during oscillatory movement of water in the flume, neglecting the effect of friction of the water on the wetted part of the vessel and the influence of elasticity of the tying devices. He arrives at the maximum value of the force

$$P = P_{max} = 2ma_x \qquad (8.11)$$

where m is the mass of the vessel; Equation (8.11) applies if the acceleration stops acting at time $t = T_0/2$, where T_0 is the period of oscillation of the water level in the flume.

An example of a detailed model study of ship inclines is the investigation for the Orlík dam incline, on the Vltava, carried out in Czechoslovakia by Vlček (1964, 1965). The prototype flume for barges up to 300 tonnes is 6.0×33.0 m in plan and 2.3 m deep; the incline is comparatively steep at 22°. Problems connected with the entry of the flume into the downstream water, fluctuations of water level in the flume with and without vessel and horizontal forces acting on the vessel during starting, stopping and sudden braking of the flume were investigated on a scale model 1:20. With the aid of a special device the size of the impact on the bottom of the flume during its landing on the water surface was measured and compared with the vertical impact of a circular disc on a smooth water surface.

For the analytical solution of the movement of the water surface in the flume Vlček assumed a plane surface in all positions. The movement of the mass of water is replaced by the movement of the centre of gravity of a trapezoid, moving along a parabola which may be approximately replaced by a circle of radius r near its apex. Thus the equation for the movement of the water mass changes into a differential equation of harmonic movement of a mathematical pendulum with a time of oscillation $T_0 = 2\pi\sqrt{(r/g)}$, giving practically the same value of the maximum fluctuation of the water surface at the head of the flume as Equation. (8.10), i.e.

$$y_{max} = l\frac{a_x}{g}$$

as the vertical component of acceleration a_y may be neglected with regard to g. The broken line [1] in Fig. 8.20 illustrates the oscillation of the water level at the head of the flume if acceleration, a, acts continuously. If at time $t = T_0/2$ the acceleration ceases, the water surface levels assume negative values, as is shown by line [2]. Line [3] shows the water levels for the case of the flume suddenly stopping when the maximum value of the water level is

$$y_{max} = \frac{lv_x}{2\sqrt{(gr)}} \tag{8.12}$$

where v_x is the horizontal component of velocity, v, of the movement of the flume. Line [4] refers to the relationship between the maximum value of oscillation y_{max} and time T_a, during which acceleration (deceleration) acts (if the flume moves always with the same velocity v). The movement of the water in the flume of the lift in reality, however, is considerably more complicated and it depends whether or not a vessel is in the flume.

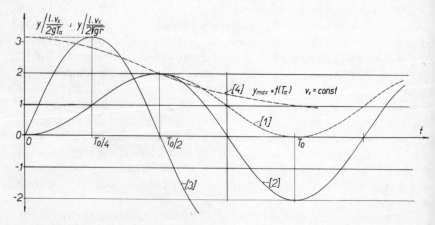

Fig. 8.20.

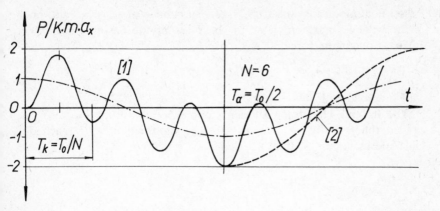

Fig. 8.21.

When studying the mooring forces Vlček assumes that the vessel is in a longitudinal direction held by two springs S_1 and S_2 with elastic constants k, of which invariably only one acts on the vessel. Again like Vasiljev he considers the force of inertia ma_x and hydrostatic pressure caused by the inclined water surface. The horizontal force, P, is dependent not only on the initial velocity, v, and the time of uniform acceleration, T_a, but also on the elastic constant, k, of the mooring device. The mass of the vessel undergoes its own oscillatory movement in a horizontal direction of period $T_k = 2\pi\sqrt{(m/k)}$. The ratio of the periods of oscillations of the water surface and of the oscillations of the vessel, N, considerably influences the maximum magnitude of the mooring force, P. If N is an even number we obtain, as did Vasiljev (Equation (8.11)), a maximum size of the force $P_{max} = 2\,Kma_x$, where $K = N^2/(N^2 - 1)$ is close to 1. The force P is illustrated on Fig. 8.21 by line [1]; the sinusoidal curve expresses the effect of the oscillations of the vessel and of the water surface. If acceleration stops acting at time $t = T_a = T_0/2$, when the vessel is at relative rest with regard to the flume the oscillating component of period T_k disappears and force P follows only the movement of the water surface in the flume as is shown by the broken line [2]. If the ratio of the period of both oscillatory movements (water level and vessel) is an odd number, greater amplitudes and a maximum value of

$$P_{max} \simeq 4Kma_x \tag{8.13}$$

occur as the flume is stopped at moment $t = T_0/2$. Model investigations, however, have shown forces considerably greater than double or even four times the forces of inertia (ma_x) up to $6.5\ ma_x$. This was due to the fact that the 'hydrodynamic mass' of water oscillated together with the vessel; this mass was determined by comparing the oscillation of the vessel floating on the water and freely suspended in air. The ratio of the hydrodynamic mass of water to the mass of the vessel was $e \approx 0.66$, giving a maximum force

$$P_{max} \approx 1.66 \times 4ma_x$$

which agreed with model results.

The limiting case for a sudden stopping of the flume has also been solved theoretically, i.e. for $T_a = 0$. The mooring force P reached its absolute maximum at time $t = T_0/4$

$$P_{max} = \frac{N}{N-1} v_x \sqrt{(km)} \tag{8.14}$$

The magnitude of force P again depends on the ratio of periods T_0 and T_k and its maximum is greatest for $N = 7; 11; 15; \ldots$. The oscillations of force P for $N = 7$ are illustrated on Fig. 8.22. It follows from Equation (8.14) that the magnitude of the tying force may be reduced by using anchoring devices with a low elastic constant k (permitting, however, extensive longitudinal movement of the vessel in the flume) or special damped mooring devices.

Model studies of this nature require special instrumentation and devices. To ensure steady movement of the model flume (Fig. 8.23) the winder was governed by an electromotor with a previously set constant number of revolutions. Braking of the movement was achieved by a belt brake of the winder activated by an electromagnet; the release of the brake was automatically registered on a recorder together with the distance travelled by the flume and the time.

Several methods were used to measure water levels. Weighted paper strips were used to determine the maximum wave height in the lower reservoir due to the flume entry. The strips were impregnated with a solution of red potassium prussiate and dried, and a small quantity of iron sulphide dissolved in the water. The level which the maximum wave amplitude reached was recorded by the paper strip turning deep blue. Wave recorders were used to record the oscillation of the water surface in the flume of the lift. At first flat steel springs with resistance tensometers were used to measure the forces acting on the vessel, but later induction recorders were exclusively used.

Below the model of the flume a horizontal plate was hung from four spring tie rods, each carrying the core of an induction meter, to measure the impact of the bottom of the flume on the water level.

The model and theoretical study of the ship incline has solved a number of important problems. It has shown that the impact of the bottom of the flume on the water surface is not dangerous for normal flume velocities (about 1 m/s), as the water level in the lower reservoir is

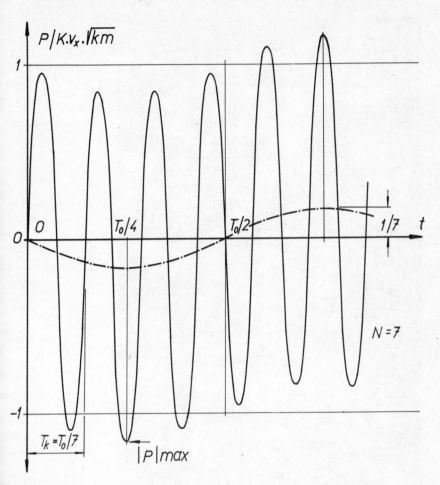

Fig. 8.22.

not absolutely horizontal. Also, the air cushion between the protruding transverse and longitudinal beams of the bottom of the flume contributes considerably to the damping of the impact. The waves in the downstream reservoir caused by the entry of the flume are negligible and the waves in the flume are not dangerous, and in particular the presence of a well tied vessel in the flume contributes substantially to their damping. Even during a sudden stoppage of the flume without a vessel, which is the most unfavourable case, model research has shown that the theoretical value of the maximum elevation of the water level is exceeded by only about 30%. The mooring forces, the magnitudes of which are limited by the construction of the vessel, determine the choice of the operational velocity and acceleration. It is unnecessary, however, to design a complicated electric

Fig. 8.23. Model of the ship incline at Orlik dam on the River Vltava [Vlček, 1964]

drive to permit an arbitrary small acceleration since a sudden stoppage of the flume (in the course of a few seconds) cannot be excluded during a failure in the power supply.

It is necessary, therefore, to use a mooring device with reliable hydraulic dampers, which brake the movement of the vessel from the first moment by a maximum permissible force, in contrast to the elastic mooring elements where the force increases linearly with their deformation. Furthermore suitable dampers do not cause an oscillation of the vessel.

8.5.3 Inclined flume

An inclined flume ('pente d'eau') is a device similar to the ship lift where vessels can overcome high heads on inland waterways. It is an inclined concrete flume with constant slope and rectangular cross-section, smooth walls and bed, and a moving and well sealed gate. In front of this gate there is a wedge of water with a horizontal surface, which is long and deep enough for a vessel or a train of barges to float on it. The gate can be moved along the length of the flume with the aid of an electric engine and thus the vessel can be transported from one reservoir to the other.

The functioning of the inclined flume has been most thoroughly studied in France (Chatou, 1964) on a model of scale 1:50, where the theoretically derived method of the computation of the oscillation of the moving water wedge in the flume, with and without a vessel, was verified and adjusted and the forces in the mooring ropes of the vessel, for various modes of movement of the water wedge in front of or behind the moving gate, determined.

Furthermore, the performance of the inclined flume was tested on a model built to a large scale of 1:10 in natural conditions at Venissieux in France (Aubert, 1970). The model was over 5 m high and 196 m long; the width of the inclined flume was 1.2 m. During studies on this model the sealing of the mobile gate was improved and it was shown that the time for safe passage of the vessel may be shorter than on a ship railway under similar conditions.

References

Annemüller, H. (1960). Der Einfluss des Turbinenschnellschlusses auf die Schiffahrt in Kraftwasserstrassen, *Der Bauingeniur*, No. 9, pp. 338–342.

Aubert, J. (1970). Amenagement de nouvelles voies navigables, *Bull. PIANC*, **IV,** No. 6, pp. 21–42.

Čábelka, J. (1949). Écluse à sas à un barrage, *Proc. 17th International Navigation Congress, Lisbon*, PIANC, pp. 201–209.

Čábelka, J. (1949a). Examen hydrotechnique du remplissage et de la vidange du sas de l'écluse de Štěchovice, *Proc. 17th International Navigation Congress, Lisbon*, PIANC, Section I, Question 2, pp. 79–85.

Čábelka, J. (1949b). Examen hydrotechnique des écluses à sas à chute petite et moyenne, avec remplissage au-dessous de la porte a bascule, *Proc. 17th International Navigation Congress, Lisbon*, PIANC, Section I, Communication 1, pp. 185–194.

Čábelka, J. (1957). Navigation lock serving as a wasteway of a canal-type power station, *Proc. 19th International Navigation Congress, London*, PIANC Section I, Question 3, pp. 127–146.

Čábelka, J. (1976). *Inland Waterways and Navigation*, (in Czech), SNTL, Prague.

Čábelka, J. and Gabriel, P. (1957). Positive surge waves in supply channels of hydro-power stations, *Proc. 7th General Meeting IAHR, Lisbon,* **I**, Paper C7, 10 pp.

Čábelka, J. and Kubec, J. (1969). Construction et modernisation des écluses sur l'Elbe en Tchécoslovaquie, *Proc. 22nd International Navigation Congress, Paris,* PIANC, Section I, Subjet 3, pp. 193–211.

Čábelka, J. and Novák, P. (1964). *Hydraulic Research 1—Research on Models* (in Czech), SNTL, Prague.

Delft Hydraulics Laboratory. (1978). *Aspects of navigability of constrained waterways,* International Symposium, Waterloopkundig Laboratorium, Delft.

Douma, J. H., Davis, J. P. and Nelson, N. E. (1969). United States practice in lock design, *Proc. 22nd International Navigation Congress, Paris,* PIANC, Section I, Subject 3, pp. 213–237.

Ehrenberger, R. (1940). Modellversuche betreffend das Donauwerk Ybbs-Persenbeug. *Wasserkraft und Wasserwirtschaft,* No. 2, pp. 41–45.

Gabriel, P. (1969). Regelung von Frequenz und Übergabeleistung in Kanal-kraftwerken, *Österreichische Zeitschrift für Elektrizitätswirtschaft,* No. 2, Wien pp. 46–59.

Gabriel, P., Grund, I. and Sikora, A. (1967). *Barrage on the Danube at Gabčikovo,* (in Slovak), Technical Report, VÚVH, Bratislava.

International Association for Hydraulic Research. (1959). Fundamental Hydraulics of Ship Locks, *Proc. 8th Congress IAHR, Subject B, Montreal.*

Mäsiar, E. (1958). *Hydraulics of Filling Systems of Navigation Locks,* (in Slovak), SAV, Bratislava.

Mäsiar, E. (1962). *Basic Methods of Increasing the Capacity of Inland Waterways,* (in Slovak), SAV, Bratislava.

Michajlov, A. V. (1966). *Navigation locks,* (in Russian), Gostechizdat, Moscow.

Novák, P. (1947). Filling and Emptying of Locks through Sluice Gates in the Lock Gates, (in Czech), *Sborník státního ústavu hydrologického, Prague.*

Puzanov, A. (1967, 1968). Mathematical modelling of time dependent hydraulic phenomena in systems of nonprismatic open channels, *Vodohospodársky časopis SAV,* No. 4, (1967) and No. 1 (1968), **5,** pp. 415–431, **16,** pp. 30–53.

Richardson, G. C. (1969). Filling system for Lower Granite Lock, *Proc. ASCE, Waterways and Harbors Div.* **95,** No. WW3, pp. 275–289.

Ries, de J. (1962). Etude sur le mouvement de l'eau et les forces d'ancorage des bateaux dans une sas mobile, *Annales des travaux publics des Belgique,* No. 3, pp. 211–242.

Sikora, A. (1961). Decreasing surges at lowhead structures, (in Slovak), *Vodohospodársky časopis SAV,* No. 3, pp. 242–254.

Vasiljev, O. F. (1959). Water Surface Fluctuations in Locks and Inclined Ship Elevators and the Conditions of Ships, *Proc. 8th Congress IAHR, Montreal,* **I,** Paper 8B, 25 pp.

Vlček, M. (1964). *Hydraulics of an Inclined Ship Lift,* (in Czech), PhD Thesis, ČVUT–VÚV, Prague.

Vlček, M. (1965). Forces acting on a floating body elastically fastened in an incline tank, *Proc. 11th Congress IAHR, Leningrad,* **4,** Paper 4.20, 9 pp.

Wittmann, H. and Bleines, B. L. (1953). Kraftwerkschwalle und Schiffahrt, *Schweizerische Bauzeitung,* No. 34.

9 Models of Outfalls and Public Health Engineering Plants

9.1 General Considerations

Hydraulic laboratories all over the world have been increasingly involved in physical and mathematical modelling of hydraulic problems associated with industrial and public health engineering plants and their impact on the environment. Model studies of industrial installations are frequently connected with problems of circulation of cooling water or flow of liquids in the technological process. In the first instance the detailed design of intakes and outfalls into the recipient can follow the procedures and criteria discussed in the previous chapters. However, the interaction of the outfall with the recipient and the need to study its siting in relation to the banks and intakes requires special consideration. Model studies are necessary to minimize recirculation of heated cooling water in thermal power stations. The situation here may be complicated by the need to consider stratified systems with three layers, i.e. cold and heated salt water and fresh river water. Waste disposal in a marine environment requires the study of jet hydraulics with a number of alternatives both for the direction of the jet and the condition of the recipient (stagnant, stratified, unidirectional or tidal currents) resulting in positive and/or negative entrainment. Model studies in these cases focus on the velocity distribution in the recipient and the change of concentration within the jet as a function of distance from the effluent.

The flow of water in industrial processes can be studied on models based on the similarity criteria for flow in pipelines and open channels discussed in Chapters 5 and 6. Frequently, however, we encounter problems where the fluid is *non-Newtonian* and where the laws of rheology have to be applied.

The criteria of similarity in these cases are still, in many instances, the subject of research and their discussion is outside the scope of this book; for further reference only a limited number of basic definitions summarized in Fig. 9.1 are included here.

In Newtonian fluids the shear stress is directly proportional to the rate of angular deformation starting with zero stress at zero deformation;

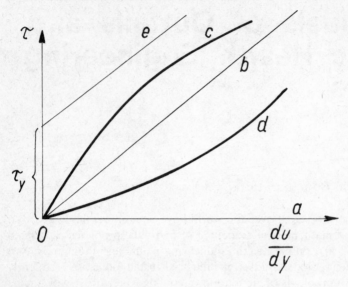

Fig. 9.1.

fluids with a variable proportionality between stress and deformation rate are called non-Newtonian; this proportionality may be variable both with the magnitude of stress and with the time of exposure to stress. In general the relationship between stress and rate of deformation can be expressed as

$$\tau = c\left(\frac{du}{dy}\right)^n \tag{9.1}$$

where c and n are constants. The apparent coefficient of dynamic viscosity μ' and the Reynolds number are in this case

$$\mu' = c\left(\frac{du}{dy}\right)^{n-1} \tag{9.2}$$

$$Re = \frac{\rho v^{(2-n)} D^n}{c\left(\frac{6n+2}{n}\right)^n} \tag{9.3}$$

According to the values of c and n we then obtain (*see* Fig. 9.1) an ideal fluid ($c = n = 0$) (a); a Newtonian fluid ($c = \mu$, $n = 1$) (b); a pseudoplastic fluid ($n < 1$) (c); and a dilatant fluid ($n > 1$) (d); the Bingham plastic fluid (e) requiring an initial stress τ_y for deformation to occur is a special case where in the ideal Bingham fluid c is a constant (μ_p) and $n = 1$. If the shear stress increases with time the fluid is rheopectic and in the opposite case it is thixotropic. Visco-plastic fluids, of course, are common in chemical industrial processes, atomic reactors, etc. Sludges and slurries are non-Newtonian fluids (often approximating the Bingham fluid).

It is evident that in model studies of flow of non-Newtonian fluids the basic properties of the fluid should be preserved even if the model fluid need not be identical with the prototype one. For example when studying the flow of the Bingham fluid in addition to the Strouhal, Euler, Froude and Reynolds numbers the Hedström number has to be taken into account

$$He = \frac{\tau_y D^2 \rho}{\mu_p^2} \tag{9.4}$$

Public health engineering works are of particular interest to the hydraulic engineer, where in some special cases non-Newtonian behaviour of fluids is also encountered. There are, however, many special cases of Newtonian flow where model research is appropriate. Because of the importance of hydraulic engineering in the design of public health engineering plants part of this chapter is devoted to model studies in this area (Section 9.4).

9.2 Basic Equations of Dispersion and Stratified Flow

It is clear that problems of diffusion and dispersion and of density currents are closely associated with modelling outfalls and public health engineering plants. Some general considerations and basic equations have therefore to be introduced at this stage.

Turbulent diffusion (molecular diffusion may usually be neglected in hydraulic engineering problems) can be described by the equation

$$\frac{\partial c}{\partial t} + u \frac{\partial c}{\partial x} - D \frac{\partial c^2}{\partial x^2} = 0 \tag{9.5}$$

resulting from the combination of Fick's law ($M = -DA\, \partial c/\partial x$) and the equation of conservation of (dissolved) matter of concentration c. In Equation (9.5) D is the diffusion coefficient applying to time averaged values of u and c in one direction (x); if additional dimensions are considered (i.e. in two- or three-dimensional flow the diffusion coefficient becomes a tensor D_{ij} and Equation (9.5) is expanded accordingly (Raudkivi and Callander, 1975). The term D/ν is sometimes described as the Schmidt number.

Due to spatial differences in temporal mean velocities, in addition to the turbulent velocity fluctuations resulting in diffusion, we get changes in concentration in time and place resulting from convection; the cumulative effect is usually referred to as (convective) *dispersion* which in three-dimensional flow can be described by the equation

$$\frac{\partial c}{\partial t} + u_1 \frac{\partial c}{\partial x} + u_2 \frac{\partial c}{\partial y} + u_3 \frac{\partial c}{\partial z} - \frac{\partial}{\partial x}\left[D_{11}\frac{\partial c}{\partial x}\right]$$

$$- \frac{\partial}{\partial y}\left[D_{22}\frac{\partial c}{\partial y}\right] - \frac{\partial}{\partial z}\left[D_{33}\frac{\partial c}{\partial z}\right] = 0 \quad (9.6)$$

where D_{11} is now the dispersion coefficient.

Adopting the procedure outlined in Chapter 2 it is evident that for the physical modelling of dispersion the following scales must apply for the dispersion coefficient:

$$M_{D_{22}} = M_{D_{11}} = M_v M_l \tag{9.7}$$

$$M_{D_{33}} = M_v M_h^2 M_l^{-1} \tag{9.8}$$

In a model operated according to the Froude law these equations result in

$$M_{D_x} = M_{D_z} = M_h^{1/2} M_l \tag{9.7'}$$

$$M_{D_y} = M_h^{5/2} M_l^{-1} \tag{9.8'}$$

It is evident from Equations (9.7) and (9.8) that a correct reproduction of the dispersion coefficients in three-dimensional flow requires an undistorted model. Further, from Equation (9.6) for steady concentration ($\partial c/\partial t = 0$) and an undistorted model, the velocity scale appears in all terms and thus similar dispersion conditions will be obtained independently of the velocity scale.

In open channel flow the dispersion coefficient is proportional to the product of depth (hydraulic radius) and shear velocity (Fischer, 1973). Thus we can write

$$M_D = M_{v_*} M_h = M_{S_e}^{1/2} M_h^{3/2} \tag{9.9}$$

If we adjust the roughness of a distorted model for $M_{S_e} = M_h/M_l$ (*see* Chapter 6) this results in

$$M_D = M_h^2 M_l^{-1/2} \tag{9.10}$$

A comparison of equations (9.7'), (9.8') and (9.10) again highlights the difficulties of modelling dispersion on a distorted model. One way of approaching similarity in special cases and small areas would be not to increase the model roughness and to operate the distorted model with $M_{S_e} = 1$ resulting in

$$M_{D_x} M_{D_y} = M_D^2 \tag{9.11}$$

allowing correct local simulation even on a distorted model.

The basic equations of *density currents* and *stratified flow* are based on continuity and the equation of motion. Thus for a two-layered system with one-dimensional flow, where suffix 1 refers to the top and suffix 2 to the bottom layer we can write

$$\frac{\partial y_1}{\partial t} + \frac{\partial(y_1 v_1)}{\partial x} = 0 \tag{9.12}$$

$$\frac{\partial y_2}{\partial t} + \frac{\partial(y_2 v_2)}{\partial x} = 0 \tag{9.13}$$

$$\frac{\partial v_1}{\partial t} + v_1 \frac{\partial v_1}{\partial x} + g \frac{\partial(y_1 + y_2)}{\partial x} + \frac{\tau_i}{\rho_1 y_1} = 0 \tag{9.14}$$

$$\frac{\partial v_2}{\partial t} + v_2 \frac{\partial v_2}{\partial x} + g \frac{\partial(y_1 + y_2)}{\partial x} + \frac{\tau_0 - \tau_i}{\rho_2 y_2} - \frac{\rho_2 - \rho_1}{\rho_2} g \frac{\partial y_1}{\partial x} = 0 \tag{9.15}$$

τ_0 and τ_i are the external (bed) and the internal (at the boundary between the two layers) shear stresses respectively.

For physical modelling the procedure in Chapter 2 leads, for $M_{y_1} = M_{y_2} = M_h$, to the Froude law and the condition $M_{\Delta\rho/\rho} = 1$. From Equations (9.14) and (9.15) or by combination of the two previous conclusions, we arrive at the condition that Fr_ρ, the Froude densimetric number, has to be the same in prototype and on the model

$$Fr_\rho = \frac{v}{\sqrt{\left(gh \frac{\Delta\rho}{\rho}\right)}} \tag{9.16}$$

$1/Fr_\rho^2$ with the velocity term referring to a vertical velocity difference is frequently denoted as the Richardson number, Ri.

$$Ri = \frac{g}{\rho} \frac{\Delta\rho/\Delta y}{(\Delta u/\Delta y)^2} \tag{9.16}$$

The Richardson number is a measure of the stability of a stratified flow; the higher Ri the more stable is the stratification.

Noting that $\tau = (\lambda/8)\rho v^2$ (Equation (5.6)) this together with the Froude law, leads back to condition $M_h/M_l = M_\lambda$ (Equation (6.9) or (III)) derived for open channel flow in Chapter 6. It must be noted, however, that this condition applies both to the friction coefficient of the boundary of the bottom layer (i.e. of the bed) and to the coefficient at the internal boundary between stratified flow, the value of which is not yet well known.

The following Section 9.3 gives some applications of the above equations and principles in models of effluent outfalls.

9.3   Models of Effluent Outfalls

9.3.1   Similarity considerations

Modelling of effluent outfalls is complicated by the fact that the effluent may disperse as a result of different mechanisms; although one may be predominant, several may be influential in many cases. For the derivation of modelling laws the various mechanisms have to be identified. The following classification summarized in Fig. 9.2 and presented by Ackers and Jaffrey (1972) can be used to identify the stages of the dispersion of a buoyant effluent:

(a) Turbulent entrainment at the effluent jet; density differences are not important, as the process is governed by the jet momentum, geometry and turbulence. The relevant criteria for modelling are therefore geometric similarity, a large enough jet Reynolds number to avoid viscous effects ($Re \geqslant 2300$) and the Froude law.

(b) Rise of the jet by buoyancy with mixing due to turbulence at the plume boundary. Clearly the same conditions as in case (a) apply with the jet Froude densimetric number (Equation (9.16)) replacing the simple Froude law, i.e.

$$M_v = M_d^{1/2} M_{\Delta\rho/\rho}^{1/2} \tag{9.17}$$

(c) The convective spread over the surface of the recipient dependent on the density difference at the origin of the spread, i.e. at boil. For a correct reproduction the densimetric Froude law has to be observed with the thickness of the buoyant layer as the length term

$$M_v = M_h^{1/2} M_{\Delta\rho/\rho}^{1/2} \tag{9.18}$$

Further the densimetric Reynolds number of the recipient has to exceed a

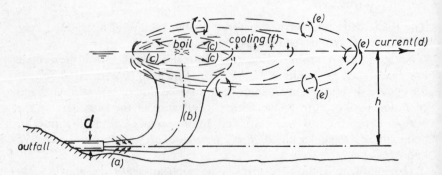

Fig. 9.2. Dispersion of a buoyant effluent. [After Ackers and Jaffrey, 1972]

limiting value which, according to Barr (1963), can be expressed as

$$\frac{\sqrt{(g\Delta\rho/\rho)}H^{5/2}}{Lv} > 150 \tag{9.19}$$

where L is the distance the convective spread will reach with a velocity given by the Froude law. Equation (9.19) frequently leads to the condition of a vertically distorted model.

(d) The mass transport of the effluent by ambient currents. The modelling of this process is governed by the laws valid for open channel flow models (*see* Chapter 6) with the model operated according to the Froude law, the ambient Reynolds number exceeding the limiting condition $(Re > Re_{sq})$, and a correct friction head loss reproduction.

(e) Diffusion and dispersion due to the turbulence of the ambient resulting in a general dilution of the effluent. From Equations (9.7) and (9.8) it follows that geometric similarity, i.e. an undistorted model of the recipient, is required to reproduce the process correctly.

(f) Loss of heat through surface cooling in case of heated effluent and bacterial and biological decay in case of sewage effluent.

The heat loss is proportional to area × time × temperature difference between the water and air and the temperature drop is proportional to mass divided by heat loss. Assuming the air temperature to be the same on the model and the prototype we must also have equal temperatures of the fluid to produce equal temperature drop. With equal model and prototype fluids and the time scale given by the Froude law, this leads to

$$1 = \frac{M_{\text{mass}}}{M_l^2 M_t} = \frac{M_l^2 M_h M_h^{1/2}}{M_l^2 M_l} = \frac{M_h^{3/2}}{M_l} \tag{9.20}$$

The modelling of surface cooling thus requires a model distorted according to Equation (9.20).

Representation of bacterial and biological decay on the model requires a tracer with a similar die-off profile, but with half-life scaled in accordance with the time scale of the model. For the Froude law this results in

$$M_{1/2\text{-life}} = M_l M_h^{-1/2} \tag{9.21}$$

In summary we see that the reproduction of stages (a), (b) and (e) require a geometrically similar, reasonably large undistorted model with $M_{\Delta\rho/\rho}$ usually chosen as 1. Stages (c) and (f), on the other hand, require a distorted model. The reproduction of stage (d), mass transport of the effluent by the ambient current, is compatible with both types of models. Bacterial and biological decay is usually neglected in physical models which use a conservative tracer; however even with this simplification the above analysis results in incompatibilities which can be resolved only by either the acceptance of scale effects or by the use of two models (undistorted for the near field, stages (a) and (b) and distorted for stages (c) and (d)). Even in this case the dispersion and diffusion would not be modelled correctly; fortunately this stage is often not of decisive importance in the outfall design and a combination of physical and mathematical modelling may be adopted.

9.3.2 Outfalls

The effectiveness of the outfall will depend on all the stages (a) to (f) discussed in Sub-section 9.3.1 (*see* Fig. 9.2). The detailed design of the outfall, however, can only influence the first three stages and primarily the first two stages characterized by the term 'initial dilution' (at the surface). For a jet with a sufficiently high Reynolds number, where viscous effects may be neglected, this initial dilution will be a function of the ratio of the depth of submergence and the jet diameter, of the jet densimetric Froude number and of the ratio of the ambient and jet velocities. For discharge into still water only the first two parameters are relevant. Thus the design of the outfall can substantially increase the initial dilution by either increasing the depth of the outfall (e.g., by extending it), or by reducing the jet diameter for a constant jet velocity (by increasing the number of outlets), or by increasing the jet velocity (by reducing the size of the outlets), or, finally, by using a combination of all these methods.

The most effective way of increasing initial dilution is by the use of a diffuser section with a number of outlet ports. The spacing of the outlets must be sufficient to ensure that there is no interference between adjacent plumes. The velocity of flow in all parts of the diffuser should be sufficiently high to prevent deposition of particles remaining after primary sedimentation, i.e. usually at least 0.5 m/s. All ports of the diffuser should flow full in order to prevent the intrusion of sea water. The outlet ports are usually circular holes at least 150 mm in diameter, with the inside edges well rounded. The number of outlet ports required is determined by the minimum size (150 mm diameter) together with the minimum velocity given by the densimetric Froude number $\geqslant 1$ and the minimum discharge; at the same time the total area of all ports should be smaller than the area of flow of the outfall. Conical devices attached to single or multiple outlet systems introduce a substantial pre-dilution, with a reduction of the subsequent dilution effect.

More detailed information about design procedures may be obtained from the following references: Abraham (1974), Agg (1978), Brooks (1960), Cederwall (1968), Hydraulic Research Station (1977), Rawn, *et al.* (1960), and particularly Gameson (1974).

Models of outfalls have been built in many laboratories, some concentrating on the detail of design and some attempting to model the overall process. In many cases special instrumentation has been developed (Dedow, 1965), e.g., the Hydraulics Research Station salinity probe capable of measuring salinity within a few millimeters volume and producing a voltage proportional to that salinity (0 to 35 parts per thousand) independent of water temperature. Special model temperature control systems have been developed for models of heated effluents and thermistors are used for temperature survey on the model.

A problem common to both field and laboratory measurements is the acquisition of sufficient data over a short time particularly where the recipient is a tidal reach. Apart from traditional methods of sampling field data, airborne infra-red techniques have been developed for obtaining surface isotherms over large areas.

For modelling of outfalls it is also interesting to compare density differences produced by salinity differences and temperature differences. Sea water with 32 ppt of dissolved salts has a density difference compared with freshwater of approximately 0.026 kg/1. The same density difference corresponds to a freshwater effluent at 78°C flowing into a freshwater ambient at 14°C. The difference, however, is that the relationship between the density difference and salinity for a fresh/saline jet is linear, whereas for a thermal jet it is non-linear with the result that the thermal jet is somewhat less buoyant at the same level of dilution. This difference becomes important when modelling effluents with a significant current in the recipient, as the jet does not rise steeply in this instance and the rates of dilution are higher than in the case where the ambient is (almost) stationary.

Figure 9.3 is an example of an undistorted model ($M_l = 25$) of an outfall from a sewage treatment plant into a tidal (saline) estuary. The study was carried out by Novak and Featherstone in the laboratory of the Department of Civil Engineering at the University of Newcastle upon Tyne and only a small part of the recipient was modelled as the main purpose of the study was to assess the interaction of the outflow and the nearby jetties and the effect of tidal levels and flows on the jet behaviour and dispersion. Density differences were reproduced on the model, which was operated according to the Froude law, and in the dispersion study tidal oscillations were reproduced as a series of steady state conditions. Freshwater was used for the jet and a saline solution for the recipient, which could be recirculated to model the ambient velocity. The discharge corresponding to the outflow was pumped to waste, and care was taken to maintain the salinity of the recipient during each experiment. A salinity probe was used to study the dispersion.

Figure 9.4 shows studied outfall positions and sampling points on a model of the Dee Estuary built at the Hydraulics Research Station, Wallingford (Ackers and Jaffrey, 1972). The model, built mainly for the study of the effect of estuary shapes, modified by a crossing scheme, on

Fig. 9.3. Model of an outfall from a treatment plant (University of Newcastle upon Tyne).

the bed configuration was adjusted to a saline model with $M_l = 1500$ and $M_h = 100$ for a pilot study of the extent of effluent movement from an outfall. Although the study was mainly qualitative some quantitative results were attempted by compounding the effects of flow characteristics at the outlet, the depth of water over the outlet and the density difference of the estuary and effluent, to give a derived constant dilution factor of 20. A dye solution diluted with saline water was introduced through a spreading device maintained just above the water surface and samples were withdrawn from various model points by a syringe for evaluation of dye intensity.

9.4 Models of Public Health Engineering Plants

9.4.1 Subject of research and similarity considerations

The reasons for model studies in connection with the design of water supply and treatment works are both economic and scientific. With the large and increasing investments in public health engineering works the savings achieved in construction and/or operational costs of one plant when applied to many others of the same design can amount to very large sums. Further, the fairly recently acquired knowledge of complicated flow

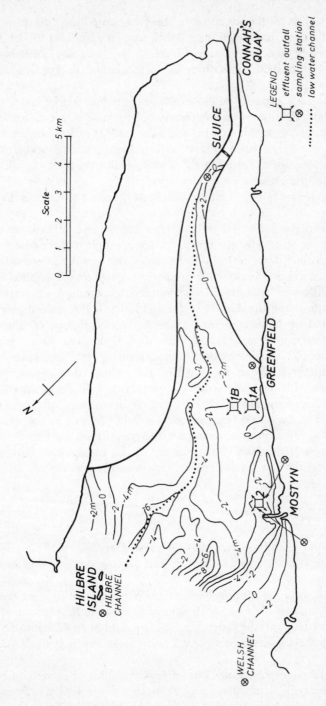

Fig. 9.4. Area of a model of the Dee Estuary with outfall and sampling points. [After Ackers and Jaffrey, 1972]

phenomena such as density currents and two-phase flow, turbulence and diffusion, flow of non-Newtonian fluids, etc., permits the modelling of many processes used in treatment plants. It also has to be borne in mind that the design in these cases often has to accommodate flow in a complicated geometry.

New materials used in public health engineering works require new hydraulic investigations. The complexity of hydraulic problems associated with the design of treatment works and the endeavours to solve some of them with the aid of scale models require measurements both for data acquisition and for verification of model results on pilot or full scale plants often using special instrumentation.

When modelling public health installations there are three possibilities:

(a) The prototype has clean water (water supply installations) or water with only some suspended matter (some water supply and treatment units or strongly diluted wastes). In these cases the standard methods and similarity criteria and limits used in previous chapters are applicable.

(b) The prototype contains a substantial concentration of suspended particles influencing the density of the fluid, whilst the viscosity remains little affected or unaffected. For example, the coefficient of kinematic viscosity of sewage is usually the same as that of clean water which is about 6°C cooler. Sedimentation tanks, clarifiers, etc., are examples of these installations. When investigating the overall flow conditions we usually work with the same criteria of similarity as in the previous case; for detailed investigations of, e.g., the sedimentation process, other criteria have to be added (*see* Sub-section 9.4.3) as well as the similarity of density currents and buoyancy, i.e. the identity of the Froude densimetric number (Equation (9.16)), observed. In cases where surface renewal and liquid film coefficients are involved the identity of Sherwood number

$$Sh = K_L \frac{d_b}{D_m} \tag{9.22}$$

on model and prototype must be observed. Here K_L is the liquid film coefficient, d_b the air bubble diameter and D_m the coefficient of molecular diffusion.

(c) The prototype fluid is non-Newtonian. When modelling, e.g., the flow in digesters and of sludges which usually behave as Bingham fluid (but also exhibit pseudoplastic properties), the model has to take into account the laws of rheology (*see* Section 9.1 and Equations (9.1) to (9.4)).

In the following paragraphs only a few examples of models of public health engineering installations will be given and some similarity aspects highlighted. Further details may be found in the references.

9.4.2 Sewer interceptors

Model investigation of storm water separators (interceptors) in combined sewers (carrying foul and rain water) is a typical example of studies of public health engineering structures where standard methods and scaling laws (i.e. the Froude law) are applied. If Q_p is the discharge to be conveyed during a flood, Q, into the treatment plant, then Q_r is the discharge to the recipient without treatment ($Q = Q_r + Q_p$). Q_p is determined by the dry weather flow in the recipient, the biological oxygen demand (BOD) in the recipient above the sewer outlet, the permissible load below the treatment plant and the population equivalent served by the sewer network. The aim of the design is to ensure that up to the flow Q_p the whole discharge through the sewer is conveyed to the treatment plant, and that for higher discharges the flow into the plant does not exceed the maximum Q_p, and that all excess flow is discharged into the recipient (Q_r).

Since we are concentrating on large discharges through the sewer during which the flow is very strongly diluted, the use of clean water in laboratory investigations is justified and the results may be extrapolated into prototype without difficulty if all limiting conditions valid for research on overflows and structures have been observed. For simultaneous modelling of parts of the sewer we must observe the conditions of similarity for discharge in pressure systems or open channels (*see* Chapters 5 and 6).

In engineering practice a number of different separators are used, the most important of which are side weirs, gravity, and vortex interceptors. A storm water separator, especially in combination with a mixing chamber, is a very complex installation from the hydraulic viewpoint and can often be only partly designed by calculation. For atypical or more important structures model studies are advisable. When studying the function of interceptors the flow of water as well as the movement of solids and suspended particles should be studied (Ackers, *et al.*, 1967).

The following examples illustrate some of the problems studied on models of interceptors. A gravity chamber, the original design of which is shown in Fig. 9.5a, was investigated on a model ($M_l = 3$) and changed to the type in Fig. 9.5b (Kutiš (1958)). Figure 9.5c compares the function of both separators. It is evident that the original design started functioning only for discharges above 150% of the design discharge and for the maximum discharge the flow to the treatment plant was 2.25 times greater than the maximum considered in the design. Figure 9.5c also shows the improvement attained by the change in the design. The resultant design is not only hydraulically more effective but also simpler and cheaper.

Model studies may result in a complete change of the interceptor type.

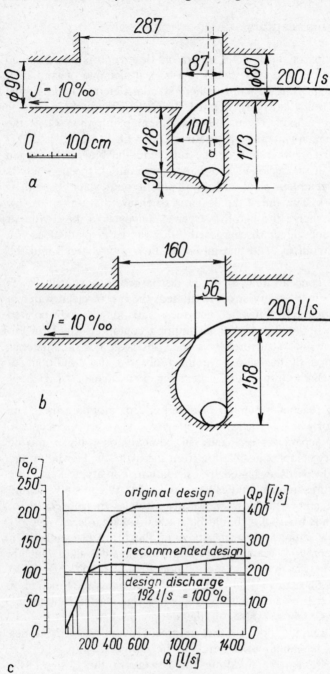

Fig. 9.5. Gravity interceptor. [Kutiš, 1958]

Fig. 9.6. Model of a sewer interceptor (original design). [Čábelka and Novák, 1964]

Thus the original design of a side weir and mixing chamber (Fig. 9.6) was changed on the basis of a model study ($M_l = 4.5$) to a centrifugal separator (Fig. 9.7). The maximum flow to the treatment plant was reduced from 590 l/s in the original design (instead of the intended 265 l/s) to 353 l/s. Although the resultant design in the given case is somewhat more complicated than the original one, the performance was greatly improved and by eliminating the mixing chamber construction costs were reduced.

9.4.3 Sedimentation tanks

Model studies of sedimentation tanks are usually pursued in one of the following three directions:

(a) Model studies of distribution systems and inlet structures. No attempts are made to model the density effects and models usually operate

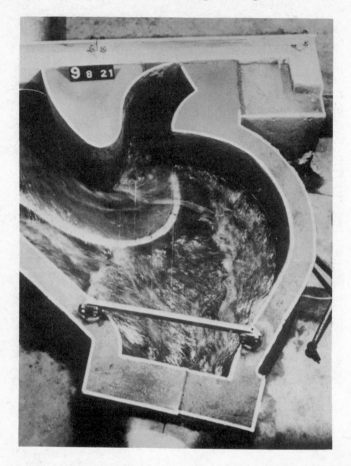

Fig. 9.7. Model of a sewer interceptor (new design). [Čábelka and Novák, 1964]

according to the Froude law with fully turbulent flow (*see* Chapter 6). The aim of the model studies is to aid the design of inlets, which should spread the inflow evenly and over as short a distance as possible throughout the tank cross-section, at the same time achieving effective energy dissipation of the inflow without erosion of the settled bed in the tank. In the tests various designs are usually compared by measuring velocity distribution and turbulence levels, and by using flow visualization methods.

(b) Model studies of the overall function of settling tanks. Here the general flow picture, circulation, tendency for the formation of 'dead corners' or density currents, etc., are usually studied. Apart from flow visualization, tracer experiments used for the estimation of retention time are most effective. The ratios of the time of the first appearance, the peak

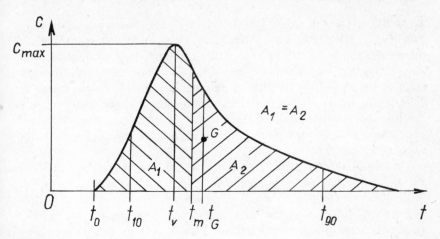

Fig. 9.8.

or the median of the tracer concentration to the theoretical retention time t_t (given by the ratio of the settling tank volume to the discharge) Fig. 9.8, are a measure of the tank performance. A very low value of t_0/t_t indicates 'short circuiting' of the tank and $t_G/t_t < 1$ indicates 'dead regions'; t_m/t_t should approach the value of t_G/t_t but not exceed it (because of secondary currents); t_G/t_t is usually 0.7 to 0.9; $t_{90}/t_{10} < 2$ is an indication of a fairly good sedimentation tank.

(c) Studies of detailed performance of settling tanks with sediment fed into the model. The scaling laws are not fully elucidated and some contradictory results are reported. Nevertheless it is clear that the laws governing the modelling of density currents on geometrically similar models must be applicable bearing in mind the criteria for the settling velocity of suspensions.

In settling tank design the surface loading or overflow rate is one of the main controlling factors (based on the classic Hazen theory) leading to the employment of the Hazen number Ha in modelling where

$$Ha = \frac{Q}{Aw} \tag{9.23}$$

and A is the surface area of the tank.

As the Reynolds number of flow for prototype tanks is often smaller than the value of Re_{sq} for fully turbulent open channel flow (Equation (6.22)), the use of the Froude flow number for scaling can lead to very small model Reynolds numbers. However as long as $Re_m > R_{cr}$ ($Re_{cr} = vh/v \simeq 850$) good results from model investigations have been reported by some researchers. A criterion, based on the Moody (or

Zegzhda) graph with $Re_m > 14h/(k\sqrt{\lambda}) \approx 0.22 Re_{sq}$ was quoted; *see* Equation (6.22): (Burdych, 1962). Because of the small values of Reynolds numbers the use of the Reynolds law for modelling settling tanks has been suggested (e.g., Clements and Khattab, 1968). However, this is not suitable for modelling the flow at inlets and retention times, where the Froude number is more appropriate. As results obtained with the use of the Reynolds law are not very encouraging, it is better to try to work with the Froude law making sure that the model is large enough for predominantly turbulent flow.

Thompson (1969) investigating the scaling law for sedimentation in rectangular tanks using two tanks of scale $M_l = 3$ (the larger tank was 3.00×1.00 m and 0.60 m deep) and feeding powder in concentrations $100 < C_i' < 1500$ mg/l at the inlet, found that good results (expressed as ratio of concentrations at exit and inlet) for the two models were obtained independently of the flow Froude or Reynolds numbers as long as the identity of the Hazen number and Froude densimetric number $\left(= \dfrac{\rho v_i^2}{C_i' g L} \right)$ was preserved.

It has been shown in Chapter 6 that the use of the Rouse criterion (Equation (6.56)) for the same values of κ on model and prototype, coupled with the equation for sedimentation velocity w (Equation (6.53)), leads to the same condition (VI) (Equation (6.41′)) as for the incipient motion of bedload. However, this implied larger suspended particles where the effect of viscosity was negligible ($W = $ const. in Equation (6.53)). The equation

$$M_w = M_{S_e}^{1/2} M_h^{1/2} \tag{9.24}$$

which follows from the Rouse criterion leads, for $M_\lambda = 1$ and the Froude law, to:

$$M_w = M_v \tag{9.25}$$

i.e. a single velocity scale for sedimentation and flow. In principle it would thus be possible to use a distorted model with larger diameter suspensions.

Combining Equations (9.25) and (6.53), for the whole range of particles, together with the Froude law leads to the identity of the Stokes number

$$St = \frac{\rho_s}{\rho} \frac{d}{h} \frac{1}{C_D} \tag{9.26}$$

on model and prototype, where C_D is the drag coefficient which is a function of wd/ν and the grain shape. For the same value of C_D on model and prototype the condition $wd/v > 20$ applies, which, for water and sediment specific gravity $S_S = 2.65$, results in $d > 0.5$ mm.

Larsen (1977) gives a full discussion of problems encountered in the analysis of the hydraulic performance of rectangular settling tanks.

Figure 9.9 is an example of a model study of inlets into circular sedimentation tanks (Burdych, 1962) where on a model of scale $M_l = 5$ only a segment corresponding to one sixth of the whole tank and only two thirds of the total length was built. The reason for this procedure was that the flow throughout the depth of the tank was observed with the use of tracers and that the emphasis was on the inlet design. The whole of the inlet was reproduced on the model but five sixths of the inflow was drawn off by an overflow at the opposite side to the segment. The model was operated according to the Froude law; even if the lowest Reynolds number was close to the critical value, the diverging shape and the inlet screen were enough to ensure a sufficient degree of turbulence. The model showed that a stilling cylinder, which is often used around the inlet, is not suitable as it directs the flow to the bed, and that a baffle reaching to only about 40% of the depth below the surface and screens arranged in two concentric circles around the sludge pit are preferable. The performance of the tank was primarily influenced by the inlet whereas the arrangement of the overflow troughs (outflow) was hardly of any importance.

Fig. 9.9. Model of an inlet into a circular tank. [Burdych, 1962]

9.4.4 Miscellaneous

The scale of treatment plants and their units is continuously increasing; this again brings specific problems which require hydraulic research. The increase in the size and power requirements of *mixing vessels* and associated equipment used in the process industries and sewage treatment has led to the laboratory investigation of mixing vessels and of vibration and fatigue failure of their mechanical parts. Scale models are used to investigate flow patterns round the baffles and paddles of mixing vessels using both Newtonian and non-Newtonian fluids and drag reducing polymers (Irving, *et al.*, 1978). The scale-up from models to prototype is difficult and the best method is to use a series of models to determine scale effects.

Laboratory studies of the performance of *aeration tanks* have to deal with the complexity of flow in mixing tanks with the added problem of characterizing the airflow in the fluid, including surface tension and liquid film effects, and in the case of diffusers also the modelling of the rising plume. The effect of aeration at hydraulic structures (weirs, gates, stepped cascades) on *oxygen transfer* has been investigated on laboratory models with encouraging results as the detailed analysis of surface tension, contact time, temperature, and liquid film effects can be 'side-stepped' and included in the effect on the resultant oxygen deficit ratio, r, and in additional coefficients.

Thus Avery and Novak (1978) showed that an equation applicable to solid (not disintegrated) jets falling into a downstream pool and based on the jet Froude and Reynolds numbers at jet impact, gave results which correlated well various laboratory and prototype data:

$$r - 1 = kFr^{1.78}Re^{0.53} \tag{9.27}$$

where

$$r = \frac{C_s - C_u}{C_s - C_d} \qquad Fr = \left(\frac{gh^3}{2q_J^2}\right)^{0.25}$$

$Re = q_J/v$, and k = coefficient dependent on the salinity of the water. (C_s, C_u and C_d are dissolved oxygen concentrations at saturation, upstream and downstream of the structure; h is the height of fall and q_J the jet water discharge per unit perimeter at impact).

Tebbutt, *et al.* (1977) developed design charts for the reaeration performance of stepped cascades again using the oxygen deficit ratio, r, as a measure. The results of these studies can be used to compare the aeration capacity of overfalls and cascades with turbine, U-tube or surface aerators and to show (Avery and Novak, 1978) that the efficiencies of an overfall or cascade (in kgO_2/kwh) are competitive with artificial aeration devices.

Other laboratory studies dealt with the oxygen transfer in rotating *biological filters* (Ouano, 1978). It was shown that the parameters most influencing the result were the ratio of the surface of the tank and the area of the contact media, and a modified Reynolds number expressed as $D^2 w/v$, where D is the diameter of the disc and ω the angular velocity of the contact media. Laboratory studies of percolating biological filters (Borghei, 1977) showed that the exit age distribution represents the function of the filter better than the mean retention time and resulted in the formulation of a flow model.

Models of *pump intakes and sumps* have been investigated in several laboratories. The criteria for the prevention and modelling of vortices were discussed in Chapter 7 (Section 7.1). A recent comprehensive study by Prosser (1977) resulted in the following recommendations for the optimum design of a pump sump with the lowest overall volume (D is the bellmouth diameter): floor clearance—$0.5D$; endwall clearance—$0.75D$; width—$2D$; submergence—at least $1.5D$; and total sump depth—at least $2.1D$.

References

Abraham, G. (1965). Horizontal jets in stagnant fluid of other density, *Proc. ASCE, J. Hydraul. Div.*, **91,** No. HY4, pp. 139–154.

Abraham, G. (1971). *The Flow of Round Buoyant Jets Issuing Vertically into Ambient Fluid*, Publication No. 81, Delft Hydraulics Laboratory, Delft.

Abraham, G. (1974). *Jets and Plumes Issuing into Stratified Fluid*, Publication No. 141, Delft Hydraulics Laboratory, Delft.

Ackers, P. and Jaffrey, L. J. (1972). The applicability of hydraulic models to pollution studies, *Symposium on Mathematical and Modelling of Estuarine Pollution*, Paper No. 16, Water Pollution Research Laboratory, Stevenage.

Ackers, P., Harrison, A. J. M. and Brewer, A. J. (1967). Laboratory studies of storm overflows with unsteady flow, *Symposium on Storm Sewage Overflows*, Paper No. 4, ICE, London.

Agg, A. R. (1978). *Investigations of sewage discharges to some British coastal waters*, Technical Report 99, Water Research Centre, Medmenham.

Angelin, S. and Flagestad, K. (1957). An investigation of intake arrangement for cooling water supply in stratified seawater, *Proc. 7th General Meeting IAHR, Lisbon*, **I,** Paper C13, 14 pp.

Anwar, H. O. (1969). The behaviour of the buoyant jet in calm fluid, *Proc. ASCE, J. Hydraul. Div.*, **95,** No. HY4, paper No. 14190, pp. 1521–1540.

Avery, S. and Novak, P. (1977). Modelling of oxygen transfer from air entrained by solid jets entering a free water recipient, *Proc 17th Congress IAHR, Baden-Baden*, **I,** Paper A59, pp. 467–474.

Avery, S. and Novak, P. (1978). Oxygen transfer at hydraulic structures, *Proc. ASCE, J. Hydraul. Div.* **104,** No. HY11, paper No. 14190, pp. 1521–1540.

Barr, D. I. H. (1964). Hydraulic considerations in model studies of sedimentation tanks, *J. IPHE*, pp. 175–182.

Barr, D. I. H. (1963, 1967). Densimetric exchange flow in rectangular channels, *La Houille Blanche*, pp. 739–766 (1963), pp. 619–632 (1967).

Bartlett, R. E. (1974). *Pumping Stations for Water and Sewage*, Applied Science Publishers, London.

Borghei, S. M. (1977). *The Effect of Hydraulic Factors on the Efficiency of Organic Transfer in a Percolating Filter*, Ph.D Thesis, University of Newcastle upon Tyne.

Brooks, N. H. (1960). Diffusion of sewage effluent in an ocean current. *Proc. First International Conference on Waste Disposal in the Marine Environment*, Pergamon Press, Oxford, pp. 246–267.

Burdych, J. (1962). Research of flow at the inlet into a circular sedimentation tank, (in Czech), *Vodní hospodářství*, 1, pp. 5–9.

Čábelka, J. and Novák, P. (1964). *Hydraulic Research 1—Research on Models*, (in Czech), SNTL, Prague.

Camp, T. R. (1945). Sedimentation and the design of settling tanks, *Trans. ASCE*, **111**, Paper 2285, p. 895.

Cederwall, K. (1968). Hydraulics of Marine Waste Disposal, Report No. 42, *Chalmers Institute of Technology*, Goteburg.

Clements, M. S. and Khattab, A. F. M. (1968). Research into time ratio in radial flow sedimentation tanks, *Proc. ICE*, **40**, Paper 7104, pp. 471–474.

Crickmore, M. J. (1972). Tracer tests of eddy diffusion in field and model, *Proc. ASCE, J. Hydraul. Div.*, **98**, No. HY10, pp. 1737–1752.

Dedow, H. R. A. (1965). The control of hydraulic models, *The Engineer*, February, part I pp. 259–263; part II pp. 301–304.

Fischer, H. B. (1973). Longitudinal dispersion and turbulent mixing in open channel flow, *Annual Review of Fluid Mechanics*, **5**, pp. 59–78.

Gameson, A. L. H. (Ed.) (1974). *Discharge of Sewage from Sea Outfalls, Proceedings of an International Symposium, Water Research Centre*, Pergamon Press, Oxford

Grace, R. A. (1978). *Marine Outfall Systems—Planning, Design and Construction*. Prentice Hall Inc., London and New York.

Harleman, D. R. F. and Elder, R. A. (1965). Withdrawal from two-layer stratified flows, *Proc. ASCE, J. Hydraul. Div.*, **91**, pp. 43–58.

Holley, E. R. (1969). Unified view of dispersion and diffusion, *Proc. ASCE, J. Hydraul. Div.*, **95**, No. HY2, pp. 621–631.

Hydraulics Research Station. (1977). *Horizontal Outfalls in Flowing Water*, Report No. EX763, HRS, Wallingford.

Ingersoll, A. C., McKee, J. E. and Brooks, N. H. (1956). Fundamental concepts of rectangular settling tanks, *Trans. ASCE*, **121**, Paper 2837, p. 1179.

Irving, J., King, R. and Bull, D. (1978). Mixing studies in a large-scale sludge digester, *The Chemical Engineer*, November, pp. 831–832.

Kutiš, L. (1958). Model studies of gravity separators, (in Czech), *Vodní hospodářství*, No. 10, pp. 314–317.

Larsen, P. (1977). On the Hydraulics of Rectangular Settling Basins, Report No. 1001, Lund Institute of Technology, Lund.

Lau, L. and Krishnappan, G. (1977). Transverse dispersion in rectangular channels, *Proc. ASCE, J. Hydraul. Div.*, **103**, No. HY10, pp. 1173–1189.

McDowell, D. M. (1975). Sediment induced density currents, *Proc. 16th Congress IAHR, Sao Paulo*, **3**, Paper C62, pp. 524–531.

Miller, D. G. (1964). Sedimentation. A review of published work, *Water and Water Engineering*, February, pp. 52–58.

Novak, P. (1977). Some aspects of hydraulic research in relation to the design of water supply and treatment works, Invited lecture, *Proc. 17th Congress IAHR, Baden-Baden*, **6**, pp. 351–358.

Ohlmeyer, F. T. (1977). Scaling of physical models with dispersion problems, *Proc. 17th Congress IAHR, Baden-Baden*, Paper B2, **3**, pp. 9–13.

Ouano, E. A. R. (1978). Oxygen mass transfer scale up in rotating biological filters, *Water Research*, **12**, pp. 1005–1008.

Prosser, M. J. (1977). *The Hydraulic Design of Pump Sumps and Intakes*, BHRA Fluid Engineering, Cranfield, UK.

Rajaratnam, N. (1976). *Turbulent Jets*, Elsevier Scientific Publ. Co., Amsterdam.

Raudkivi, A. J. and Callander, R. A. (1975). *Advanced Fluid Mechanics*, Edward Arnold, London.

Rawn, A. M., Bowerman, F. R. and Brooks, N. H. (1960). Diffusers for disposal of sewage in seawater, *Proc. ASCE, J. Sanitary Engineering Div.*, **86**, No. SW2, pp. 65–105.

Smisson, B. (1967). Design, construction and performance of vortex overflows, *Symposium on Storm Sewage Overflows*, Paper 8, pp. 99–110, ICE, London.

Stefan, H. (1970). Modelling spread of heated water over a lake, *Proc. ASCE, J. Power Div.* **96**, No. PO3, pp. 469–482.

Tebbutt, T. H. Y., Essery, T. S. and Rasaratnam, S. K. (1977). Reaeration performance of stepped cascades, *J. Inst. Water Engrs Sci.* **31**, No. 4, pp. 285–297.

Tesařík, L. (1954). Discussion of the gravity and diffusion theory of motion of suspended particles, (in Czech), *Sovětská věda—vodní stavitelství*, No. 1.

Thompson, D. M. (1969). Scaling laws for continuous flow sedimentation in rectangular tanks. *Proc. ICE Technical Note* 11, **43**, London, pp. 453–461.

Twort, A. C., Hoather, R. G. and Law, F. M. (1974). *Water Supply*, 2nd Edn, Edward Arnold, London.

Vreugdenhill, C. B. (1977). *Use of Computers for Hydraulic Engineering Problems*, Publication No. 185, Delft Hydraulics Laboratory, Delft.

Vries, A. H. de (1974). *Hydraulic Aspects of Cooling Water Systems for Thermal Power Plants*, Publication No. 136, Delft Hydraulics Laboratory, Delft.

White, J. B. (1970). *The Design of Sewers and Sewage Treatment Works*, Edward Arnold, London.

10 Models of Estuaries, Coastal and Maritime Engineering Works

10.1 General

The objectives of models of estuaries, coastal engineering works and maritime structures are manifold: they include investigations of the effect of tides, currents and wave action on coastal and estuarine morphology, beach formation and littoral drift, studies of coastal protection, land reclamation works and harbours, of the effect of dredging and dredging techniques, of the development of tidal and wave power utilization, etc. The interaction of structures with the sea bed and currents resulting in local erosion as well as the study of forces exerted by all types of waves under different conditions, form an important area of research in connection with the design of off-shore structures.

The wide scope of research objectives as well as the scale of engineering works and operations at sea give an additional stimulus to research on all aspects of wave hydraulics and above all stress the need for prototype wave and other field data as the basis for model studies.

It is only natural that the greatest development of tidal models has been in countries with an extensive coastline, e.g., Great Britain, the Netherlands, France, U.S.A., etc. Historically it was particularly research work in Great Britain which, together with the studies of Osborne Reynolds, formed the basis of subsequent development of estuarine scale models (Allen, 1947). In 1885 Reynolds built a model of part of the Mersey estuary using scales $M_l = 31\,800$ and $M_h = 960$ with a distortion of approximately 33. Although the original aim was to demonstrate the circulation of water in the estuary the investigations proved fundamental to the development of similarity and scaling procedures. Soon a larger model ($M_l = 10\,560$) with a distortion of about 27 followed. In 1888 Vernon-Harcourt built a model of the Seine estuary (to study methods of improving navigation) with a horizontal scale $M_l = 40\,000$ and distortion 100.

After these pioneering studies and a number of other attempts at constructing tidal models (Wheeler, Cruttwell, McClure—Bombay harbour tidal model) model studies of the Severn estuary were initiated at Manchester University by Gibson in 1926; these are described in detail by Allen (1947). The original model of about 135 km of the estuary was built to a horizontal scale $M_l = 8500$ and vertical scale $M_h = 100$; this was later changed to $M_h = 200$. The distortion was therefore 85 and 42.5. The main objective of the model investigations was to study the effect of a proposed tidal barrage on the regime of the estuary.

There followed tidal models of the Mersey, Humber, Dee and Parrett estuaries, which elucidated problems of simulation of silt and salinity. These studies together with the subsequent development of hydraulics and modelling techniques laid the foundation for the present large tidal models of the Rhine, Thames, Scheldt and many other estuarine and coastal engineering models all over the world.

Because of the nature of the model investigations special methods and instrumentation have frequently to be introduced; wave tanks and wave and tide generators are used (*see* Section 10.3). In large models the effect of the rotation of the earth on currents (geostrophic acceleration of the flow) has to be simulated by the use of 'Coriolis tops' (*see* Sub-section 10.2.2). The full range of instrumentation briefly described in Chapter 4 and extensive data processing facilities are often required.

The area covered by a single model study of coastal regions is steadily increasing. As the model boundaries have to be taken sufficiently far away not to affect the changes in the region under consideration it is not surprising that physical tidal models in spite of large distortions and large values of horizontal scales require very large laboratory areas and even the construction of special halls (e.g. the model of the Eastern Scheldt of the Delft Hydraulic Laboratory at de Voorst in the Netherlands, covers an area of $180 \times 80 \ m^2$).

The modelling procedure for some models of estuaries and of, e.g., locks situated between salt and fresh water areas has to take into account the density difference between fresh and sea water and the resulting density currents and stratification (*see* Section 9.2).

Because of the complications and often great cost of tidal, coastal and maritime models, mathematical models are particularly important in this field and are increasingly being used. The degree of schematization required in mathematical models makes them a useful tool particularly in studies of overall effects over large areas. These investigations are often followed by studies using scale models and dealing with more detailed aspects of the problem or more restricted areas. Such 'hybrid' modelling can lead to very good results particularly if the complexity of the problem can be expressed mathematically only with a great degree of approximation. Both mathematical and scale models have to rely on good prototype data (*see* Sub-section 6.4.1 and Chapter 12).

10.2 Basic Equations of Wave Motion and Similarity Considerations

10.2.1 Basic equations of wave and tidal motion

A brief statement only of some of the basic equations for oscillatory waves is given here. These equations, together with the equations of unsteady flow and sediment transport given in Chapter 6, form the basis of the similarity criteria and design of tidal, coastal and maritime models. A fuller treatment of the equations of motion may be found in more specialized textbooks (Stoker, 1957).

The general equation for the celerity c of an oscillatory (periodic) wave is

$$c = \sqrt{\left(\left(\frac{gL}{2\pi} + \frac{2\sigma\pi}{\rho L}\right)\tanh\frac{2\pi h}{L}\right)} \tag{10.1}$$

where L is the wave length and h the depth. The influence of surface tension σ can be neglected in prototype waves simplifying Equation (10.1) to the 'Stokesian' gravity wave equation

$$c = \sqrt{\left(\frac{gL}{2\pi}\tanh\frac{2\pi h}{L}\right)} \tag{10.2}$$

For the assumption of negligible influence of surface tension to be valid $gL/2\pi \gg 2\sigma\pi/\rho L$. For $gL/2\pi < \sigma\pi/\rho L$ the influence of surface tension is dominant signifying capillary waves. Thus for gravity waves

$$L \gg \sqrt{\left(\frac{4\pi^2\sigma}{g\rho}\right)} \gg 0.017\,\text{m} \tag{10.3}$$

taking σ for the air–water interface as 0.075 N/m. If $h < 0.05L$ in Equation (10.2), the function $\tanh 2\pi h/L \simeq 2\pi h/L$ and

$$c = \sqrt{(gh)} \tag{10.4}$$

Equation (10.4) is the equation for the celerity of a *shallow water* wave or *long wave*. If, on the other hand, $h > 0.5L$ then $\tanh 2\pi h/L \simeq 1$ and

$$c = \sqrt{\left(\frac{gL}{2\pi}\right)} \tag{10.5}$$

Equation (10.5) signifies a *deep* water or *short* wave. For $0.05L < h < 0.5L$ the full Equation (10.2) must be used.

The wave length L and the wave celerity c are linked by the equation

$$L = cT \tag{10.6}$$

where T is the wave period ($2\pi/T$ is the wave frequency). Equations

(10.2), (10.5) and (10.6) can be used to calculate the wave length L and celerity c of an originally deep water wave of a known period T and wave length L_0 or celerity c_0 as it approaches the shore. As the wave period T must remain constant throughout it follows that:

$$c = c_0 \tan h \frac{2\pi h}{L_0} \frac{c_0}{c} \tag{10.7}$$

Equation (10.7) can be rewritten as

$$\frac{2\pi h}{L_0} = \frac{c}{c_0} \ln \sqrt{\left(\frac{c_0+c}{c_0-c}\right)} \tag{10.7'}$$

For any value of depth h and c_0 and L_0 (or T), c (and L) can be found from Equations (10.7) and (10.7').

The kinetic energy of one wavelength per unit width of wave crest is given by

$$E_k = \tfrac{1}{16} H^2 \gamma L, \tag{10.8}$$

where H is the wave height; the total energy (kinetic and potential) is twice this value. Figure 10.1 is a diagrammatic representation of the estimated relative ocean wave energy, wave period and respective generating forces (Sorensen, 1978).

It is evident from the above equations that as the wave approaches the shore its length, and therefore celerity, must decrease ($\tan h\, 2\pi h/L < 1$).

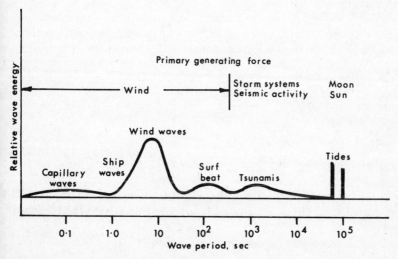

Fig. 10.1. Ocean wave energy. [After Sorensen, 1978]

The orbital velocity v' of a particle and the wave height H are linked by the equation

$$v'_y = \frac{\dfrac{2\pi}{T} H \cosh \dfrac{2\pi}{L} y}{2 \sinh \dfrac{2\pi}{L} h} \cos \left(\frac{2\pi}{T} t - \frac{2\pi}{L} x \right) \tag{10.9}$$

In modelling the effect of oscillatory waves their deformations have to be taken into account. These are, particularly, wave *refraction* and wave *diffraction* (due to an obstacle; *see* Sub-section 10.4.1).

The tidal motion in estuaries with complicated boundaries and density stratification and currents can be very complex and extremely difficult to express mathematically. In principle, however, and for the purpose of modelling, the tidal motion is described by the equation for unsteady flow in open channels, i.e. the continuity equation

$$\frac{\partial A}{\partial t} + \frac{\partial Q}{\partial l} = 0 \tag{6.32}$$

and the Saint-Venant dynamic equation

$$S_0 - \frac{\partial h}{\partial l} - \frac{1}{g} \frac{\partial v}{\partial t} - \frac{v}{g} \frac{\partial v}{\partial l} - \frac{v^2 \lambda_R}{2gR} = S_f \tag{6.33}$$

10.2.2 Similarity criteria

For modelling *tidal motion* in estuaries the conditions and laws resulting from Equations (6.32) and (6.33) as explained in Chapter 6 (Sub-sections 6.2.1 and 6.2.4) are applicable. They are primarily the conditions of identity on model and prototype of the Froude and Strouhal numbers and criteria used for the design of models with nonuniform flow, i.e.

$$M_{S_0} = M_{S_e} \tag{6.7)(II}$$

and

$$M_\lambda = M_{S_e} \frac{M_R}{M_h} \tag{6.9)(III}$$

For the modelling of the *gravity oscillatory waves* the following considerations apply:

From Equation (10.3) it follows that if $L \gg 0.017$ m surface tension will not produce a scale effect. A value of $L_{min} \simeq 10 \times 0.017 = 0.17$ m is usually observed.

For long shallow water waves from Equation (10.4)

$$M_c = \sqrt{M_h} \tag{10.10}$$

For short deep water waves from Equation (10.5)

$$M_c = \sqrt{M_L} \tag{10.11}$$

For intermediate waves from Equation (10.2) it follows that for no scale effect

$$\tanh\frac{2\pi h_p}{L_p} = \tanh\frac{2\pi h_m}{L_m}$$

and thus

$$M_c = \sqrt{M_L} = \sqrt{M_h} \tag{10.12}$$

From Equation (10.6)

$$M_L = M_c M_T \tag{10.13}$$

If in the general case we choose two scales, e.g., M_T and M_h, M_c and M_L can be calculated.

From Equations (10.12) and (10.13) it follows that in this case:

$$M_c(=\sqrt{M_L} = \sqrt{M_h}) = M_T \tag{10.14}$$

In general, Equations (10.10) to (10.14) do not exclude distorted models with $M_h \neq M_l$. For the reproduction of wave refraction, which depends only on the depth, Equation (10.10) is sufficient and a distorted model is permissible. For wave refraction from currents according to Bijker (1967) correct results may be obtained if the current is modelled according to the Froude law which is consistent with Equation (10.10) for $M_c = M_v$. The wave height in the model can be determined arbitrarily, as long as the waves are not too steep. For reproducing wave diffraction, however, the wave height at any point along the obstacle must be reproduced correctly and thus the wave length scale, M_L, must be equal to the horizontal length scale, M_l of the model. This, in turn, means that for studies of wave diffraction an undistorted model with $M_h = M_l$ is necessary if scale effects are to be avoided.

From Equation (10.9) it follows that scale effects for the orbital velocity reproduction can be avoided only if $M_L = M_h$. For the maximum orbital velocity at $x = t = 0$, the scale will be given by

$$M_{v'} = M_H M_T^{-1} \tag{10.15}$$

Combining Equations (10.15) and (10.14) and for $M_H = M_h$, results in

$$M_{v'} = M_H M_h^{-1/2} = \sqrt{M_h} = M_v \tag{10.16}$$

i.e. the reproduction of the orbital velocity according to the Froude law requires the reproduction of the wave height according to the depth scale.

The above equations (10.10) to (10.16) apply equally to fixed bed and movable bed models. In the latter case, however, the equations and conditions for incipient sediment motion and sediment transport discussed in detail in Sub-sections 6.2.2 to 6.2.4 and 6.3.2 have also to be taken into account. It follows that the modelling of morphological processes may require a distorted model even where wave diffraction occurs; in this case scale effects have to be accepted and great care taken in the interpretation of model results. Furthermore it must be noted that for vertical velocities on a distorted model operated according to the Froude law

$$M_w = \frac{M_h^{3/2}}{M_l} \qquad (10.17 = 6.37)$$

Equation (10.17) applies to the rate of rise and fall of water levels and must be taken into account in the design of tidal models. Equally it applies to the settling velocity of particles in suspension. As the settling velocity in sea water is substantially higher than in fresh water it may be necessary to simulate the suspended particles on a model with fresh water by grains of a higher settling velocity or to use coagulants.

In models where the interface between fresh water and sea water and density currents are not relevant it is customary and certainly more convenient to use fresh water. However, where density differences, $\Delta\rho$, have to be taken into account, the densimetric Froude number has to be the same in the model and prototype:

$$M_{Fr_o} = 1 \qquad \text{with} \qquad Fr_\rho = \frac{v}{\sqrt{(gh)}} \sqrt{\left(\frac{\rho}{\Delta\rho}\right)} \qquad (9.16)$$

A fuller discussion of the densimetric Froude number and of related dispersion problems can be found in Sections 9.2 and 9.3.

An analysis of the conditions of similarity for tidal models and models with gravity-oscillatory waves shows that the great distortion used in early models and mentioned in Section 10.1 must lead to scale effects in the reproduction of morphological details. Nevertheless in these cases good overall results relating to water levels and general flow patterns can be and have been obtained.

As mentioned in Section 10.1 the large area simulated by tidal and maritime models sometimes requires the simulation of the geostrophic acceleration of flow. In a distorted model operated according to the Froude law the horizontal acceleration should be reproduced to a scale

$$M_{a_x} = \frac{M_v}{M_t} = \frac{M_h^{1/2}}{M_l/M_h^{1/2}} = \frac{M_h}{M_l} \qquad (10.18)$$

The acceleration due to earth rotation is

$$a_g = 2v\omega \sin\phi \qquad (10.19)$$

where ω is the angular velocity of earth rotation ($=0.73 \times 10^{-4}$ rad/s) and

ϕ the latitude.

Thus

$$M_{a_z} = M_v = \sqrt{(M_h)} \neq M_{a_x}$$

for the model in the same latitude as the prototype. The model acceleration is therefore too small by $M_l/M_h^{1/2}$.

It is possible to rectify this by placing the model on a rotating platform (impractical in most cases) or by using the Magnus effect to reproduce the geostrophic acceleration (Schoemaker, 1958). A cylinder of diameter D rotating with N revolutions per second in a fluid with velocity v exerts a force F at right angles to the flow:

$$F = c\pi^2 \rho D^2 h v N \qquad (10.20)$$

where c is a constant ($c \simeq 0.4$).

From Equations (10.18) and (10.20) the number of rotating cylinders n per m^2 of model required to produce the correct acceleration can be determined as

$$n = \frac{\rho h_m \dfrac{a_{g_p}}{M_{a_x}}}{c\pi^2 \rho D^2 h_m v_m N} = \frac{a_{g_p} M_l}{0.4\pi^2 D^2 v_m N M_h} \text{ cylinders/m}^2. \qquad (10.21)$$

10.3 Methods and Instrumentation Used in Laboratory Investigations of Waves and Tidal Models

As mentioned briefly in Section 10.1 models reproducing tidal motion and oscillatory waves require certain special methods and instrumentation in addition to those used for river models (*see* Chapters 4 and 6). The most frequent are wave tanks with wave and tide generators.

Wave generators are usually of the wedge or paddle type driven through gear boxes and/or by variable speed motors (*see also* Figs. 10.11 and 10.13); they can generate regular or random waves. Irregular waves can be generated by wind superimposed on waves produced by a regular movement of the wave generator or by a continuous variation of the speed and magnitude of motion of a generator whose mechanism is suitably programmed. This type of generator can reproduce waves according to actually measured data or use a random electronic signal filtered in accordance with the required energy spectrum. Even then the wave steepness on the model may be adjusted by blowing air over the generated waves. These combined wave and wind flumes must be of sufficient substantial length to achieve the required wave form. The wave generator may influence the time scale for the wave M_T and the ratio of wave length and period M_L/M_T then determines the length scale M_l of the model.

Sometimes it is necessary to simulate an oblique rather than frontal approach of the waves to a structure (attack under an angle). In this case wide wave basins with several wave generators, which may be operated with a gradual shift in their movement creating a random wave effect, are used. Wave generators can also be installed in flumes with a current and the wave pattern superimposed on it. The inlet arrangement in this case is best designed by trial and error to achieve the desired combination of current and wave action in the test section; this should be sufficiently far removed from either end of the flume not to be affected by the boundary conditions.

At the end of the flume opposite the wave generator, a wave absorber must be provided to prevent disturbing the generated waves and the test section by wave reflection. This is usually provided in the form of a sloping rough beach, but bales of steel wool, expanded metal, plastic fibre, etc., have also been used successfully. The best design is again achieved by preliminary experiments.

When studying the interaction of oscillatory flow with sediment movement or structures, *tunnels with pulsating flow* under pressure can also be used. It is important to realize that the vertical motion of orbiting particles cannot be reproduced correctly in this type of flow without a free water surface. Nevertheless relevant results may be obtained particularly when studying oscillatory flow in the boundary layer.

Tidal models, usually models of estuaries, need *tide generators* placed at their seaward boundary. There are many different generator designs but in principle they are of two types: gate operated or pneumatic. The weir type tide generator usually has one or several flap gates raised or lowered according to the tidal movement reproduced on the model and always discharging the excess model inflow to waste (or the recirculating system). Modern servo-control techniques permit an easy reproduction of whole cycles of tides by following the movement of an eccentric cam or previously plotted curves of tidal movement. Figure 10.2 shows a view of a weir tide generator at the seaward limit of the Thames estuary model built at the Hydraulics Research Station, Wallingford (1969) with scales $M_l = 600$ and $M_h = 60$ for the study of the Thames estuary flood prevention scheme.

Figure 10.3 is a schematic diagram of a pneumatic tide generator. A tide cam mechanism or automatic curve reading apparatus or automized steering signal with punch tape (1) is connected to a model float and float-operated pot (2) through a comparing, stabilizing and amplifying circuit (3); the output from this circuit operates an air-control valve (6) through a servo-amplifier (4) and servomotor (5), which regulates the pressure in the tank (7) provided with an air bleed valve (8) and connected to the suction side of a fan (9).

Fig. 10.2. Weir tide generator at the seaward limit of the Thames estuary model. [Crown Copyright. Reproduced by permission of the Controller HMSO, courtesy of the Hydraulics Research Station, Wallingford]

In some models it is possible to concentrate on the maximum ebb and flood flow rather than the whole tidal cycle. In this case it is possible to use steady state conditions and it is even possible to simulate the whole tidal cycle by a series of steady state conditions (*see also* the example quoted in Sub-section 9.3.2).

When investigating the resonance of *seiches*, i.e. slow mass oscillations due to the variations in wind induced slopes, *in harbours* the 'starry sky'

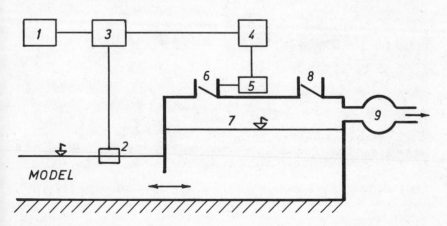

Fig. 10.3.

technique can be used. As seiches have a period of several minutes a photograph taken of light reflections during one wave period can give a very good indication of absolutely calm areas and areas affected most strongly by the water surface movement. Numerous points of light on a ceiling reflected by the water surface are photographed with an exposure time equal to one wave period. The trace of the light reflection on the water surface provides a measure of the horizontal water movement and thus of movement of ships about their moorings. Figure 10.4 (Hydraulics

Fig. 10.4. 'Starry sky' harbour model. [Crown Copyright. Reproduced by permission of the Controller HMSO, courtesy of the Hydraulics Research Station, Wallingford]

Research Station, Wallingford, 1972) is an example of the application of this technique.

Density currents may of course be important in tidal models. If fresh water effects are negligible in prototype then salt water is usually reproduced by using fresh water on the model as using salt water could be costly and cause corrosion problems. If, however, the density differences and stratification effects are important, then this is controlled on the model by brine injection into the 'sea water' circulation. Salinity distribution in a model may also be maintained in some cases by extracting at the model periphery the surface layer of freshwater brought into the estuary by the modelled river (*see also* the example quoted in Sub-section 9.3.2).

When reproducing *tidal volumes* and flows in estuaries a great degree of schematization may be used as illustrated by Fig. 10.5, which shows the model of the Humber estuary from the confluence of the Yorkshire Ouse and the Trent to the sea. To save space the tidal flows in both rivers were reproduced by folding them into labyrinths. The scales of the model are $M_l = 720$ and $M_h = 72$.

The design of 'Coriolis tops' simulating the effect of *geostrophic acceleration* on the flow has already been discussed in Section 10.2. Figure 10.6 shows part of a model of the Oosterschelde (Easter Scheldt) estuary built by the Delft Hydraulics Laboratory with a number of the Coriolis simulators on the model and in the foreground.

Fig. 10.5. Humber estuary model. [Courtesy British Transport Docks Board]

Fig. 10.6. Easter Scheldt model with 'Coriolis tops'. [Courtesy Delft Hydraulics Laboratory]

For tests on harbour entrances and berthing *radio controlled models of ships* are used as described in Chapter 8.

Distorted tidal models may require adjustment of *bed roughness* just as river models. The same techniques as are described in Chapter 6 are used (Sub-section 6.4.2). Vertical rods or strips may often be required to produce sufficient local roughness.

Artifical bed models are used to simulate bed reaction forces when investigating the action and performance of dredgers.

10.4 Models of Coastal Engineering Works

10.4.1 Waves in shoaling water

The design of coastal engineering works is closely associated with the behaviour of waves in shoaling water and coastal sediment transport, which includes on- and offshore, and particularly longshore transport of material, i.e. the littoral drift.

When deep sea waves approaching a shore reach a depth smaller than half their wavelength their transition to shallow water waves begins (*see*

Sub-section 10.2.1). Orbiting liquid particles are slowed down by their contact with the bed, their path changes to elliptical and the wave front eventually over-rides the trough and collapses into it. This 'break point' occurs at a mean depth of about 1.20 wave height. The wave steepness and particularly the steepness of the shore affect the character of the breaking waves: *surging breakers* occur at the steepest beach slopes (steeper than $1:10$) and low wave steepness, *plunging breakers* form on a medium slope with relatively steep waves, and *spilling breakers* on a mildly sloped sandy beach with steep waves ($H_0/L_0 > 10^{-2}$).

The uprush of water from a wave breaking on a shore is called the *swash*. The steeper or more impermeable the slope the bigger the swash height, which is defined as the vertical distance from the lowest level of the uncovered beach as the wave breaks to the top of the swash. The swash height varies from about $1.4H$ for a $6:1$ permeable slope to $2.6H$ for a $2:1$ impervious smooth slope. For composite slopes the method suggested by Thorndike (1958) may be used to determine the swash.

Due to bed friction the wave fronts bend to approximate the underwater contours; although the waves have thus a tendency to approach in a line approximately parallel to the shore, there is often a net longshore transport of material due to a wave approach component normal to the shore (depending on the strength, duration and directions of winds and fetches corresponding to the wind directions).

Waves approaching a steep wall in sufficiently deep water (depth over $1.5H$) in a line parallel to the wall are *reflected* and form a series of standing waves or clapotis with the wall in an anti-nodal position (with the maximum vertical movement). A wall slope $2:1$ (horizontal:vertical) is about the steepest for waves to break on it; if the apron is steeper the wave is reflected (Thorn and Simmons, 1971).

The wave celerity c is initially a function of h/L (*see* Equation (10.2)), and in shallow water a function of h only (Equation (10.4)). If α is the angle between a wave crest and a contour marking a change in bed level, from Snell's law of *refraction* it follows that

$$\frac{c_1}{c_2} = \frac{\sin \alpha_1}{\sin \alpha_2} \qquad (10.22)$$

where α_1 and α_2 are the angles between the wave crest and contour line for celerities c_1 and c_2 corresponding to the depth at each side of the contour line, which is considered as a step. Equation (10.22) may be used to draw the approximate refraction pattern by tracing paths of initially equidistant orthogonals, assuming that steps in bed level occur midway between contours (Muir Wood, 1969).

From Equation (10.22) it follows that where a wave approaches a sudden drop of bed level total reflection occurs for $\alpha_1 > \alpha_c$ (with

$\alpha_2 = \pi/2$):

$$\alpha_c = \sin^{-1} \frac{c_1}{c_2} \tag{10.23}$$

Equation (10.23) has its implication, e.g., for wave patterns at a deep channel leading to a harbour, because for shallow waves approaching the channel boundary with celerity c_1 at an angle bigger than the critical (α_c) total reflection occurs since the waves cannot enter the channel ($c_1 < c_2$).

At an obstruction, e.g., at a breakwater, *wave diffraction* occurs. The presence of an obstruction sets up radiating disturbances which give rise to wave trains in the lee (shadow) of the obstruction. Figure 10.7 shows a diffraction diagram at a long breakwater (Penney and Price, 1952) and Fig. 10.8 at a wide gap between two breakwaters at a harbour entrance, where the gap width $B \geq L$ (Johnson, 1953).

10.4.2 Coastal sediment transport

The offshore sediment profile development takes place in three zones: in the backshore (above the wave run-up limit), in the real developing

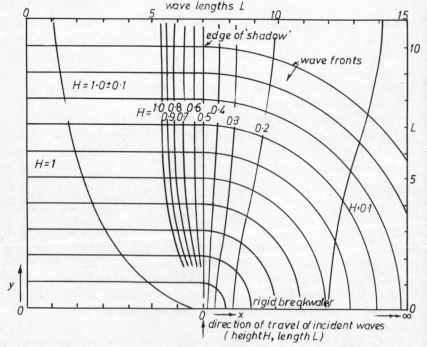

Fig. 10.7. Wave diffraction at a long breakwater. [After Penny and Price, 1952],

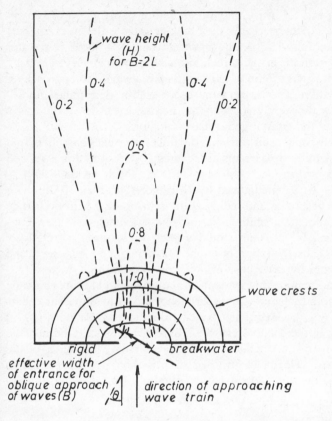

Fig. 10.8. Wave diffraction at a wide harbour entrance. [After Johnson, 1959],

profile with transport constituting the difference between the actual and equilibrium profile and in the transition zone below the developing profile. Tracers with labelling by fluorescence, magnetism, radioactivity or rare elements are frequently used for essential field studies of sediment movement.

Coastal sediments are derived mainly from sediment brought down-stream by the rivers into their estuaries and from sediment produced by wave attack on coastal formations, and coastal sediment transport will be primarily a function of wave height, steepness and period, shore profile, and sediment size and grading. According to Russell (1960) waves of 2.5 m height and 8 s period just move 25 mm pebbles in a 8 m depth, 50 mm in 4 m depth and 75 mm pebbles only in the breaker zone (these results do not take into account the possible effect of tidal currents). As the type of movement of sediment particles, i.e. rolling (pebbles), salta-tion (coarse sand) and movement in suspension (fine sand), is influenced by different aspects of wave motion a natural 'sorting' of sediment particles by waves takes place. As the breaking wave is the chief cause of movement of sand and shingle the main movement is above low water and along the foreshore in the direction of the breaking wave.

Beaches, as also rivers, tend to change in such a way as to approach an equilibrium situation. The form of the beach will be determined, therefore, primarily by the supply of sediment, the characteristics of the waves and currents, and the coastal geological formations.

In the breaker zone offshore bars parallel to the coast line and occasionally broken by rip currents are formed. Their formation is related to the sand transport in the swash and surf zone (Muir Wood, 1969).

Figure 10.9 shows a schematized beach profile (Sorensen, 1978).

The threshold of motion and sediment transport in tidal currents can be determined by the same methods as in open channel flow (*see* Subsections 6.2.2 and 6.3.2). One would expect wave action at relatively shallow depth to cause agitation of the bed resulting in an increase of the sediment transport by tidal currents (*cf.* the case without waves). Although the phenomenon is dependent on the wave climate, the principle was confirmed both by laboratory experiments and by field measurements carried out, e.g., by the Hydraulics Research Station, Wallingford (1979) at Maplin Sands in the Thames estuary. There it was established that the tidal flux of sand was independent of the wave activity for values of the rms wave-induced velocity at the bed of less than $v_0' = 50$ mm/s. For higher values of the rms velocity fluctuations v' the tidal flux of sand increased as $\left(\dfrac{v'}{v_0'}\right)^2$

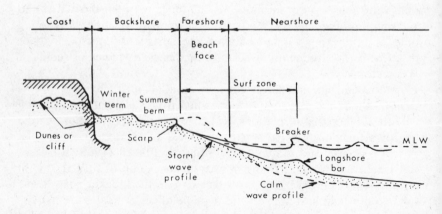

Fig. 10.9. Schematized beach profile. [After Sorensen, 1978]

10.4.3 Coastal engineering works

The design of coastal engineering works and sea defences is based on three main factors; (i) the analysis of the cause of the problem, (ii) the determination of the direction and magnitude of predominant storm waves, sediment transport and the tidal range and current, and (iii) the selection of the appropriate type of engineering works and their detailed hydraulic and structural design based on model tests if necessary.

The analysis of the cause of the problem, e.g., beach erosion, may often reveal that this is due to human activity interfering with the upstream littoral drift and thus the possibility of eliminating the cause should be investigated first.

Wave prediction for a particular location is essentially based on the knowledge of wind speed and its duration and direction, the area of generation (fetch), and of intermediate wave decay. Empirical tables and graphs relate these parameters to the wave characteristics. For example, the Darbyshire and Draper (1963) chart based on observations around Britain is widely used (*see* Fig. 10.10). It facilitates the determination of wave height H_{max} and period as a function of wind speed (knots) and duration (hrs) and the fetch in nautical miles. The maximum wave height may be determined by the fetch or by the duration of the storm depending upon which limiting condition is first encountered by an ordinate representing the wind speed (traced from left to right).

H_{max} refers to the maximum wave height in a typical wave record of 10 minutes length. To determine H_{max} for longer storm durations a multiplier f is used ($H_{max} = fH_{max_{10}}$), $1.17 < f < 1.49$ for storm duration $1 < t < 48$ hrs. The significant wave height H_s is commonly used in model tests of wave attack, e.g., on rubble mounds of breakwaters, which can fail by the erosion of their foundations; this is the mean height of the one-third highest waves, and it may be expressed from $H_{max} \simeq 1.6H_s$. A wave height of the average height of the highest 10% of all waves, denoted as $H_{1/10}$, with $H_{max} \simeq 1.25H_{1/10}$, is also used for design purposes, (e.g. Muir Wood, 1969). For the testing of possible failure of monolithic structures, which fail by overturning, the design wave should be the absolute maximum wave.

Beach stability can be achieved artificially either by artificial feeding or by the construction of groynes. Whenever technically and economically feasible, artificial sediment feeding (beach nourishment) is preferable to permanent engineering measures. Groynes are low barriers constructed usually at right angles to the beach and their function is to intercept the littoral drift and thus build up the bench. Without littoral drift they are ineffective or even harmful. On a shingle beach they are carried seawards only a short distance beyond the toe of the shingle, whereas on a sandy beach they usually extend to the low water mark. Their height and

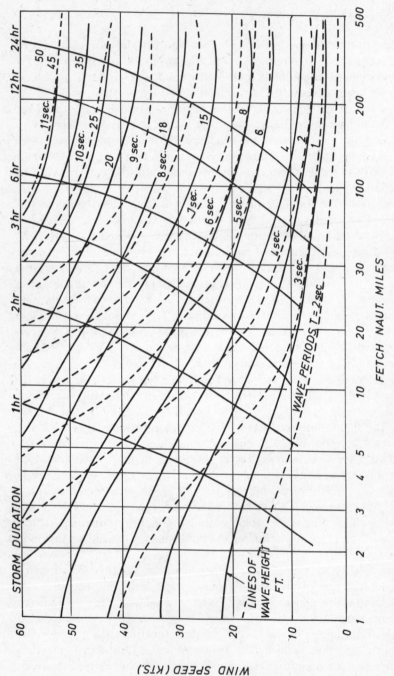

Fig. 10.10. Wave heights around British coasts. [After Darbyshire and Draper, 1963]

spacing is important as an incorrent design could result in material being washed from the beach; generally they should not be too high and their spacing should be about equal to their length depending on the direction of the wave attack. If there is doubt about the best groyne spacing it is better to start with a bigger spacing (say 1.5 to 2 times the length) and to add intermediate groynes later, if necessary. Timber is the most frequently used material facilitating easy modification, although permeable steel, articulated concrete or willow fascine groynes (reducing scour on the down-drift side) are also used. Construction should start at the end furthest from the direction from which the sediment feed is coming. By placing this first groyne in a position where accretion is taking place the 'terminal groyne' problem can be reduced (Thorn and Simmons, 1971).

Russell (1960) reports among other findings from extensive coastal model studies at the Hydraulics Research Station, Wallingford, that a system of groynes 1 m high and 55 m apart lost one eighth of the drift that was arrested from each compartment. Thus, in a large number of groynes the last ones become ineffective. At the last groyne on the down-drift side a scour hole forms as the material is being swept away at an annual rate of nql, where n is the number of groynes, l the distance between them and q the loss of material from the beach in m^3/year per m length. Figure 10.11 illustrates the formation of the scour on the leeside of the last of a

Fig. 10.11. The terminal groyne problem. [Crown Copyright. Reproduced by permission of the Controller HMSO, courtesy of the Hydraulics Research Station, Wallingford]

system of groynes on a hydraulic model (Hydraulics Research Station, 1960).

Models for coastal problems where beach erosion and protection are being studied naturally have movable beds. From the analysis in Sub-section 10.2.2 it follows that, for the scale of the current and orbital velocities to be equal, the reproduction of the wave height must be in accordance with the depth scale (Equation (10.16)).

As the reproduction of sediment motion on the model almost inevitably requires a distorted model, scale effects may result and additional local roughness may be required. One possibility is to choose the horizontal model scale M_l and adopt a provisional depth scale M_h, which can be adjusted after comparing the beach profile on the model and in prototype until good agreement is obtained. If necessary a slight departure from the Froude law in the velocity scales is also possible.

Sea defence works are built for the prevention of coastal flooding and for the protection of the shore. Sand dunes form a good natural defence against flooding. Structures preventing flooding of low-lying land are often earthen embankments, which need not be as substantial as concrete or masonary walls protecting the shore from erosion and required to withstand direct wave attack. Sea walls must be high enough to prevent overtopping in the worst conditions of tide and wave action, to provide a suitable form of wave energy dissipation and to be stable enough to withstand wave and earth pressures. If breaking waves enclose pockets of air against the wall this may result in additional intense shock pressures. The wave energy dissipation and stability are best determined by model tests in wave flumes the results of which are given in design equations (Muir Wood, 1969; Bruun and Gunbak 1976; Denny 1951; etc.). Figure 10.12 gives a schematic guide for the forces caused by waves breaking on a vertical wall. The dynamic component of the force is approximately given by the equation

$$P_v = \rho g h \left(1 - \frac{x^2 \tan^2 \beta}{4H^2}\right) \tag{10.24}$$

For the design of rubble mound breakwaters the Iribarren–Hudson (1953) equation is widely used:

$$W = \frac{KH^3 \mu^3 \rho^2 \rho_s}{(\rho_s - \rho)^3 (\mu \cos \alpha - \sin \alpha)^3} \tag{10.25}$$

where K is a coefficient the value of which is a function of stone shape and the stable angle α of the exposed face of the mound, W is the minimum stable weight of stone of specific mass ρ_s, μ is the coefficient of friction between the capping and the core of the mound, and H is the wave height. Hudson (1959) simplified Equation (10.25) for constant

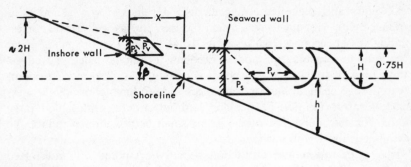

Fig. 10.12.

values of h/L and H/L to

$$W = \frac{\gamma_s H^3}{K'(s_s - 1)^3 \cot \alpha}$$ (10.26)

where K' is a non-dimensional factor obtained by model tests (US Coastal Engineering Research Center, 1966).

As an illustration Table 10.1 gives the values of K' for two layers in the mount armour:

Table 10.1

	Structure Trunk		Structure Head	
	A	B	A	B
Smooth quarry stone	2.1	2.6	2.0	2.0
Rough quarry stone	2.8	3.5	2.7	3.2
Tetrapod or quadripod*	6.6	8.3	5.0	6.5
Hexapod*	7.2	9.0	5.0	7.0

(A = breaking wave, B = non-breaking wave)

* Many other types of breakwater armour blocks (giving different values of stability) are now available (Hydraulics Research Station, 1979).

10.5 Models of Harbours and Maritime Engineering Works

The design of an ocean harbour involves the study of the sea approaches and of many inter-linking hydraulic, engineering and economic parameters. In major designs model studies form only one, albeit very important, stage (e.g., Agar and McDowell, 1971; van Rees, *et al.*, 1974). Scale models are mainly used to study wave penetration and diffraction behind breakwaters and the effect of incident and reflected waves and their resonance with irregular waves inside the harbour, as well as the corresponding vessel response (*see also* Fig. 10.4).

With the development of modern dredging techniques (suction dredges, trailing hopper dredgers and mechanical cutting) it is often more economical to dredge channel harbour entrances than to have enormous lengths of breakwaters (Vinjé, 1977). The harbour mouth is designed large enough for safe entry but otherwise as small as possible to reduce the wave height inside the harbour.

Wave penetration and diffraction should be studied on undistorted models (*see* Sub-section 10.2.2). If no breaking waves are present then for the study of the harbour proper a distorted model may be used. Model studies may be used to indicate areas inside the harbour where wave height reduction by absorption on sloping boundaries is effective and advisable.

The studies of the new harbour entrance at Rotterdam-Europoort described in detail by van Rees, *et al.* (1974) may serve as an example of a comprehensive model investigation of an important harbour design. A tidal salinity model, with scale $M_l = M_h = 64$, was constructed with part of the North Sea and Rotterdam Waterway included. The model was used for predicting flow patterns during and after construction, the solution of harbour problems, the prediction of cooling water circulation and of salinity intrusion, etc. 50 mm cubes were used on the fixed bed model, operated in accordance with the Froude law, to produce the required additional roughness. Prior to the construction of the final model a pilot model with scales $M_l = 600$ and $M_h = 100$ was tested. It was found that in spite of the size of the model (a special hall 3000 m^2 was built for it) there was no need to simulate the Coriolis force in this case (*see* Sub-section 10.2.2), the effect of which was implicit in the boundary conditions. The flow on the model was controlled by 12 overflow gates on the seaward side and 3 underflow gates on the river side. Density was controlled by brine injection into the sea water circulation.

Figure 10.13 shows the Port Talbot model (scale 1 : 180) built in the laboratory of the British Transport Docks Board Research Station, Southall. The figure shows wave diffraction and reflection inside the harbour and, in particular, the reflection from the vertical wall on the left, which was eliminated in later stages of the model investigations by adding a wave absorption rock face to this wall. Navigation tests to simulate berthing at jetties using radio-controlled model boats and strain gauges to measure forces on moored ships were also carried out.

Figure 10.14 shows the complicated wave pattern arising from a combination of wave diffraction and reflection in a harbour model (Hydraulics Research Station, Wallingford).

The determination of wave forces acting on cylinders and of their

Fig. 10.13. Port Talbot harbour model. [Courtesy British Transport Docks Board]

Fig. 10.14. Wave diffraction and reflection on a model. [Crown Copyright. Reproduced by permission of the Controller HMSO, courtesy of the Hydraulics Research Station, Wallingford].

oscillations is an important topic for laboratory and prototype studies associated with the design of coastal works and harbours. With the development of offshore oil and gas exploitation these problems have become even more important, as wave forces in deep water have to be considered (anchored oil rigs operate now in depths exceeding 150 m and may be subjected to forces exerted by open sea storm waves).

The full treatment of this subject is outside the scope of this book, but certain aspects of it may be found in some of the quoted literature. In principle research centres on the determination of the drag and mass coefficients, C_D and C_m, in the equation for the exerted force F over a length dz

$$F = \left[\frac{C_D \rho D u^2}{2} + \frac{C_m \rho D^2 \pi}{4} \frac{\partial u}{\partial t} \right] dz \qquad (10.27)$$

where u is the horizontal particle velocity and D the cylinder diameter. Combining Equation (10.27) with the wave equations, permits its solution for known values of C_D and C_m. For steady flow conditions C_D is a function of the cylinder Reynolds number ($C_D \simeq 1.2$ for $Re < 2 \times 10^5$ and $C_D \simeq 0.3$ for $Re > 5 \times 10^5$). Wiegel (1964) quotes $C_m \simeq 2.5$ and $1 < C_D < 2$ for a simple cylinder in a wave. Paape and Breusers (1966) related the values of C_D and C_m to the ratio of the particle orbital length and cylinder diameter.

Apart from investigating forces on simple cylindrical piles laboratory investigations in this area are concerned with forces acting on a number of piles in different configurations (e.g., Hayashi, *et al.*, 1966), on submarine pipelines and cables, and on flexible moorings (e.g. Wilson, 1964).

References

Agar, M. and McDowell, D. M. (1971). The sea approaches to the Port of Liverpool, *Proc. ICE*, **49**, June, pp. 145–156.

Allen, J. (1947). *Scale Models in Hydraulic Engineering*, Longmans, Green and Co., London.

American Society of Civil Engineers. (1975). Modelling techniques, *2nd Annual Symposium of the Waterways, Harbors and Coastal Engineering Division, San Francisco*, ASCE, New York.

Bagnold, R. A. (1947). Sand movement by waves: some small-scale experiments with sand at very low density, *J. ICE*, **27**, No. 4, pp. 447–469.

Bakker, W. T. and Doorn, T. van (1978). Near bottom velocities in waves with a current., *Proc. 16th Conference on Coastal Engineering, Hamburg.*

Bijker, E. W. (1967). *Some Considerations About Scales for Coastal Models with Movable Bed*, Publication No. 50, Delft Hydraulics Laboratory, Delft.

Bishop, R. E. D. and Hassan, A. Y. (1964). The lift and drag forces on a circular cylinder oscillating in a flowing fluid, *Proc. Roy. Soc., Series A*, **277**, pp. 51–75.

Bonnefille, R. and Perkecker, L. (1966). Le début d'entrainment des sédiments sous l'action de la houle, *Bulletin du Centre de Recherches et d'Essais de Chatou*, No. 15.

Brebner, A. and Riedel, H. P. (1973). A new oscillating water tunnel, *J. Hydraul. Res. IAHR*, No. 2, pp. 107–121.

Bretschneider, C. L. (1957). Hurricane design wave practice, *Proc. ASCE, J. Waterways and Harbors Div.*, **83**, No. WW2, Paper 1238, 33 pp.

Breusers, H. N. C., Nicollet, G. and Shen, H. (1977). Local scour around cylindrical piers, *J. Hydraul. Res. IAHR*, No. 3, pp. 211–252.

Brorsen, M., Burcharth, H. F. and Larsen, T. (1974). Stability of dolos slopes, *Proc. 14th Conference on Coastal Engineering*, **111**, pp. 1691–1701.

Bruun, P. (1956). Destruction of wave energy by vertical walls,. *Proc. ASCE, J. Waterways & Harbors Div.*, **82**, No. WW1, Paper 912, 13 pp.

Bruun, P. and Gunbak, A. R. (1976). *New Design Principles for Rubble Mound Structures*. The Norwegian Institute of Technology, Trondheim.

Connor, J. J. and Brebbia, C. A. (1976). *Finite Element Techniques for Fluid Flow*, Newness–Butterworths, London.

Darbyshire, M. and Draper, L. (1963). Forecasting wind generated sea waves, *Engineering*, April, pp. 482–485.

Denny, D. F. (1951). Further experiments on wave pressures. *J. ICE*, **35**, No. 4, pp. 330–345.

Dronkers, J. J. (1964). *Tidal Computations in Rivers and Coastal Waters*, North-Holland Publ. Co., Amsterdam.

Eagleson, P. S. (1965). *Theoretical Study of Longshore Currents on a Plane Beach*, Hydraulics Laboratory Report No. 82, Massachusetts Institute of Technology, Boston.

Francis, J. R. D. (1959). Wind action on a water surface, *Proc. ICE*, **12**, pp. 197–216.

Gravesen, H., Kirkegaard, J. and Nielsen, A. H. (1975). Problems of physical model tests with harbours, *Proc. ASCE, Symposium on modelling techniques. San Francisco* **II**, pp. 1422–1447.

Harris, R. W., Inman, D. L., Bailard, J. A. and Oda, R. L. (1976). Study and Evaluation of Remedial Sand Bypassing Procedures, Report H 76–1, Waterways Experimental Station, Vicksburg.

Hayashi, T., Kano, T., Shirai, M. and Hattori, M. (1966). Hydraulic research on the closely spaced pile breakwater, *Proc. 10th Conference on Coastal Engineering, Tokyo*, **2**, pp. 873–884.

Hudson, R. Y. (1953). Wave forces on breakwaters, *Engineering Aspects of Water Waves: A Symposium, Trans. ASCE*, **118**, p. 653.

Hudson, R. Y. (1959). Laboratory investigations of rubble-mound breakwaters, *Proc. ASCE, J. Waterways Harbors and Coastal Eng. Div.*, **85**, No. WW3, pp. 93–121.

Hydraulics Research Station. (1960, 1969, 1979). Notes No. 12, No. 15 and No. 21, HRS, Wallingford.

Ippen, A. T. (1966). *Estuary and Coastline Hydrodynamics*, McGraw-Hill, New York.

Ippen, A. T. (1968). *Hydraulic Scale Models. Osborne Reynolds and Engineering*

Science Today, edited by D. M. McDowell and J. D. Jackson, Manchester University Press, Manchester.

Johnson, J. W. (1953). Engineering aspects of diffraction and refraction, *Trans. ASCE*, **118,** Paper 2556, p. 617.

Johnsson, I. G. and Carlsen, N. A. (1976). Experimental and theoretical investigations in an oscillatory rough turbulent boundary layer, *J. Hydraul. Res. IAHR*, No. 1, pp. 45–60.

Kamphuis, J. W. (1972). *Scale Selection for Wave Models*, CE Research Report No. 71, Queen's University, Kingston, Ontario.

Kendrick, M. P. and Derbyshire, B. V. (1978). *Effects of a Barrier on Existing Estuary Regime. Thames Barrier Design*, ICE, London.

Kobus, H. (Ed.) (1978). *Wasserbauliches Versuchswesen*, Mitteilungsheft No. 4, Deutscher Verband für Wasserwirtschaft, Bonn.

Koopmans, F. and Oorschot, J. H. van (1976). *Random Wave Generation for Research on Immersed Marine Vehicles*, Publication No. 167, Delft Hydraulics Laboratory, Delft.

McDowell, D. M. (1969). Scale effects in models of shallow tidal water. *Proc. ICE*, Paper 7209S.

McDowell, D. M. and O'Connor, B. A. (1977). *Hydraulic Behaviour of Estuaries*, Macmillan, London.

Muir Wood, A. M. (1969). *Coastal Hydraulics*, Macmillan, London.

Ogink, H. J. M. (1975). *Investigations on the Hydraulic Characteristics of Synthetic Fabrics*, Publication No. 146, Delft Hydraulics Laboratory, Delft.

Paape, A. and Breusers, H. N. C. (1966). Influence of pile dimensions on forces exerted by waves, *Proc. 10th Conference on Coastal Engineering, Tokyo*, **2,** pp. 840–849.

Penney, W. G. and Price, A. T. (1952). The diffraction theory of sea waves by breakwaters and the shelter afforded by breakwaters, *Phil. Trans. Roy. Soc. Series A*, **244,** March, pp. 236–253.

Postma, H. (1967). Sediment transport and sedimentation in the estuarine environment, in *Estuaries*, Edited by Lauff Publication No. 83, *Am. Ass. Adv. Sci.*

Rees, A. J. van, Kuur, P. van der and Stroband, H. J. (1974). *Experiences with Tidal Salinity Model Europoort*, Publication No. 125, Delft Hydraulics Laboratory, Delft.

Rouse, H. (1964). *Engineering Hydraulics*, 4th Edn, John Wiley and Sons, New York.

Rouse, H. and Ince, S. (1957). *History of Hydraulics*, Iowa Institute of Hydraulic Research, State University of Iowa, Iowa.

Russell, R. C. H. (1960). *Coast Erosion and Defence*, Hydraulics Research Paper No. 3, DOE–HRS, HMSO, London.

Russell, R. C. H. and Osorio, J. D. C. (1958). An experimental investigation of drift profiles in a closed channel. *Proc. 6th Conference on Coastal Engineering, University of Florida*, pp. 171–183, U.S. Council on Wave Research. Berkeley. California.

Saville, T. Jr. (1958). Wave run-up on composite slopes, *Proc. 6th Conference on Coastal Engineering, University of Florida*, pp. 691–699, U.S. Council on Wave Research, Berkeley, California.

Schijf, J. B. (1959). Generalities on coastal processes and protection, *Proc. ASCE*, **85**, pp. 287–304.

Schoemaker, H. J. (1958). Influence of the earth rotation in hydraulic research, (in Dutch), *De Ingenieur*, No. 49, pp. 608–609.

Shaw, T. L. (Ed.) (1979). *Mechanics of Wave-Induced Forces on Cylinders*, Pitman Publishing, London.

Silvester, R. (1974). *Coastal Engineering*, (2 Volumes), Elsevier Scientific Publ. Co., Amsterdam.

Sleath, J. F. A. (1974). Velocities above a rough bed in oscillatory flow, *Proc. ASCE, J. Waterways Harbors and Coastal Eng. Div.*, **100**, No. WW4, pp. 287–304.

Sorensen, R. M. (1978). *Basic Coastal Engineering*, John Wiley and Sons, New York

Stoker, J. J. (1957). *Water Waves*, Interscience Publ. Inc., New York.

Swart, D. H. (1974). *Offshore sediment transport and equilibrium beach profiles*, Publication No. 131, Delft Hydraulics Laboratory, Delft.

Thorn, R. B. and Simmons, J. C. F. (1971). *Sea Defence Works*, 2nd Edn, Butterworths, London.

U.S. Coastal Engineering Research Center. (1966). *Shore Protection Planning and Design*, Technical Report No. 4, 3rd Edn, U.S. Coastal Engineering Research Centre, Washington D.C.

Vinje, J. J. (1977). *Recent Developments in Hydraulic Research*, Publication No. 183, Delft Hydraulics Laboratory, Delft.

Vries, M. de (1977). *Scale Models in Hydraulic Engineering*, International Institute for Hydraulic and Environmental Engineering, Delft.

Wiegel, R. L. (1964). *Oceanographical Engineering*, Prentice-Hall, London.

Wilson, B. W. (1964). Characteristics of anchor cables in uniform ocean currents, Bulletin No. 11 and 12, PIANC, Brussels.

Yallin, M. S. (1971). *Theory of Hydraulic Models*, Macmillan, London.

11 Aerodynamic and Analogue Models and Models of Groundwater Flow

11.1 General

The preceding chapters dealt almost exclusively with the theory of scale models, the results of their use and the applications of these results in civil engineering practice. Models of groundwater flow were not discussed. As the majority of groundwater flow problems are solved either by analogue or mathematical modelling techniques and as a detailed discussion of mathematical models has, from the onset, been excluded from this book, the brief treatment of some groundwater flow problems is combined in this chapter with a more general discussion of analogue models and techniques.

Aerodynamic modelling of flow under pressure, in conduits, at valves, etc., is of course governed in principle by the same similarity considerations as pressurized liquid flow. The technique of modelling open channel flow using aerodynamic models falls into a slightly different category forming a transition to analogue models. Therefore a short treatment of this subject is also included in this chapter.

An analogue model of a hydraulic phenomenon is a physical model where the flow field is represented in a different (physical) medium in such a way that the equations of the variables in both systems are mathematically identical.

To illustrate the principle of analogue models let us consider three cases: a simple surge tank as used in hydroelectric power stations with automatic turbine regulation; a bar fixed at one end with a horizontal disc attached to the other; and an electric circuit with resistance, capacitance, and inductance, and connected to a DC supply (*see* Fig. 11.1). Examining

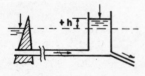 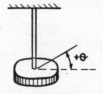

Fig. 11.1.

the changes with time of the water level h in the surge tank, of the angle θ through which the disc turns in torsional oscillations of the bar, or of the voltage U after disconnecting the DC supply, we find that in each case they are represented by an identical differential equation with identical constraints:

$$\frac{d^2x}{dt^2} + a\frac{dx}{dt} + bx = 0 \tag{11.1}$$

for $t = 0$; $d^2x/dt^2 = dx/dt = 0$; $x = -x_0$.

Thus the torsional vibrations of the bar become the analogue of the water level oscillations in the surge tank and vice versa. We can therefore use one to analyse the other. The surge tank is a hydromechanical analogue of the bar and the electric circuit an electrohydrodynamical analogue of the surge tank.

Similarly an electrical resistance network may represent a groundwater aquifer; here the voltage corresponds to water levels, current to discharge, resistance to the reciprocal of transmissivity, and capacitance to storage capacity.

We should differentiate between an analogue model, physically representing a flow situation, and an analogue computer which uses an electric circuit for the solution of simultaneous differential equations. A circuit with potentiometers, sign changers, summers, multipliers, integrators, and function generators can be used, e.g., to solve a flood routing problem. Digital and analogue computers and techniques each have their advantages and disadvantages. The analogue has the advantage of offering the possibility of testing different situations quickly and relatively cheaply and of quickly introducing alternatives; however, the final output is limited, e.g., to an xy plotter. Further, it is not possible to 'freeze' the model at intermediate times to investigate specific situations more closely and the overall result only is available. On the other hand, for the digital computer output there is a choice between a tabulated result and a graphical display. The computer also facilitates a study of intermediate stages; changes are easily incorporated, but for an extensive and complicated problem both the programming time and the length of computer runs tend to be substantial (and expensive). In some cases the use of hybrids, i.e. a combination of analogue and digital techniques, a similar principle as the combination of physical scale and mathematical models, produce the best and most economical results.

11.2 Aerodynamic Models in Hydraulic Engineering

The basis of aerodynamic modelling of open channel flow is the change of flow with a free water surface into pressure flow. The reader will recall

(Chapter 5) that for similarity of flow under pressure in hydraulically rough conduits, apart from the equality of conduit shapes and relative roughness, the only condition is that the model (and prototype) should be in the hydraulically rough region, i.e. $Re_m > Re_{sq}$. For flow with a free water surface, however, it is necessary to add the condition of identity of Froude numbers in model and prototype (Chapter 6). Since the Froude number determines the position and shape of the free water surface, this surface, if known, may be replaced on the model by a smooth surface (simulating the water–air interface) to create a pressure model with the pressure heads simulating the free water surface and where it is sufficient to fulfil the condition $Re_m > Re_{sq}$. In principle we could use water or air as the fluid on this pressurized model; the use of air, however, is more convenient from the technical point of view, more economical (pumping costs and need for a circuit with inlet and outlet tanks) and permits the placing of a model in any position as gravity effects may be neglected. As in air models we are replacing an incompressible fluid (water) by a compressible one, we must further ensure the independence of the flow from the value of the Mach number. For air this limit is given by a velocity $v \leqslant 60$ m/s.

The main advantage of aerodynamic modelling of open channel flow is that the models can be much smaller than normal free surface hydraulic models, which are governed by the relationship of the Froude numbers on the model and prototype with a permissible minimum Reynolds number for the model, since the necessary value of Reynolds number may be achieved by the corresponding increase in velocity (and thus also discharge) of air without regard to the Froude number. (It is necessary to remember, however, that the coefficient of kinematic viscosity for air at temperature 20°C and atmospheric pressure is about 15×10^{-6} m²/s, i.e. about fifteen times greater than the coefficient of viscosity for water).

The introduction of a smooth plane surface, e.g., a glass plate, instead of the free surface distorts the boundary conditions and a number of studies dealt with the influence of this surface on the deformation of the velocity field. It follows that air models are particularly useful wherever this deformation does not substantially influence the total flow picture and where the water level in prototype does not deviate considerably from a plane surface.

Theoretical and experimental studies aimed at establishing the type of free surface flow suitable for study on air models have been carried out in the USSR by Averkiev (1952) and Latcher and Prudovskij (1959). All used the basic scheme of a sudden expansion and its influence on the extent of the reversal of flow (Fig. 11.2). On the assumption that $M_\lambda = 1$ Averkiev found that the percentage error in the relative length of the vortex $l/(b_2 - b_1)$ due to the use of a fixed plate instead of a free surface depends on geometric parameters b_1/b_2 and b_1/h as shown by Fig. 11.3

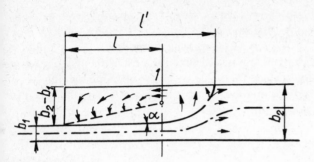

Fig. 11.2.

(h = depth of flow simulated by the height of the smooth plate above the bed). Averkiev also assumed free surface on the model and a roughness (for a plasticine model) of $k = 0.2$ mm for the calculation of λ_m. Latcher and Prudovskij, however, using the same procedure calculate λ_m including the roughness of the glass plate (but do not include the glass in the wetted perimeter) and conclude that, when observing geometric similarity for $Re_m > Re_{sq}$ and $M_\lambda = 1$, very good agreement may be obtained between the air and water model (and, respectively, between the air model and prototype), both as far as the relative length of the vortex and the distribution of the mean vertical velocities beyond the expansion are concerned. But even on the assumption that Averkiev's deduction is correct it is possible, with the aid of the graph on Fig. 11.3, to determine the regions where air models may be used. Accepting an error of 5% the aerodynamic model may be used for all open channels where $b_1/b_2 > 0.75$ and $b_1/h > 30$, i.e. in the case of the vast majority of natural rivers. In

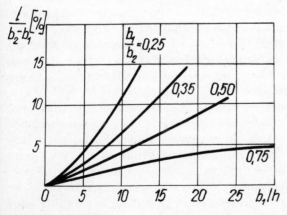

Fig. 11.3.

settling tanks which are comparatively deep we can work with a 10% error in the region $b_1/b_2 < 0.5$ and $b_1/h < 10$, etc. It is thus evident that there is a wide field of use for the aerodynamic models.

Averkiev also found, by analysing Rachmanov's experiments, that for a practically plane water surface the value of $l/(b_2 - b_1)$ depends only very slightly on the flow Froude number up to the critical value of Fr_{cr}. This value may be expressed by the equation

$$Fr_{cr} \leqslant 0.03 \frac{b_1}{b_2} \tag{11.2}$$

With limited laboratory space, which determines the horizontal scale M_l, and bearing in mind the condition $Re_m > Re_{sq}$ it is necessary, at least in some cases, to use a distorted model. Recalling the condition of similarity of distorted open channel flow models derived in Chapter 6, i.e.

$$M_\lambda = \frac{M_R}{M_l} \simeq \frac{M_h}{M_l} = M_{S_e}$$

(Equation (6.9) and condition (III)) it is important to note that, in aerodynamic models of open channel flow, M_R cannot be approximated by M_h as the top surface should be included in computing the wetted perimeter of the model for the modified condition (III) which with $R_m \simeq h_m/2$ becomes

$$M_\lambda \simeq \frac{2M_h}{M_b} = \frac{2M_h}{M_l} \tag{11.3}$$

There is sufficient evidence that observation of the above criteria gives good results even for detailed flow phenomena and head losses on distorted aerodynamic models of river flow up to a distortion of about 2.5. Should total losses only in a river stretch be required for qualitative studies (e.g., pressure losses for an arbitrary position of the water surface, i.e. glass cover) very good results have been obtained with a much greater distortion. Thus Hincu, et al. (1961) report good agreement between the study of water levels on an aerodynamic model of the Danube delta with $M_l = 10\,000$ and $M_h = 500$ (i.e. a distortion of 20) and a hydraulic model of the same region constructed to a scale $M_l = 900$ and $M_h = 65$.

As far as velocity distribution, tangential stresses and the resistance coefficients in aerodynamic models are concerned it may be concluded from the results obtained so far that with a suitable distortion it is possible to achieve the same distribution of velocities as for an open channel in the lower part of the cross-section (below the zone of maximum velocity). The distortion in the velocity distribution produced by the cover could be partially offset by placing the cover in a slightly more elevated position than would correspond to the water level. The dependence of λ on Re for various values of relative roughness in an air flow was investigated primarily by Giljarov (1959) and further by Kahan and Hincu (1959). For equal roughness on the model bottom and cover they attained, as expected, a good agreement with Zegzhda's results, but for different roughness on the bed and on the cover (or for a smooth cover) the results deviated and attained values corresponding to as much as double values of R/k. It follows from the experiments that the total frictional resistance coefficient, for a cross-section of varying roughness on the bottom and covering plate, may be sufficiently accurately calculated as the arithmetical mean of the resistance coefficients for even roughness on the entire section and the same depth.

From the experiments of Soviet and Roumanian authors, some of which were elaborated further by Sumbal (1961), it is evident that the beginning of sediment movement occurs in air at analogous tangential stresses and velocities, as in water; this means that the condition (VI) for modelling incipient sediment motion derived in Chapter 6 is also valid for aerodynamic models. The sediment discharge increases with air discharge much faster than is the case for water. Qualitative studies of local scour and bed deformation may thus be carried out on aerodynamic models as long as we are not concerned with the development of these deformations with time and as long as they are not substantially influenced by three-dimensional flow effects.

As the Froude law is no longer applicable beyond the condition expressed by Equation (11.2), and as the model discharge may be chosen arbitrarily (as long as $v_m < 60$ m/s and $Re_m > Re_{sq}$) the scale of the velocities is given by

$$M_v = \frac{Q_p A_m}{Q_m A_p} = \frac{M_Q}{M_l M_h} \tag{11.4}$$

This scale is valid for mean cross-sectional velocities and also for the mean velocities in a vertical and for local velocities.

The scale of pressures taking Equation (11.3) into account is given by

$$M_p = \frac{M_\rho M_\lambda M_v^2 M_l}{M_R} = M_\rho M_v^2 = M_\rho \frac{M_Q^2}{M_l^2 M_h^2} \tag{11.5}$$

From Equation (11.5) for the difference of water levels above datum between two sections in prototype we obtain

$$\Delta z_p = \frac{\Delta p_p}{\gamma_p} = \frac{\Delta p_m}{\gamma_p} M_p = \frac{\Delta p_m}{\gamma_m} \frac{M_Q^2}{M_l^2 M_h^2} \tag{11.6}$$

assuming that the difference in corresponding elevations of the cover of the model is given simultaneously by

$$\Delta z_m = \frac{\Delta z_p}{M_h} = \frac{\Delta p_m}{\gamma_m} \frac{M_Q^2}{M_l^2 M_h^3} \tag{11.7}$$

If this difference is not initially known we proceed by iteration and gradually adjust the position of the model cover until condition (11.7) is satisfied.

On aerodynamic models, apart from the pressures which are measured by manometers connected to normal piezometric openings, velocities are measured by small pressure head (Pitot) tubes or hot wire anemometers and flow paths are studied using various tracers (smoke, sparks, etc.) or light threads. The models are usually placed on tables or trestles with access from below for the insertion of velocity probes and pressure tappings. The morphological features are usually modelled, with the use of thin templates, in plasticine, with a small amount of linseed oil added to prevent cracking, or sometimes layers of plywood have been used. Due to the small size of the models great care and accuracy is required in their construction. The cover is usually of glass or perspex 5 to 10 mm thick and the contact between the cover and the model has to be carefully sealed, e.g., with putty.

Air may be either driven into the model or exhausted from it by fans discharging 1000 to 10 000 m³/h at a pressure of about 500 to 600 mm of water, and air discharge is usually measured by an orifice. An arrangement with the outlet from the model connected to the suction side of the fan is used more frequently, as it allows an easy introduction of tracers at the model inlet. In this case, it is necessary to check carefully and prevent the bending of the model cover by supporting it at intervals by thin rods acting as distance pieces; for this reason a combination of driving air into the model and extracting it at the end is sometimes used so that atmospheric pressure is maintained approximately in the middle of the model.

Because of their small dimensions and the possibility of speedy adjustments, aerodynamic models of open channel flow are particularly well suited for preliminary studies of various alternatives of the layouts of complex low head hydraulic structures, intakes, river training schemes, etc. The 'optimum' solution is then often tested in greater detail on a conventional hydraulic model, but in less important cases it is possible to base the final design on the aerodynamic model alone. Reliable quantitative results may be achieved, especially for river studies, with a fixed bed and predominantly two-dimensional flow.

The following example of the model investigations of the regulation of the river Elbe illustrates some of the advantages of aerodynamic models (Novak, 1967). It was necessary to increase the low flow depths for purposes of navigation by at least 100 mm (prototype) and measures were sought which would achieve this in the most economic way. The river channel is very irregular both in plan and in longitudinal section, with substantial 'macroroughness' due to pools and protrusions in the bed (as opposed to 'microroughness' caused by the sediment size), and analysis

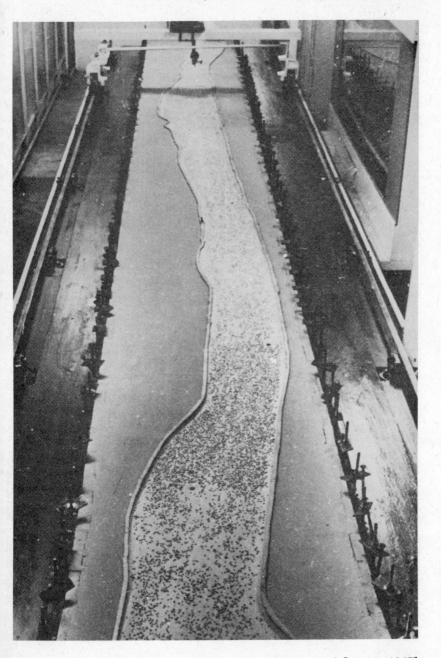

Fig. 11.4. Aerodynamic model of the River Elbe (without cover) [Novak, 1967]

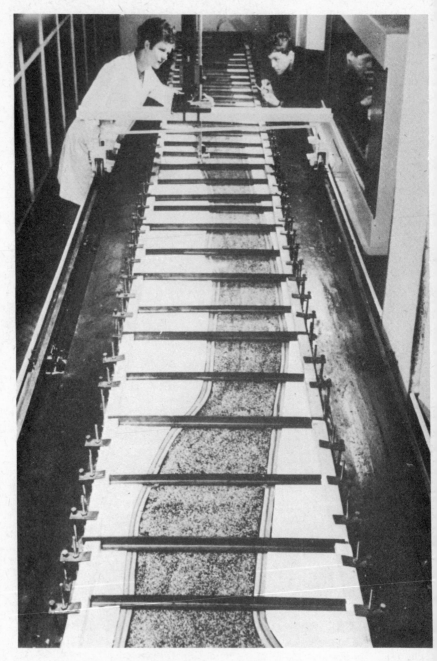

Fig. 11.5. Aerodynamic model of the River Elbe (with cover). [Novak, 1967]

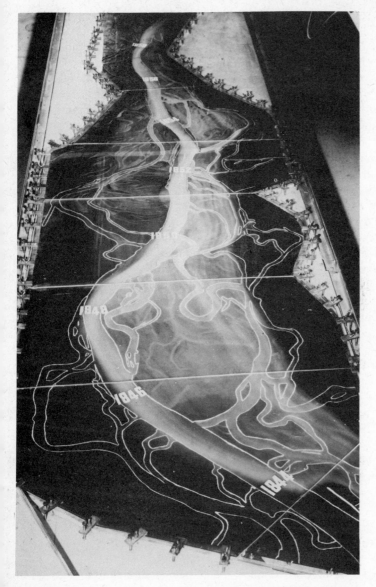

Fig. 11.6. Aerodynamic model of the River Danube (VÚV Bratislava).

has shown that in the given case 40 to 50% of the energy losses were caused by this irregularity in the channel section. An increase in depth could be achieved by concentrating the flow and narrowing the section, by employing longitudinal river works or groynes. Completely or partly eliminating the influence of channel irregularities, however, could decrease energy losses to such an extent that even with the narrower channel, the depth remained practically the same. Therefore, it was decided to investigate the problem on a distorted and tilted hydraulic model with $M_l = M_z = 65$, $M_h = 25$, and $M_s = 1$ (distortion 2.6). Although the model was useful it could not cope with the possible effects of dredging and overall nonuniformity of flow, (because of the changed slope which was adopted to preserve the effect of 'macroroughness'); the demands on accuracy of depth measurements were almost unrealistic and results of comparative studies were, therefore, somewhat uncertain as the required minimum increase of depth was only $100/25 = 4$ mm on the model (built in open air).

Both these disadvantages were removed by the use of an aerodynamic model with $M_l = 350$ and $M_h = 130$, i.e. with a practically identical distortion as the hydraulic model (2.69). The model was constructed in plasticine and roughened by fixed sand grains; the cover was also roughened by sand of a somewhat smaller size than the bed and raised by the same value. The model was designed with atmospheric pressure approximately in the middle of its length by connecting both the inlet and outlet to a fan, and was operated according to the previously stated principles and equations in such a manner that the sought after change of depth of 100 mm in prototype corresponded to about 60 mm of water gauge on the model ($M_Q = 2000$). It was, therefore, much easier and safer to judge the effect of various alternative designs on the model.

A comparison of the results achieved on hydraulic and aerodynamic models, as far as the type of investigated training measures and the limited accuracy of the hydraulic model permitted, gave good results. Figures 11.4 and 11.5 show the aerodynamic model without and with the cover.

Figure 11.6 shows a part of an aerodynamic model of the Danube below Bratislava, constructed at VÚV Bratislava, to study river training problems and the effects of a planned barrage.

11.3 Analogue Models in Hydraulic Engineering

The principle and a few examples of analogue models were already given in Section 11.1. Returning to Equation (11.1) and using the procedures established in Chapter 2 the following criteria or 'indicators' of analogy can be derived:

$$M_b M_t^2 = M_a M_t = 1 \tag{11.8}$$

Therefore, also

$$\frac{M_b}{M_a^2} = 1 \tag{11.8'}$$

From the boundary conditions it follows that

$$M_h(=M_\theta) = 1 \tag{11.8''}$$

Equation (11.8) enables us to determine the numerical relationship between analogous physical parameters. (It is evident that a single system of units has to be used throughout.)

Hydraulic analogues utilizing the similarity of flow patterns in a two-dimensional potential flow and in a thin layered viscous flow are often used together with flow visualization methods to study flow past obstacles or streamlines in seepage flow. A typical example are horizontal or vertical thin *layer* models or so-called *Hele–Shaw* models. In these models a viscous fluid flows in a thin slot between two smooth plates with a small, constant velocity giving laminar flow throughout. Neglecting inertia forces, the velocity in the horizontal (x) and vertical (y) directions (in the case of the vertical models) or in the horizontal x–z plane (horizontal models) is given by the equation

$$v_x = \frac{a^2 g}{12\nu\gamma}\frac{\partial p}{\partial x} = \frac{a^2 g}{12\nu}\frac{\partial h}{\partial x} = k\frac{\partial h}{\partial x} \tag{11.9}$$

$$v_y = \frac{a^2 g}{12\nu}\frac{\partial h}{\partial y} = k\frac{\partial h}{\partial y} \tag{11.9'}$$

where a is the distance between the plates.

Equations (11.9) and (11.9') correspond, e.g. to the equation of laminar flow through a porous medium and when combined with continuity

$$\frac{\partial v_x}{\partial x} + \frac{\partial v_y}{\partial y}\left(+\frac{\partial v_z}{\partial z}\right) = 0$$

satisfy the Laplace equation

$$\frac{\partial^2 h}{\partial x^2} + \frac{\partial^2 h}{\partial y^2} + \frac{\partial^2 h}{\partial z^2} = 0 \tag{11.10}$$

Hele–Shaw models using a fairly viscous fluid (e.g., glycerine) usually have a slot thickness of about 2 mm and a length of 1 to 2 m, with overfalls at the inlet and outlet simulating the boundary conditions, which may also be time dependent. Models using water have an appreciably smaller thickness of about 0.1 to 0.3 mm. Figure 11.7 shows a vertical Hele–Shaw model used to study seepage flow under a foundation. A change in the space between the plates could be used to simulate conditions of different permeabilities in stratified soils. The flow between the plates must of course remain laminar, i.e. the Reynolds number $Re = va/\nu < 500$ (Aravin and Numerov, 1958). Slot models are simple to construct and operate, although care and accuracy in the positioning of the plates are required.

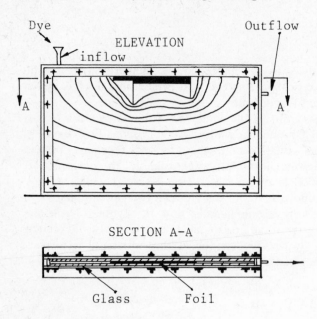

Fig. 11.7. Hele–Shaw model of seepage flow.

The use of Hele–Shaw models is limited to the solution of two-dimensional flow problems. No such limitations apply to *sand seepage models*, which, however, have disadvantages resulting from large capillary elevation and difficulties in the determination of the free water surface, and problems of entrapped air. Uniform glass balls or pellets of up to 4 mm diameter are sometimes used to overcome these difficulties.

The *membrane analogy* can be used to study the flow field around obstacles. A rubber membrane is fixed under uniform tension in a metal ring. If placed in an inclined position the lines of equal elevation (dotted lines on Fig. 11.8) show the streamlines of parallel flow. If a rod of similar cross-section as the shape of the body, whose effect on the flow field is under investigation, is then pressed from below into the inclined membrane its deflections at various points give a very good indication of the resultant streamlines (the full lines on Fig. 11.8 indicate the resulting flow net of streamlines and equipotential lines). By changing the orientation of the 'body' to the flow an optimum position with no separation of flow can be determined.

As mentioned earlier *electrical analogues* are widely used for the solution of groundwater flow problems. They can also be used for other hydraulic engineering problems, e.g., surge tank oscillations, flow in distribution networks, etc., although in these cases mathematical modelling is usually more convenient and appropriate.

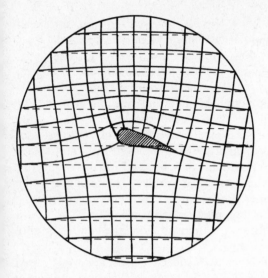

Fig. 11.8. Flow net determined by membrane analogy. [After Hálek, 1965]

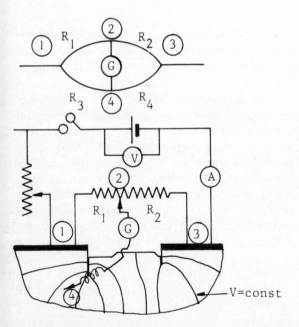

Fig. 11.9. Electrical circuit of an electroanalogue model of seepage flow.

The analogy between liquid flow and electrical current, pressure head or water level and voltage, and permeability and electrical resistance are best explored in groundwater flow problems with linear equations.

In principle a two-dimensional model uses a *two-dimensional conductor* in the shape of the considered porous medium with the contours simulating the boundary between the permeable and impermeable ground. The inlet and outlet is simulated by electrodes (brass or copper). As the geometry of the resulting flow net is independent of the absolute value of the filtration coefficient (conductivity; this follows from the Laplace Equation (11.10)) a variety of materials may be used for the conductor, e.g., tin foil sheets, electrolytes, varnished surfaces containing graphite powder, electroconductive paper, etc. The flow net is determined by using a probe to find lines of equal potential. In principle (*see* Fig. 11.9), a Wheatstone bridge is used with probe 4 moved along the conductor until the galvanometer, G, indicates zero.

Direct analogues using *linear resistors* and *capacitors* are widely used for groundwater resources analysis. An example of their use is given in Section 11.5.

11.4 Basic Equations for Groundwater Flow and Criteria of Similarity

Some basic equations only and the resulting criteria of similarity are given here; fuller treatment is given in some of the quoted references (Bear (1972), Cedergren (1977), Hálek (1965), Kovács (1978), Todd (1959), Verruijt (1970) etc.).

In dealing with flow through porous (granular) media only flow under the influence of gravity, i.e. filtration or seepage, is considered; movement under the influence of capillary forces, adhesion, etc., is excluded. The geometric properties and the porosity coefficient n (void ratio) of the granular medium may vary in location and direction, or they may be invariant forming an homogeneous, isotropic, cohesionless medium, which can be characterized by an effective grain size d. (An effective grain size is the diameter of uniform spheres which have the same porosity and produce the same filtration velocity as the actual nonuniform granular medium for the given gradient.) By dimensional considerations we can arrive at the equation

$$\frac{\gamma S d}{\rho v^2} = f\left(n, \frac{vd}{\nu}\right) \tag{11.11}$$

where v is the seepage (filtration) velocity given by the discharge divided by the gross area and $S = -\partial H/\partial x$ is the slope of the energy line or the hydraulic gradient $= -\partial h/\partial x$ (as $v^2/2g$ is negligible compared to the pressure head).

For small values of the Reynolds number the effect of inertia is negligible and thus Equation (11.11) will have the form

$$v = \left[\frac{\gamma d^2}{\mu} \frac{1}{f'(n)} \right] S = -k \frac{\partial h}{\partial x} \qquad (11.12)(=11.9)$$

where k is the coefficient of permeability (discharge per unit area giving a unit hydraulic gradient; in m³/day/m²). Equation (11.12) is the well-known Darcy law and is identical with Equation (11.9) derived in a different way. The limit of validity of Equation (11.12) is $Re = vd/\nu \leqslant 1$ signifying laminar filtration. For flow through coarse sand and gravel the seepage may be non-linear due to inertial effects in the flow round the particles and the onset of turbulence. If the effects of viscous forces are negligible, Equation (11.11) will reduce to

$$v^2 = \left[\frac{\gamma d}{\rho} \frac{1}{f''(n)} \right] S = -C \frac{\partial h}{\partial x} \qquad (11.13)$$

Equation (11.13) is valid for turbulent filtration at $vd/\nu \geqslant 10^4$. Equations (11.12) and (11.13) could be combined and written in the form

$$S = av + bv^2 \qquad (11.14)$$

where a and b are constants dependent on d and n, or

$$v^n = -C \frac{\partial h}{\partial x} \qquad (11.15)$$

with $1 < n < 2$ and both n and C varying with the Reynolds number.

Another way of expressing Equation (11.14) taking into account experimental results is (Yalin, 1971)

$$\frac{\gamma S d}{2\rho v^2} = \frac{1}{n^6} \left(0.01 + \frac{1}{Re} \right) \qquad (11.16)$$

The permeability coefficient in laboratory conditions is usually determined by tests in a filtration column, through which the flow Q is maintained under a constant head. By measuring the head loss, ΔH, over a distance ΔL and knowing the cross-sectional area, A, of the column, the coefficient is computed from $k = Q\Delta L/(A\Delta H)$. The value of the coefficient of permeability in the field is best determined by pumping tests, which, e.g., for a steady state condition in an unconfined homogeneous aquifer, are characterized by the equation

$$\frac{Q}{\pi k} \ln \frac{r_2}{r_1} = y_2^2 - y_1^2 \qquad (11.17)$$

where Q is the discharge from the abstraction well and y_1 and y_2 are the heights of the water table above the impermeable stratum in observation wells at distances r_1 and r_2 from the abstraction well. Equation (11.17) is the equation of the depression curve and permits the computation of k from the other measured quantities.

From Equation (11.11) the following criteria of similarity may be stated:

$$\frac{M_{\gamma Sd}}{\rho v^2} = M_n = M_{Re} = 1 \tag{11.18}$$

As the free surface in the filtration model has to be reproduced without distortion

$$M_S = 1 \tag{11.19}$$

Equations (11.18) and (11.19) can be satisfied using the same fluid on the model as in prototype ($M_\rho = M_\mu = 1$), only if $M_d = M_v = 1$ (which does not preclude a reduced model).

Using Equation (11.16) as a starting point the similarity criterion can be written as

$$\frac{M_{\gamma Sd}}{2\rho v^2} = 1 = \frac{1}{M_n^6} \frac{0.01 + \dfrac{1}{Re_p}}{0.01 + \dfrac{1}{Re_m}}$$

which results in

$$M_n^6 = \frac{0.01 Re_p + 1}{0.01 Re_p + M_{Re}} \tag{11.20}$$

The conditions $M_{\gamma Sd}/(\rho v^2) = 1$ and $M_S = 1$ for the same fluid on model and prototype results in

$$M_d = M_v^2 \tag{11.21}$$

($M_d = M_v = 1$ is a special case of Equation (11.21)). The values of M_n, M_d and M_v must thus satisfy both Equations (11.20) and (11.21).

For unsteady filtration the Strouhal criterion $M(vt/l) = 1$ must also be observed. If $Re < 1$ the first term in the bracket of Equation (11.16) can be neglected and it reverts back to the Darcy equation (Equation (11.12)) with

$$M_v = M_k \tag{11.22}$$

Modelling filtration with granular media is difficult (*see* the structure of the expression for k in Equation (11.12)); it is used, therefore, mainly when Darcy's law is not applicable, as otherwise analogue models, particularly electrical analogues, are more convenient in the domain of validity of linear filtration.

11.5 Examples of Groundwater Flow Models

As an example of seepage flow under the foundations of a weir Fig. 11.10 shows the flow net determined by a combination of two electrical analogues (*see* Section 11.3). One analogue was used for the determination of equipotential lines, the other for the solution of the streamlines. The usual procedure is to determine only one set of lines (the equipotential lines by the method illustrated in Fig. 11.9) and to complete the flownet by drawing the streamlines crossing the equipotential lines at right angles using a mesh of squares or rectangles (Fig. 11.10). In the given case the seepage flow per unit width is given by

$$Q = k \frac{H}{n} \frac{a}{b} m \tag{11.23}$$

where n and m are the number of spaces between the equipotential lines and streamlines respectively. The flow net also permits the determination of the pressure distribution on the foundations of the weir as well as in the ground below it.

With reference to well hydraulics models can be used, e.g., to determine the flow conditions for wells with horizontal filters extending radially from a central shaft. Figure 11.11 shows the streamlines as determined by Nemecek (1964). Owing to the flow before the well construction the flow pattern is asymmetrical, in spite of the fact that the filters are arranged symmetrically about the shaft; the upstream filters receive more water than the downstream ones. A modification of the position of the filters can be sought that would give equal flow through each filter.

The models of the groundwater flow in the Mishraq region in Iraq, built in the hydraulics laboratory of the University of Newcastle upon Tyne by

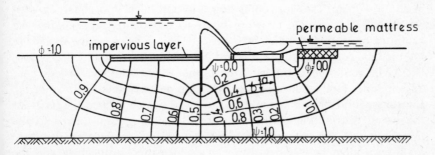

Fig. 11.10.

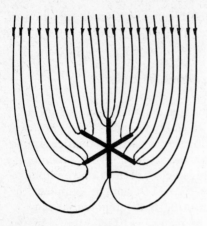

Fig. 11.11. Streamlines to a horizontal filter well. [After Nemecek, 1964]

Featherstone and Al Samarrie (1975), can serve as an example of models used for investigation of groundwater flow in a complex engineering situation. The Mishraq region situated on the west bank of the Tigris in northern Iraq has large sulphur deposits mined by underground melting by the injection of super-heated water through a borehole (Frasch process). The economics of the mining process depend on the water consumption which, in turn, depends on the geohydrology of the deposits. It was necessary, therefore, to study the hydraulics of groundwater flow in a large field by simulation. Since the natural flow in the sulphur bearing horizon can be considered as practically steady and some observed hydrogeological data were available, it was decided to study the problem initially on an analogue model and supplement the results by mathematical modelling. The objectives of the analogue were the study of the distribution of the transmissivity, the interconnection with the river and the quantities of natural flow all influencing the control of the mining process.

The area investigated was about 9 km^2 and was divided into a square mesh of 100 m. The horizontal flow through each grid square is represented by orthogonal resistors fitted to the points representing the centre of each square, which were spaced 20 mm apart on the model. In the model a transmissivity of 50 mm^2 p.d. was represented by 3300 ohms and 1 volt represented 1 m head. From the permeability determined near 23 boreholes (and assuming linear variation between them), a map of the transmissivity distribution could be produced, which formed the basis for the initial distribution of the resistors. By making adjustments to the distribution of the resistors, an arrangement was produced which gave good agreement between pressure heads measured in the field and the model voltages.

The potential along the boundary was automatically adjusted for river level changes by joining the nodes along the river line by a low resistance wire which was connected at one end to earth through a variable resistor. Figure 11.12 shows the analogue model with the boundary and river connections and some associated instrumentation.

The analogue proved to be very useful for the evaluation of the geohydrology in the natural state and for the identification of the locations most suitable for exploitation (avoiding areas of high permeability). The model permitted the determination of natural flows as a function of river stages, which in turn served as the basis for further studies of the pollution of the river as a result of sulphur exploitation. Further applications of the analogue were the study of methods of groundwater control and the determination of storage coefficient and smelting index by comparing undisturbed permeability with that after sulphur extraction.

The effect of sulphur extraction on the hydraulic flow parameters was investigated in the laboratory by measuring the permeability before and after extraction on a number of samples cut from cores from several boreholes. Further, a qualitative physical model with an artificial rock produced by immersing crushed dolerite in molten wax was built in a sealed metal container with a glass front. Cold water flowed horizontally through the model from a reservoir and, simultaneously, water flowing

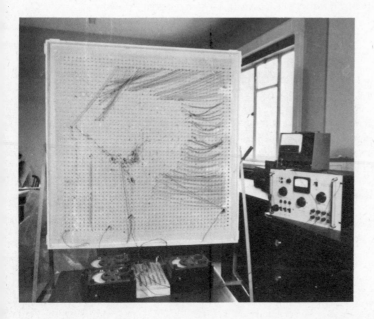

Fig. 11.12. Analogue model of the Mishraq region with river connection. [Featherstone and Al Samarrie, 1975]

under pressure into the model through a vertical 'borehole' melted the wax. The hot water and wax flowed upwards simulating an asymmetrical core of exploitation, the shape of which might influence ground subsidence and sulphur production.

References

Aravin, V. I. and Numerov, S. N. (1958). *Filtration in Hydraulic Structures*, (in Russian), Gostechizdat, Moscow.

Averkiev, A. G. (1952). New method of hydraulic model studies, (in Russian), *Izv. VNIIG*, No. 47.

Averkiev, A. G. (1957). *Methodology of Study of Open Channel Flow on Pressurised Models*, (in Russian), GEI, Moscow.

Bear, J. (1960). Scales of viscous analogy models for groundwater studies, *Proc. ASCE, J. Hydraul. Div.*, **86**, HY2, pp. 11–23.

Bear, J. (1972). *Dynamics of Fluids in Porous Media*, American Elsevier Publ. Co., New York.

Cedergren, H. R. (1977). *Seepage, Drainage and Flownets*, 2nd Ed, John. Wiley and Sons, London.

Druzhinin, N. I. (1956). *Method of Electrohydrodynamic Analogy and its Application to the study of Filtration*, (in Russian), Gosenergoizdal, Moscow.

Featherstone, R. E. and Al Samarrie, A. M. (1975, 1976). Geohydrology of Mishraq – groundwater study with electrical analogue simulations, *Sulphur*, No. 120, September/October 1975, pp. 44–49; No. 124, May/June 1976, pp. 20–24.

Gair, F. C. (1959). Unifying design principle for the resistance network analogue. *Brit. J. Appl. Phys.*, **10**, pp. 166–172.

Giljarov, N. P. (1959). *Use of Aerodynamic Models in River Research—New Methods and Instrumentation for Research of River Processes*, (in Russian), Izd ANSSSR, Moscow.

Hálek, V. (1965). *Hydraulic Research 3—Methods of Analogy in Hydraulics*, (in Czech), SNTL, Prague.

Hincu, S., Ionescu, S. and Finkelstein, A. (1961). Hydraulic laboratory study of the improvement of the Danube delta, (in Roumanian), *Sesiunes anuala ISCH*, Bucarest.

Ivicsics, L. (1975). *Hydraulic Models*, VITUKI, Budapest.

Johnson, C. L. (1956). *Analog Computer Techniques*, McGraw-Hill, New York.

Kahan, M. and Hincu, S. (1959). Study of free surface flow on aerodynamic models, (in Slovak) *Vodohospodársky časopis SAV*, No. 3, pp. 247–258.

Karplus, W. J. (1958). *Analog Simulation*, McGraw-Hill, New York.

Kovács, G. (1978). *Mathematical Modelling of Ground-Water Flow*, VITUKI, Budapest.

Landau, H. G. (1958). High order accuracy in the solution of partial differential equations by resistor networks, *J. Appl. Mech.*, pp. 17–20.

Latcher, V. M. and Prudovskij, A. M. (1959). *Some Problems of Aerodynamic Modelling of Open Channel Flow—New Methods and Instrumentation for Research of River Processes*, (in Russian), Izd. ANSSSR, Moscow.

Levi, I. I. (1960). *Modelling of Hydraulic Phenomena*, (in Russian), Gosenergoizdat, Moscow.

Liebman, G. (1954). Resistance network analogues with unequal meshes or subdivided meshes, *Brit. J. Appl. Phys.*, **5**, pp. 362–366.

Nemecek, E. P. (1964). Die Berechnung des Horizontalfilterbrunnens Östern. *Wasserwirtschaft*, **16**, Nos 1/2, pp. 20–32.

Nemeth, E. (1957). Hydrological research in Hungary, *Proc. Congress of the Int. Geodetic and Physical Union, Toronto*.

Novak, P. (1967). Model similarity and training of rivers with large channel irregularities, *Proc. 11th Congress, Fort Collins*, **I,** Paper A47, pp. 379–388.

Peattie, K. R. (1956). A conducting paper technique for the construction of flow nets, *Civil Engineering and Public Works Review*, **51,** pp. 62–64.

Pirkovský, M. (1970). Aerodynamic models, (in Slovak), *Vodní hospodárství*, No. 2.

Prickett, T. A. (1975). *Modelling Techniques for Groundwater Evaluation*, Advances in Hydroscience, Academic Press, Oxford.

Rushton, K. R. and Herbert, R. (1970). Resistance network for three-dimensional unconfined groundwater problems with examples of deep well dewatering. *Proc. ICE*, **45,** pp. 471–490.

Schneider, P. J. and Cambel, A. B. (1953). Membrane apparatus for analogic experiments, *Rev. Sci. Instr.*, **24**, No. 7, pp. 513–514.

Sumbal, J. (1961). The use of aerodynamic models for the determination of the position of the free water surface for steady nonuniform flow, (in Slovak), *Vodohospodársky časopis SAV*, No. 3, pp. 237–241.

Todd, D. K. (1959). *Groundwater Hydrology*, John Wiley and Sons, New York.

Vallentine, H. (1969). *Applied Hydrodynamics*, 3rd Edn, Butterworths, London.

Verruijt, A. (1970). *The Theory of Groundwater Flow*, Macmillan, London.

Yalin, M. S. (1971). *Theory of Hydraulic Models*, Macmillan, London.

12 Field Investigations of Hydraulic Parameters

12.1 Subject and Aims of Research

Investigation on rivers and hydraulic structures in field (prototype) conditions, as compared with highly developed model research of all types, is perhaps less used nowadays than several decades ago, though its importance has increased; as a result of the present use of physical and analogue models, and because of the great development of mathematical models, it serves many purposes. The three most important are:

(a) *Direct investigation* of hydrodynamic phenomena and natural processes and their effects on the river and hydraulic structures, the correct simulation and study of which has so far not been successfully achieved on physical or mathematical models;
(b) measurements and investigations under natural conditions to obtain initial *data* for *designing and proving* physical or mathematical models;
(c) prototype measurements to *verify* the results obtained on physical or mathematical models.

Depending on the aims and purposes of field measurements and investigations, their methodology and the hydraulic and other parameters to be measured are determined. In general it will be the aim of field studies to cover a wide range of conditions, e.g., spring and neap tides, floods and low flows, and various conditions when investigating hydraulic structures, etc. Field investigations can be very demanding in terms of manpower and instrumentation and, therefore, require careful preparation and planning.

A very brief account only of the relevant instruments and techniques for field measurements is given here, since they are undergoing rapid development. Further details are available in the references.

12.2 Investigations on Rivers, Canals, Reservoirs and in Coastal Regions

12.2.1 Bed topography

The topography of movable river beds and canals and of the gradual bed changes (erosion, deposition) is usually measured by taking surveys in permanently established cross-sections. At separate verticals in every section, the distances of which from a fixed bench mark on the bank are determined by measurement, the depth of the bed is ascertained (the position of the water level is determined by gauge or levelling). For small streams a steel rope with longitudinal divisions stretched across the river in the measuring section is sufficient as reference. The depth of the bed is measured by soundings taken from a boat. For large rivers and canals, reservoirs and estuaries, surveying methods are used to determine the position of the verticals and the depth is often measured by ultrasonic depth gauges, i.e. echosounders and echographs, based on the principle of reflection of ultrasonic waves from the bed. The error of echosounders is usually only a few centimeters. In oceanographic surveys more sophisticated techniques may be used.

12.2.2 Water levels

During steady or slowly changing unsteady flow direct readings of the water level on a vertical or inclined depth gauge, with sufficiently detailed divisions, are sometimes sufficient. By levelling the zero of the gauge the absolute height of the water level above sea level (ordnance datum) can be obtained. The simplest measurement of the water level change with time is done by recording the levels with stage recorders, the drums of which turn at a rate that can be altered according to the expected speed of oscillation of the water level and the aims of the measurements.

The vertical shafts of permanent recorders are built into the river or canal bank at the measuring section and are linked to it by a horizontal pipe sited beneath the lowest possible water level. In important gauging stations long-distance water level recorders with floats are fitted; the movement of the water level is linked mechanically to an electric transmitter.

Temporary transportable recorders are often used for measuring water levels on rivers and canals (Fig. 12.1). The float of the recorder moves in a vertical steel pipe closed at the lower end and with several small orifices symmetrically distributed over the circumference. The drum of the limnigraph is fitted at the top of the pipe, and a bench mark on the bank and an auxiliary mark on the vertical pipe of the limnigraph facilitate

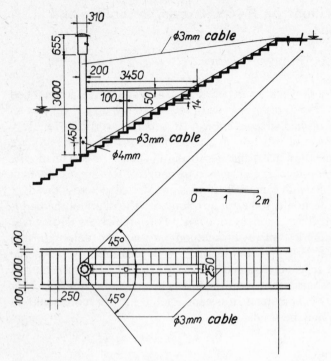

Fig. 12.1. Temporary water level recorder.

marking of the initial values of the height of the water level, together with time, before measurement on the recorder charts.

12.2.3 Waves

The same principles and instrumentation as given in Sub-section 12.2.2 can be used for measuring tidal levels in estuaries or oscillatory waves on reservoirs.

The study of wind waves on reservoirs has also been effectively carried out with the aid of a slit photowavegraph, taking photographs of undisturbed waves from the bank. From the photographs taken by two cameras placed at a known distance above each other, the basic elements of the windwaves are determined (i.e. period T, celerity c, length L and height H (Fig. 12.2). On large reservoirs instruments for measuring ocean waves may also be used.

Tide gauges are usually sited in deep water in a fairly sheltered area where surface waves only occur. Their principle is the same as that of ordinary water level recorders (*see* Fig. 12.1). At important locations automatic recording tide gauges giving a continuous record may be used. Tide gauges are also suitable for the measurement of seiches.

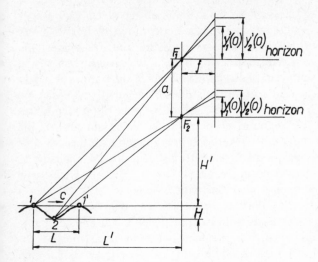

Fig. 12.2. Measurement of waves from the bank of a reservoir.

Ocean waves may be measured and recorded by a number of methods: pressure gauges or inverted echosounders, resting on the sea bed; vertical gauges working on the principle of electrical resistance or pressure and attached to a structure; floating wave recorders usually in the form of a buoy, e.g. the wave-rider buoy, which has an accelerometer and transmits data by radio; and ship-borne wave recorders combining data from an accelerometer and from pressure sensors attached to the hull (Draper, 1961).

12.2.4 Surface velocities

Surface velocities are measured either indirectly with the aid of special apparatus or by direct observation of floats.

One-shot photogrammetry has been used in some countries (e.g., France and Hungary) to determine the directions of surface flow on large rivers and canals. This method is based on photographing the investigated locality twice on one plate from a fixed point; one short exposure during the day, one long (or regularly interrupted) exposure during the night, recording the paths (and velocities) or a number of floats with torches inserted across the entire width of the flow. This method clearly illustrates the plan of a river reach with the corresponding streamlines but has the disadvantages of low accuracy (the shot is in central perspective) and of great laboriousness.

The stereophotogrammetric method based on the use of ground stereophotogrammetry has been found to be most suitable for observing surface streamlines. This is a two-shot method, based on obtaining stereoscopical pairs of shots of the float paths on the river reach under observation and their stereoscopic, spatial observation and assessment. Light floats are again most suitable for illustrating the streamlines; the moving light exposure is interrupted simultaneously on both shots of the stereoscopic pair, resulting in photographs on which the path of the light floats is pictured as a series of broken lines. The length of each line depends on the length of exposure, the distance from the phototheodolites and the surface velocity at the given point in the flow. For analysis the normal methods of topographical stereophotogrammetry can be used.

Floats and drift recorders are frequently used in coastal engineering and tidal streams studies. Both in river and coastal engineering the floats usually consist of a vertical timber bar with a pennant, light, or even a radar aerial, at the top and ballast at the bottom end. The float often also has wooden vertical vanes at its bottom end to stabilize it and to enable it to react to the prevailing current. It is usually two-thirds submerged; for tidal streams, a typical length is about 3 m. In some cases, e.g., when measuring close inshore, floats with a drogue suspended at the required level below them are used.

Drift cards, i.e. reply paid cards in plastic envelopes, may be used when studying the wind drift of surface layers of the sea.

Special apparatuses, e.g. the Hungarian VITUKI or the French VOLTURNO, consist fundamentally of a small current meter placed in a special cardan suspension, a small compass and an electrical recording device. With these instruments it is possible to measure the flow velocity at separate measuring points by means of the current meter and changes in the direction of flow at various depths below the water level relative to the basic flow direction on the water surface. These changes in the flow direction are recorded as changes in electrical resistance, which can be directly read off in degrees. The basic direction of flow on the water surface is measured by the compass. The accuracy of measuring the velocity vector depends on the flow velocity and is within a range from $\pm 2°$ to $\pm 4°$. Measurements are usually taken from a boat moving across the river in the measuring section and the position within the section is determined by surveying. The method is very time consuming and of low accuracy, due to the need for interpolation between the measuring points.

12.2.5 Velocities of flow

The most widely used instrument for measuring flow velocity on rivers and canals is the current meter which is reliable and comparatively accurate when correctly used. It may have different forms (propeller, cup, electromagnetic, drag body) and purposes (indicating, recording, directional). The most common type, i.e. the propeller current meter, is based on the principle that the rate of its propeller revolutions is proportional to the flow velocity at the point of measurement. After a certain number of propeller revolutions an electric circuit with a device for counting the revolutions is closed. During the metering period the average number of revolutions per second is ascertained and from the calibration certificate of the meter the value of the flow velocity at the measured point is determined. The meter is either fixed to a rod or suspended. It is lowered into the flow from a boat, a bridge, or a cableway. With the aid of current-meters it is possible to measure the velocity at separate points in the flow and in individual verticals, or to investigate velocities in the whole section (isovels) and also the mean cross-sectional velocity. At every point the flow velocity is measured over a period of time, which is long enough to exclude the influence of flow fluctuations, but short enough to ensure that time errors in measurements are small and a certain steady state of flow is recorded. For this reason several meters are usually used simultaneously, either fixed to a mobile perpendicular set of poles or to a horizontal frame of a measuring carriage (in a rectangular section) moving in a vertical direction (Fig. 12.3).

Point measurements with a current meter should last at least one minute (40 s according to British Standards Institution (1964)) and during periodically recurring pulsations they should be at least as long as two periods. The distance of the extreme measuring points from the water surface, the bed and the sides, must not exceed 0.2 m and the maximum distance between the points can be 1 m; the spacing of the measuring points near the bed and the channel sides, where there is a great velocity gradient, should be smaller. To obtain a sufficiently accurate picture of the velocity field in a section during point measurements of velocity, the number of measuring points x must lie within $24\sqrt[3]{A} < x < 36\sqrt[3]{A}$, where A is the cross-sectional area (m^2) of the measured section.

Instead of placing several propellers on a perpendicular system of poles for point measurements of velocity in separate verticals, the integration method of measuring with the aid of a special current meter is now often used. The meter moves along a vertical pole at an even, low velocity of 2 to 4 cm/s from the water surface to the bed (or in the opposite direction; Taus, et al., 1963). By recording the number of propeller revolutions for the entire period necessary to cover the vertical from the water level to the bed or vice versa the mean flow velocity in the vertical is directly measured. The integrating meters give an impulse after every, or every other, revolution so that the values of velocities along the entire vertical may be observed from an oscillographic record.

If the measuring section is rectangular (e.g., in an inlet) a number of integrating meters may be fitted on the horizontal frame of a measuring carriage and placed at suitably chosen distances from each other and the lateral wall (Fig. 12.3). The measuring carriage suspended on a special

Fig. 12.3. Integrating current meters at a power station inlet.

device is lowered or raised at even velocity (2 to 4 cm/s), so that simultaneously the mean flow velocity in all verticals of the measuring section is measured (areal integration of velocity). Since in current metering it is often impossible to fulfil the condition that the axis of the propellers should always correspond to the direction of flow at the point of measurement, component propellers are used measuring the velocity component perpendicular to the measuring section (up to an inclination of about 30° of the propeller axis from the flow direction).

In ocean engineering work special current meters recording the required information within the immersed instrument in coded form, e.g., on magnetic tape, are used. In more refined instruments telemetry may be used to 'interrogate' the meter.

12.2.6 Discharge

The most frequently used method for measuring discharges on rivers and canals consists of measuring the cross-sectional area A (corresponding to the water stage h) and the simultaneous measurement of the mean flow velocity, v, with the aid of current meters (*see* Sub-section 12.2.5). The steady discharge Q corresponding to the stage h is then given by $Q = Av$. If a number of similar measurements for various steady stages h is carried out, the rating curve $Q = f(h)$ can be established. From this the discharge Q through the section for any arbitrary water level h can be determined. A necessary assumption is that the section should be situated in a river or canal reach unaffected by backwater and should have a stable bed. In case of a change (e.g., erosion) of the gauging section a new rating curve has to be established.

Another method is the use of temporary or permanent gauging structures for discharge measurements. If a permanent structure is available in or near the river reach of interest, it should be used to provide a long-term record of discharge. These structures are usually notches or weirs of simple or more complicated shape such as a Crump weir, flat Vee weir, etc. These structures have been developed on the basis of laboratory studies. To measure low discharges, only the central part is used, and this is sometimes separated from the rest of the weir by piers (Fig. 12.4). The discharge is calculated as a function of the head above the crest of the spillway, usually measured by a level recorder situated on the bank of the river. Although the structures have been investigated on models, in special circumstances (effect of bends, sedimentation, etc.) it is advisable to verify several discharges by direct measurements in the field.

On smaller canals and rivers it is also possible to use a sharp-edged notch or a Venturi or Parshall measuring flume for discharge measurement. Under suitable conditions the notch or flume may be used as a

Fig. 12.4. Crump weir on the River Greta near Barnard Castle (Northumbrian Water Authority).

permanent installation for continuous measurement of discharges. Even if the equations for the calculation of the discharge on these devices are known on the basis of measured geometric and hydraulic parameters, in special circumstances their accuracy should again be verified by calibration.

Other methods are also used for discharge measurement on rivers and canals, e.g., ultrasonic and dilution gauging. In the dilution method a known quantity of tracer (e.g. isotope) solution at known concentration is injected into the stream with the aid of special dosing equipment and at a downstream section, after perfect mixing, its concentration in the water is measured, e.g. with the aid of a radiation counter. The discharge is then calculated from the equation

$$Q = q \frac{C_1 - C_2}{C_2 - C_0} \tag{12.1}$$

where q = injection rate,

C_0 = background concentration,

C_1 = tracer concentration at injection,

C_2 = downstream sample concentration.

Methods of discharge measurements in rivers and canals are described in greater detail in books on hydrology and hydrometry (e.g., Ackers *et al.* 1978) and in many cases standard specifications for the whole procedure have been published (e.g. BSI (1964–1974)).

12.2.7   Friction coefficients

The calculation of the discharge capacity or of the necessary dimensions of river channels and canals depends to a large extent on the correct determination of the value of their head loss coefficients. Their value is influenced by a number of factors such as the shape of the channel and its changes, the condition of the channel surface, the composition of the material of its bed and banks, the degree of silting up or constriction (e.g., by weeds) of the channel cross-section, etc.

Friction coefficients are measured under steady flow conditions, i.e. with steady water levels in the chosen sections of the canal or river, the shape and cross-sectional area of which have been measured. Movable (temporary) level recorders are placed at suitably chosen points and their bench marks sited on the bank surveyed. Before every measurement of the water level the initial values of the water level height is transferred from the bench-marks to the registration paper of the limnigraph and time recorded. The measurement is repeated for several different water levels and, simultaneously, the steady discharge is measured. Thus all the hydraulic parameters necessary for the calculation of the channel friction coefficient are obtained.

When assessing water levels from the records, time intervals must be chosen during which there has been a steady flow regime along the entire reach of the channel.

The channel is not usually prismatic and the flow in it, therefore, is not uniform. The friction coefficients of the channel can be computed using the basic equation for steady nonuniform flow:

$$\Delta h = \frac{\bar{v}^2 \Delta l}{\bar{C}^2 \bar{R}} + \frac{\alpha(v_{i+1}^2 - v_i^2)}{2g} + \xi \frac{\alpha}{2g}(v_i^2 - v_{i+1}^2) \tag{12.2}$$

where Δl = the length of the reach with steady flow,

$\bar{v} = \dfrac{Q}{\bar{A}}$ = the mean cross-sectional velocity in the

channel reach,

$\bar{A}$ = average cross-section,

$\bar{R}$ = mean hydraulic radius,

$\bar{C}$ = mean value of the Chezy velocity coefficient,

v_i, v_{i+1} = mean sectional velocities in sections i and $(i+1)$,

ξ = coefficient of local head loss.

From the mean values of the velocity coefficients $\bar{C}$ calculated from Equation (12.2) it is then possible to express, e.g., the value of the mean roughness coefficient n, with the aid of the known equations (*see* Chapter 6).

12.2.8 Unsteady flow and its effect on navigation

The flow regime in rivers and canals with a system of locks or power stations is hardly ever steady, since their operation causes unsteady flow in the reaches (reservoirs) between them. This may have an unfavourable effect on the hydraulic structure itself, on the bank stability, and on navigation. The operation of such a system of power stations must, therefore, be backed by conclusive evidence based on the results of investigations of the hydraulic regime, carried out using physical and/or mathematical models or by direct field measurements. During these measurements, apart from recording the water levels, (*see* Sub-section 12.2.2) the change of discharge with time $Q = f(t)$ must also be measured within the studied reach. For measurement of variable discharges through the power station turbines it is possible to use a calibrated pressure difference meter or other measuring devices (*see* Sections 12.4 and 12.6).

The study of hydraulic phenomena on power station and navigation canals in connection with navigation is concerned either with the effect of unsteady flow on vessels (at rest or moving) or with the waves occurring during the movement of vessels and their effect on the canal bed and banks and on other vessels.

To assess the forces exerted by translatory waves on vessels, either computational methods or direct measurements of the forces (e.g., in lashings) may be used. When using a mathematical method the various hydraulic parameters, e.g., the slopes of water levels, length of waves with regard to the length of vessels, height of waves, velocities of flow, etc., must be known in order to calculate the forces exerted on the vessel. To ensure the safety of the vessels and of navigation, the maximum force occurring in the lashings during unsteady flow must be smaller than the permissible force the ropes can withstand. If the lengths of the surge waves are considerably shorter than the vessel their height must not be such that they pass over the sides of a fully loaded vessel. Furthermore, the continuity of the movement of the vessels on a water surface with waves must not be disrupted (when sailing against the slope of the wave and against the direction of their propagation the speed of the vessel is decreased and vice versa). If calculation proves that the safety of the vessels and continuity of navigation are not fully ensured, it is necessary to reduce the rate of change of discharge and thus favourably influence the hydraulic parameters of unsteady flow by technical and/or operational measures (*see* Chapter 8).

Direct measurement of forces in the vessel lashings is carried out simultaneously with the investigation of hydraulic parameters of the unsteady flow regime. Such measurements have been carried out, e.g., on the Dortmund-Ems canal in Germany in the Meppen-Varloh reservoir. The purpose of the research was to show whether simultaneous filling of the two locks placed side by side at Meppen was consistent with safe navigation. Simultaneous filling causes negative waves in the upstream reservoir, since the draw off of water from the reservoir increases from $0 \text{ m}^3/\text{s}$ to the maximum $113 \text{ m}^3/\text{s}$ in about 285 s.

A total of 13 limnigraphs was installed in the upper Meppen reservoir to record the water level oscillations. To measure and record the forces arising in the lashings of the barges and tugs, measuring elements with double, suitably protected tensometers were used and changes in the electric resistances of the loaded elements were recorded. The time-discharge relationship was assessed from the progress of filling, $h = f(t)$, recorded by level recorders in both locks (*see also* Chapter 8).

Large scale studies of the hydraulic phenomena occurring during the movement of vessels along a water-way (especially in a canal) and their effects on the bed and banks, and also on other vessels, were carried out in a number of countries, especially in the German Federal Republic and the Netherlands. These results of field experiments complemented and verified research in laboratories and the results of theoretical studies of the influence of the vessel speed and of the values of the blockage ratio $n = A/A_1$ (where A is the canal cross-sectional area and A_1 is the immersed sectional-area of the vessel) on the complicated flow along the vessel and its effects, both on the water-way and on the other vessels. Important results were obtained, particularly in experiments on a new section of the Main–Danube canal near Bamberg with a value $n = 7$ for fully loaded vessels (Schäle, et al., 1968).

Experiments have shown that flow caused in the canal by the movement of vessels is three-dimensional. Back-flow of water and the lowering of the water level along the vessel are subject to considerable acceleration. The velocities of this flow are unevenly distributed in the canal section (the greatest are at the surface) and change both in direction and magnitude. Flow along a fully loaded vessel becomes steadier with the increasing length of the vessel; the greater the length, the smaller the danger of deformation of the canal section due to the effects of back-flow (this also applies for the maximum permissible navigation speed $v = 0.6c_{cr}$, where c_{cr} is the celerity of a translatory wave in the canal $c_{cr} = \sqrt{(gh)}$). This finding is particularly important for comparatively long push-tow systems for it confirms their suitability as compared with tow navigation.

12.2.9   Sediment transport and morphology

Under certain conditions the flow transports sediments either along the bed (sand, gravel, boulders) or in suspension (fine particles). Erosion and sedimentation change the channel and coastal morphology. For a technically correct and hydraulically effective design of a river training or coastal protection scheme, or for the undisturbed operation of a hydraulic structure, the beginning and end of sediment transport, the quantity transported, the sediment petrographic composition, its grain size and distribution, the particle shape and mode of movement should be known. The mechanics and computation of sediment movement is dealt with in greater detail in Chapters 6 and 10.

The bed material may be sampled by using grabbing devices or more sophisticated bed material samplers (e.g. the American US BM-60).

Suspended sediment concentration is measured either directly by taking individual or pumped samples from the flow (Crickmore and Aked, 1975), or indirectly with the aid of turbidity meters based on the principle of photoelectric effect. A number of commercially produced meters exist for the measurement of suspended sediments. The simplest instrument is a sampling bottle with an inlet and de-aeration orifice, which is placed in the stream until it is full. Instead of point sampling it may also be used for integration sampling vertically. More sophisticated devices have been developed, e.g., in the Netherlands ('Delft Bottle'), the USA (USP-61), the USSR and France, where, for example, the Neyrpic Turbidisonde is fitted on both sides with Venturi nozzles to compensate for the resistance at the inlet orifice of the sampling device by additional suction. Thus the disturbance to flow and sediment transport caused by the presence of the samplers is minimized.

Coarser sediment transport along the bed is measured either by direct mechanical methods or indirectly. Direct measurement in small streams is achieved by retaining a certain volume in a pit, and in larger rivers with the aid of a bed load meter lowered to the bed of the river. Indirect methods include acoustic, electric and optical methods, the use of radioactive or fluorescent tracers, etc.

For direct measurement of bedload, various wire mesh (Bogardi, Shamov, etc.) and full-walled samplers (Novak, Karolyi, Goncharov, Helley-Smith, etc.) have been developed. Figure 12.5 shows the VÚV bedload meter developed by Novak (1957). The efficiency of these bedload meters, defined as the ratio of actually retained quantities of sediment to the quantity which would otherwise pass through the same section of the river bed without the presence of the sampler and which can be ascertained only by fairly complicated laboratory investigations, is at most about 70% for good designs (Novak, 1959).

Indirect methods of sediment measurement are still being developed. Tracers and possibly the acoustic method (hydrophonic detectors) are most promising, but so far both are suitable only for a qualitative study of sediment movement (except for certain cases where it is possible to examine the distribution of tracers with respect to depth and hence make a limited quantitative assessment), and/or for the determination of the

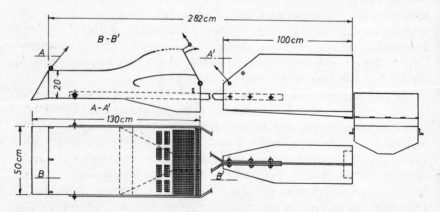

Fig. 12.5. VÚV bedload meter. [Novak, 1957]

beginning of sediment movement and of the width of the sediment band moving along the bed of the channel.

The height, length and velocity of continuously moving sediment banks on the river bed can be measured by electrical gauges, using the difference in resistance between water and gravel or sand saturated with water. For the measurement of the dune velocity two gauges placed at a given distance from each other in the direction of the flow can be used. The state and development of gravel banks and the aggradation and erosion of the river or reservoir bed at certain time intervals may be observed with the aid of an echograph (*see* Sub-section 12.2.1).

The measurement of bedload is difficult because its movement is very irregular, unevenly distributed over the whole width of the channel and part of it may only be transported across the river channel. The results of field measurements and the correlations between the transported quantity of sediment and the discharge may be compared with results obtained by computation according to various equations and/or from scale models (*see* Chapter 6).

Littoral drift may be measured directly at certain barriers by measuring, e.g., the rate of sediment accumulation on the updrift side, or by computing beach quantities at fixed section from regular aerial surveys. Indirect methods again rely mostly on radioactive or fluorescent tracers (Crickmore, 1976).

12.2.10 Temperature and other reservoir parameters

In deep reservoirs water temperature is usually measured twice a week at 3 to 5 m depth intervals, always in the same vertical in the centre of the reservoir at a distance of about 200 m from the dam. At the same time the water temperature downstream of the dam and the air temperature are measured. To measure the water temperature in the reservoir either special mercury or electric thermometers, often several in one vertical at various depths, are used. The results are processed graphically as a function of time and lines of equal temperature (isotherms) are determined. A sudden jump in temperature in a certain layer below the water level is not developed as clearly in reservoirs as in natural lakes.

The winter regime in reservoirs with almost stationary water develops in a somewhat different way from rivers and canals. The formation, dissolution and physical properties of the reservoir ice cover must be constantly observed. It begins to form near the banks and gradually spreads over the entire water surface. The more the water surface is disturbed by wind during freezing up, the more uneven the surface of the ice cover will be. Near the banks and the dam the ice cover is thicker than in the centre of the reservoir and it lasts on average a fortnight longer than in the river above it; this is why attention must be paid to the formation of ice barriers at the end of the backwater. In large reservoirs the ice cover as well as the ice floating in from the upstream reach of the river dissolves completely, but in small reservoirs ice floes have to be passed over the spillway of the dam or through the barrage (*see also* Section 12.3).

Apart from the temperature regime the quality parameters of the water in the reservoirs are monitored using physical, chemical and biological methods. Since the quality of the reservoir water is influenced to a large extent by the quality of its surface tributaries these are investigated as well. In some larger reservoirs density currents which considerably influence the quality of water withdrawn from the reservoir are also investigated. For a description and discussion of the methods used for the investigation of the quality of water in rivers and reservoirs, which is outside the framework of this book, the relevant technical literature should be consulted.

12.3 Investigations of the Winter Regime of Rivers and Canals

12.3.1 Basic forms of ice and ice phenomena

Long term observations have revealed the following basic forms of ice on rivers and canals:

(a) *Surface ice*, forming an ice cover on the water surface, usually of crystalline, homogeneous structure, due to cooling and freezing of the surface layer of the water only. Because of continuing low temperatures the thickness of the ice cover increases from below;
(b) *Internal ice*, forming small crystals in a fast stream of water through general cooling, and causing the separate ice grains to rise to the surface and combine there to form a carpet or flow of frazil (brothlike) ice of spongelike structure, the underside of which is not clearly defined and divided from the water on which it floats, as is the case in surface ice;
(c) *Depth (or even bottom) ice*, forming on contact of the water with solid, mainly metal, overcooled objects submerged in the water or positioned on the river bed. Its compact structure considerably differs from internal water ice which is light and porous.

Through the action of these three basic forms of ice, together with natural factors such as morphology, hydraulic and hydrological parameters and local climatic conditions, ice phenomena may occur, which are of great importance in the design and operation of hydraulic structures, i.e. congestion of frazil ice, ice barriers, ice on screens and gates, etc.)

The ice cover on rivers and canals begins to form mainly at the banks and progresses towards the centre as air heated by the water flows in this direction. Both the thickness of the snow cover, the heat conductivity of which is considerably lower than that of ice, and the heat generated by the friction of the flowing water on the underside of the ice cover, influence its growth and thickness.

Due to intensive long term cooling, if the velocity of flow is greater than 1.0 m/s, a large quantity of internal ice constantly forms in the stream and covers part of the water surface in the form of 'cakes' of frazil ice. The constant formation of ice causes complex conditions at some sharp bends and meanders, at fords with small water depth (on the gravel banks of which bottom ice also forms), and at any other point in the river where the water surface slope suddenly decreases, due to either a discontinuity in the bed slope or to backwater from a hydraulic structure. At these points the flow velocity is also reduced and conditions for the formation of a continuous ice cover arise. Frazil ice, brought by the flow from the upper reaches of the river, accumulates under this cover, freezes on to it, and gradually blocks the flow cross-section of the channel causing a speedy rise in the water level above the blockage point. As similar blockages may also occur in sharp bends and meanders of the river, the radius of curvature within a backwater (according to Potapov, 1955) should not be smaller than

$$R_{\min} = \frac{0.02h_s}{\alpha(v-1)^2} \tag{12.3}$$

where h_s is the thickness of the floating frazil ice, α is an empirical coefficient (e.g., for $h_s = 0.4$ m $\alpha = 0.0025$) and v is the mean velocity of flow in m/s.

The influence of wind on the formation of ice on rivers is complex. Although it facilitates easier heat transfer from water to air, it slows down the formation of an ice cover by generating waves (mixing of water particles and of layers of different temperature, rough water surface). This is the case particularly on large reservoirs and lakes where the height of waves caused by the wind does not depend only on its velocity, but also on the fetch. Sometimes wind and morphology may have a greater influence on the formation of ice processes than the flow velocity. During the period when ice floes are passing, usually at the end of the winter when the ice softens, ice barriers frequently form on rivers with lower flow velocities under the same conditions as blockages of frazil ice. According to investigations the criterion for the formation of an ice barrier is the Froude number (Kivisild, 1959). As long as the Froude number $Fr \leqslant 0.08$ the ice floes are not drawn beneath the ice cover, but remain in front of it on the surface. At greater values of the Froude number an ice barrier begins to form.

12.3.2 Flow in an ice-covered channel

Due to the influence of the ice cover in a river channel or canal, the hydraulic parameters and flow regime change. The ice cover influences the velocity distribution, increases the wetted perimeter and thus reduces the hydraulic radius and causes an increase in the resistance to flow. To elucidate the problem of flow in channels with ice cover, investigations of all necessary hydraulic parameters are carried out under natural conditions, as for channels with a free surface (Brachtl, 1963).

Stage recorders at regular intervals are used for measurements of the water levels on a reach of the frozen river or canal, and the methods are the same as for measuring water levels without an ice cover (*see* Subsection 12.2.2). The limnigraphs are installed before the ice forms and to prevent the water level in their vertical steel pipes from freezing, a layer of non-freezing liquid is used. Since the ice cover follows changes of the water level in the river, suitable methods must be used to prevent the vertical pipes of the limnigraphs from freezing to it (*see* Sub-section 12.3.3).

Measurements of the flow velocities beneath the ice cover are most frequently carried out with the aid of current meters in the verticals in openings cut in the ice cover. The method of measurement is similar to that used in channels without ice cover (*see* Sub-section 12.2.5).

The discharge of water under the ice during steady flow is most frequently measured indirectly by measuring the cross-sectional area of flow (immediately before ice formation) and the velocity; the thickness of the ice cover must be taken into account. Other methods can also be used to measure steady discharges under the ice cover, e.g., dilution gauging techniques.

For measured or derived hydraulic and geometric parameters it is possible to determine the mean value of the friction coefficient of the channel with ice cover for steady flow conditions.

Unsteady flow in rivers and canals with ice cover can be investigated using similar methods as those outlined in Sub-section 12.2.8. The study of this problem, however, has not advanced far enough to draw general conclusions beyond the fact that the velocity of propagation of surges and smooth translatory waves in channels with ice cover is greater than in the same channels with a free water surface.

12.3.3 Prevention of ice formation at hydraulic structures

A hydraulic structure may considerably influence the ice phenomena in a river reach, e.g., due to the reduced flow velocity in the reservoir upstream an ice cover begins to form sooner and more quickly, and the movement of the ice floes from it begins later than on a free river without the backwater effect. This causes certain operational difficulties which must be prevented by suitable measures tested in the field to guarantee a smooth and safe operation of the hydraulic structure under winter conditions (Sikora, 1962).

Therefore, to prevent the formation of dangerous ice barriers at the end of the backwater it is necessary to disrupt the ice cover in the reservoir at a certain time prior to the ice passage from the upper reaches and to pass the floes over the barrage.

On the Danube in Austria the opening and closing of the gates and the resultant lowering and raising of the water level in the reservoir above the barrages was found to be an effective way of breaking the ice cover (and passing it over the gates; Böck, 1957). To break up the ice cover and ice barriers ice-breakers and explosives (small charges beneath the ice, light bombs) are also used. The passing of the broken ice floes and frazil ice from the reservoir over partially lowered barrage gates has not been found very effective because of low flow velocities, especially when the water level in the reservoir was not lowered. Considerably more effective results were obtained by completely opening one barrage gate (section), which resulted in the ice floes starting to move not only near the opened gate but also at a distance of several kilometers above the barrage across the entire width of the reservoir. An evaluation of the experiments has shown that on $1 \, m^2$ of reservoir surface completely freed from ice a discharge of $7.5 \, m^3/s$ of water was used for passing ice in this way through one completely open weir section. In comparison with the previously mentioned method it was found that the consumption of water per $1 \, m^2$ of freed surface is only one tenth of that necessary for passing the same amount of ice floes over all the gates lowered 1.5 m beneath the upstream water level. Thus losses in power production in the power stations next to the barrages are also reduced. The time necessary to pass ice from one square kilometer of reservoir surface over the barrage greatly decreases with the increasing specific discharge through the sections through which the ice is passed. This time is also reduced by the increasing ratio of width b/B, where b is the width of all barrage sections (including the piers), through which the ice passes and B the width of the reservoir (influence of lateral contraction). Evidently a barrage situated in the streamline of the river has the best conditions for passing ice floes and frazil ice from the reservoir (*see also* Sub-section 7.3.3).

The directions of the movements of the ice floes on the water surface and the formation of ice barriers can be investigated with the aid of stereophotogrammetric methods of measurement (*see* Sub-sections 12.2.2 and 12.2.4).

A necessary condition for the successful passing of the ice through barrages is that their gates should always be in working condition. In winter an ice cover may freeze to the gates and this could not only exert considerable pressures but also prevent gate movement. Furthermore the gates may freeze both to the piers and to their sills and deep ice form on their upstream face. Finally ice also forms on the downstream part of the gates where water seeping through imperfectly sealed joints freezes. Such ice phenomena must be eliminated or at least drastically reduced by measures which have been investigated by field experiments.

To preserve strips of free water surface in the ice cover in front of the gates infra-red heaters can be suspended above the water surface or heated cooling water from the power station sprayed (*see* Fig. 12.6), but for the most part forced water circulation is used, whereby the warm bottom layers are brought to the surface in front of the weir gates. The most frequently used method for inducing artificial circulation is the use of air bubbles, which are driven into the water under excess pressure at a maximum of 0.8 atmospheres at a depth of about three to five meters (depending on temperature) through orifices of about 2 mm diameter in pipes connected to a compressor. The distance between the orifices is usually between 1.5 and 2.0 m; they should be placed as closely as possible to the protected structure. The air consumption per orifice of

Fig. 12.6. Spraying the ice cover upstream of gates with heated water.

Fig. 12.7. Breaking up the ice cover at barrages by spraying with a water jet (River Váh).

2 mm diameter at operational excess pressure 0.7 atmospheres is about 0.6 l/s.

The freezing of gates to piers and the sill is prevented by electric heating (direct or indirect) of the steel parts on which the rubber sealing of the joints rests. This also reduces ice formation on the downstream face of the gates due to seepage. Ice from gates and piers can also be removed by spraying with a concentrated fast water jet, and such a jet may also be used to break up ice forming upstream of the gates (*see* Fig. 12.7).

Direct electrical heating has also been found effective as a protection for the fine screens of intakes against the formation of deep and frazil ice, which may completely block the flow cross-section of unprotected screens and prevent the draw-off of water.

12.4 Investigations on Pressure Conduits

12.4.1 Discharge and friction losses

For a certain steady discharge Q the hydraulic gradient along a conduit is measured with the aid of accurate manometers placed in characteristic measuring sections, i.e. always upstream and downstream of a straight length of constant cross-section or of each part where local losses are occurring.

To measure pressure four piezometrical orifices are drilled into the walls of the conduit in every measuring section. These are distributed symmetrically over the circumference and connected to each other by a circular pipe terminating in a manometer, the elevation of which is found by levelling. During every measurement taken for steady discharge the pressure on the manometers is read off several times and its arithmetical mean calculated; in determining the pressure the rating of the manometer and temperature effects should be taken into account.

The most commonly used method of measuring discharge in large conduits under pressure (if there is no reliable differential head device available) consists of the measurement of the cross-sectional area and the corresponding velocity distribution (velocity-area method). In pipes of smaller diameters one current meter fixed on a pole perpendicular to the pipe is usually used, which can be shifted along one of its diameters or along two diameters perpendicular to each other. In bigger conduits a larger number of current meters is used, usually mounted on a cross temporarily fixed to the walls of the pipe (*see* Fig. 12.8; Kutiš, 1970).

Fig. 12.8. Mounting current meters inside a pressure conduit [Kutiš, 1970]

One meter must be placed in the axis of the conduit and the spacing between corresponding propellers fitted to the various parts of the cross should be the same. Towards the wall of the pipe this spacing is smaller because of the steep velocity gradient. Usually propellers of a diameter of 100 mm are used (50 mm near the walls of the pipe). The necessary number x of the current meter propellers on each arm of the cross is calculated from the relationship

$$4\sqrt{D} < x < 5\sqrt{D}$$

where D is the inside diameter of the pipe (m) in the measuring section. Point velocities are measured simultaneously throughout the section, as this speeds up the measurement and represents the steady discharge better. The measuring section should be placed in a straight section of the conduit in such a way that upstream of it there is a straight length equal to at least 20 and downstream of it 5 diameters. The minimum diameter of a conduit still suitable for this method of measurement is 1200 mm. In the case of smaller diameters the influence of the supporting cross on which the current meters are fitted is felt and the measured velocities are greater than correspond to a free flow section (Tonini, 1965)

Discharge in conduits under pressure may also be measured in other ways, e.g., by measuring the pressure differences between two sections. Venturimeters or orifices are used as also is the measurement of the difference in pressures between the inner and outer side of a pipe bend. Both methods are suitable for continuous measurement of pressure and discharge and may be calibrated using other methods of discharge measurement. If standard conditions for the installation of the meter are available, no further calibration is required (BSI, 1964)

Gibson's waterhammer method may also be used to measure the discharge in pressure pipes. When closing a gate (or turbine) at the discharge end the pressure in the pipe increases by Δp which changes with time t according to the waterhammer equations. The function $\Delta p = f(t)$ is measured on sensitive manometers and recorded. From the recorded pressure diagram (a sinusoid with gradually damped oscillations), and after taking into account losses due to friction and the velocity head, the mean cross-sectional velocity at steady flow before the closing of the gate (turbine) is determined by integration. This method is suitable for long straight pressure conduits, e.g., pressure penstocks of high-head power stations. When carefully carried out its accuracy is relatively high (about ±1%) and it is thus comparable with careful current-meter measurements or possibly also with dilution gauging.

Other methods for the measurement of discharge in conduits include electromagnetic meters and the ultrasonic Doppler meter.

12.4.2 Waterhammer and oscillations in surge tanks

Every sudden change in discharge causes a pressure wave (waterhammer) the computation of which before construction often gives only approximate results due to the uncertainty in boundary conditions. This is also the case for variations in the water level in surge tanks placed between the pressure conduit and the penstock of high-head power stations to reduce the effects of the waterhammer in the conduit. Therefore, oscillations of the water level in surge tanks and waterhammer in pressure pipes are often investigated by direct measurements on completed structures.

For the measurement of pressure waves in pipes mechanical or electrical instruments are normally used (Ludewig, 1965). The most important mechanical instrument is the pressure gauge, the frequency of which is suitable for most measurements. The pressure spreads from the pipe into a small pipe branching off from it and then into a small cylinder in which a spring loaded piston is placed, the position of which depends on the pressure in the pipe. A shift in the piston, which is directly proportional to change in pressure and indirectly proportional to the stiffness of the spring, is magnified and registered. The disadvantage of this mechanical pressure indicator is that during pressure oscillations in the pipe the pressure acting on the piston is not quite equal to the pressure in the pipe since pressure losses occur in the branch pipe.

Electrical devices for the measurement of variable pressure consist of a pressure sensing unit transforming pressure changes into corresponding changes of an electrical parameter. The sensor is fitted to a device transforming its signal to a current suitable for registering; the frequency of the electrical measuring instrument must again be taken into account.

During measurement of water level oscillations in surge tanks, changes in pressure are usually measured simultaneously, both on the pressure conduit upstream of the surge tank and on the penstock leading from the surge tank. Oscillations of the water level in the surge tank are recorded by a suitably adopted stage recorder.

12.5 Investigations on Spillways

The discharge over the spillway of a dam is best ascertained from the known stage-discharge curve in a measuring section downstream of the structure; at the same time the water level in the upstream reservoir is measured. The computation of the discharge coefficients from the measurements depends on whether we are dealing with a free or a gated spillway and is carried out according to equations known from hydraulics for overflow or outflow. The evaluation of the discharges is more complicated for drowned weirs where the downstream water level must also be measured.

If there is no section with a known rating curve downstream of the dam, e.g., if it is influenced by the backwater from a downstream structure, the discharge must be determined by one of the methods mentioned in Sub-section 12.2.6.

The shape of the overflow jet on the spillway surface of a dam can be measured by poles fitted perpendicular to the spillway surface in several sections. Better results (without disturbing the jet) may be obtained with the use of ground photogrammetry. This measurement is simplified by marking coordinates on the lateral walls of the spillway piers.

Flow velocity anywhere on the spillway may be ascertained either indirectly from the discharge and the depth of the spillway jet (mean sectional velocity) or by direct measurement with the aid of, e.g., a Pitot tube (point velocity) or floats (surface velocity).

The last mentioned methods of velocity measurement were used in France on the ski jump spillway surfaces of dams on the Rivers Cère and Dordogne. Surface velocities were measured with floats, the position of which was filmed at five points along the spillway. To measure velocities at the bottom of the overflow jet (about 20 m/s) a streamlined Pitot tube was used, which was sealed to the concrete surface of the spillway and connected to a differential manometer inside the dam. Apart from the velocity gradient the value of the relative roughness of the spillway surface may be ascertained in this way (*see* Sub-sections 5.1.1 and 6.3.1).

Hydraulic pressures on the spillway surfaces of dams, their baffles, etc., are measured with the aid of piezometric tubes set in the concrete and connected to manometers in the control passage. The tubes have a diameter of about 10 mm and must be insulated against frost. The surface of the spillway must be carefully smoothed round the opening of the piezometer tubes to prevent local negative pressures and before every measurement air must be removed from the piezometers.

Aeration of high-velocity flows is another important phenomenon investigated on some hydraulic structures. The point where aeration begins on the surface due to turbulence (*see* Sub-section 7.3.3b), the progress of the aeration from the surface towards the bottom of the chute and the coefficient of aeration of the flow (expressing the proportion of water in the aerated flow) may be determined by measurement (Kratochvil, 1964).

Vibrations of gates, valves and members surrounded by fast flowing water are also investigated on completed structures. The purpose of measurement is to find both the cause of vibration and means of limiting or eliminating it (*see* Sub-section 7.6.3 and Fig. 12.9 showing a vibrating jet flowing over a partially lowered flap gate).

Fig. 12.9. Vibration of an overfall jet at a weir gate (Klavary on the River Elbe).

12.6 Investigations on Hydroelectric Power Stations

Measurements at hydroelectric power stations serve for the determination of the coefficients of efficiency of the turbines and generators guaranteed by the manufacturer. In the case of Kaplan turbines the measurements also permit determination of the optimal linkage between the guide and propeller vanes.

The output of the power station aggregate

$$P = \frac{\gamma Q H}{102} \eta_g \eta_t \text{ (kW)} \tag{12.4}$$

depends on the discharge Q, the effective turbine head H, and the efficiency of the generators η_g and the turbine η_t. Turbine efficiency is usually determined indirectly on commissioning the power station by simultaneously measuring the power P on the output of the generator, the steady discharge Q through the turbine and its effective head H, the efficiency of the generator being known from the previous tests. Further, there are direct methods for the determination of the turbine efficiency, i.e. a thermodynamic method or computation from values of efficiency measured on large and accurate turbine models in the laboratory.

The discharge through the turbine during steady flow is measured by one of the standard methods (*see* Sub-sections 12.2.6 and 12.4.1) chosen according to whether the measurement takes place in an open inlet or outlet channel of the power station, in the intake or in the pressure conduit of the turbine; and also according to the head of the power station and the length of measurement (instantaneous or continuous). The most frequently used method is that of measuring the cross-section and velocity using current meters (*see also* Fig. 12.3).

Since in high-head power stations situated at the foot of dams the penstocks are comparatively short and curved, the measuring section for the current meters cannot be placed in accordance with standard specifications (Sub-section 12.4.1). To exclude errors, in important cases measurements are carried out simultaneously in two sections of the same conduit or in the intake (Fig. 12.3) and in the penstock (Fig. 12.6). Experience has shown that with carefully conducted measurements the differences between the values of the measured discharge in the two sections does not exceed ±1%.

When continuous measurements are needed during the operation of the power station, measuring pressure differences in the turbine spiral casing is suitable. Comparatively accurate results may be obtained if the pressure tappings are placed so as to record the greatest difference in pressure and, at the same time, to be outside the influence of pressure pulsation, which is caused, e.g., by the guide vanes of the turbine. Pressure tappings (diameter about 10 mm) are usually placed on the outside and inside walls in the first quadrant of the turbine spiral casing and connected by copper or bronze tubes (diameter about 20 mm) to a differential manometer placed as near as possible to the turbine spiral.

The effective head acting on the turbine and defined as the difference in energy immediately upstream of the entry into the turbine spiral and at the exit from its draft tube must be measured simultaneously with the discharge (hydraulic losses occurring in the spiral and draft tube of the turbine are included in the total turbine losses).

In the case of low head plants the upstream water level is measured in the inlet, if possible downstream of the fine rack, usually with an accurate water level recorder. The downstream water level is ascertained either by lowering a heavy grate from a rope with the zero position levelled or with the aid of a stage recorder. Since the cross-sectional area of the inlet and outlet are measured beforehand and the steady discharge is known, the mean value of inlet and outlet velocities and the velocity heads may be calculated and the energy levels in both sections and the effective head of turbine H found.

For high-head power plants the level of the energy line at the beginning of the turbine spiral is measured by a manometer. The head losses in the supply pressure conduit (*see* Sub-section 12.4.1) may be measured simultaneously.

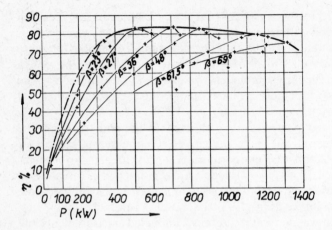

Fig. 12.10. Determination of the optimum linkage of guide and turbine vanes.

Investigations of the optimum linkage of the (Kaplan turbine) guide vane angles, α, and the turbine vane angles, β, are carried out by measurements of the flow through the turbine, the effective head and the output for several values of β and for four to six values of α for each guide vane angle β. The whole measurement must be made with the same head (difference between upstream and downstream water levels). The envelope representing the most suitable linkage guaranteeing the optimum turbine efficiency for a variable flow through the turbine and constant head can be determined from the plot of efficiency, η, against power, P (see Fig. 12.10).

After a period of operation the flow conditions and efficiency may change, e.g., due to wear in the turbine, and a correction of the chosen setting may have to be made on the basis of new measurements.

References

Ackers, P., White, W. R., Perkins, J. A. and Harrison, A. J. M. (1978). *Weirs and Flumes for Flow Measurement*, John Wiley and Sons, Chichester, UK.

American Society of Civil Engineers. (1978). Verification of mathematical and physical models in hydraulic engineering, *Proc. 26th Annual Hydraulics Division Speciality Conference, University of Maryland*, ASCE, New York.

Böck, H. (1956, 1957). Die Eisverhältnisse der Donau in Stauraum Jochenstein; Neue Wege der Eisbekämpfung bei Staukraftwerken, *Österreichische Wasserwirtschaft*, No. 5/6, pp. 97–102, pp. 123–125.

Brachtl, I. (1963). *Steady Flow under Ice Covers*, (in Slovak), Ph.D. Thesis, Slovak Technical University, Bratislava.

British Standards Institution. (1964). *Methods for the Measurement of Fluid Flow in Pipes*, BS1042, BSI, London.

British Standards Institution. (1964–1974). *Methods of Measurement of Liquid Flow in Open Channels*, BS3680, BSI, London.

Cornick, H. F. (1959). *Dock and Harbour Engineering*, Vol. 2, Chapter 10, Charles Griffin, London.

Crickmore, M. J. and Aked, R. F. (1975). Pump samplers for measuring sand transport in tidal waters. Conf. on Instrumentation in Oceanography; Inst. Electr. and Radio Eng., Bangor.

Crickmore, M. J. (1976). Tracer techniques for sediment studies – their use, interpretation and limitations, *Diamond Jubilee Symposium, Central Water and Power Research Station, Poona, India.*

Draper, L. (1961). Wave recording instruments for civil engineering use, *Proc. Conference on Wave Recording for Civil Engineers*, National Institute of Oceanography.

Gaspar, E. and Oncescu, M. (1972). *Radioactive Tracers in Hydrology, Developments in Hydrology*, Elsevier, Amsterdam.

Graf, W. H. (1971). *Hydraulics of Sediment Transport*, McGraw-Hill, New York.

Helley, E. J. and Smith, W. (1971). *Development and Calibration of a Pressure Difference Bedload Sampler*, Open file report, US Geological Survey.

Herschy, R. W. (1978), *Hydrometry: Principles and Practices*, John Wiley and Sons, Chichester, UK.

International Standards Organisation. (1977). *Liquid Flow Measurement in Open Channels – Functional Requirements and Characteristics of Suspended Sediment Load Samples*, ISO 3716; *Methods for Measurement of Suspended Sediment*, ISO 4363; *Bed Material, Sampling*, ISO 4364, ISO, Geneva.

Kivisild, H. R. (1959). Hanging ice dams, *Proc. 8th Congress IAHR, Montreal*, **III,** Paper 1-S1, 3 pp.

Kratochvil, S. (1964). *Hydraulic Research 2—Measurements on Hydraulic Structures*, (in Czech), SNTL, Prague.

Kutiš, L. (1970). Discharge measurement using current meters, (in Czech), *Vodní hospodářství*, No. 12, pp. 330–335.

Ludewig, D. (1962). Einige Verfahren zur Messung von Druckstössen in Rohrleitungen, *Wasserwirtschaft-Wassertechnik*, No. 3, pp. 102–108.

Novak, P. (1957). Bedload meters – development of a new type and determination of their efficiency with the aid of scale models, *Proc. 7th General Meeting IAHR, Lisbon*, **I,** Paper A9, 11pp.

Novák, P. (1959). *Bedload Meters—Study of their Performance and Efficiency*, (in Czech), Práce a štúdie No. 99, VÚV, Prague.

PIANC (1969). Principles governing the design and construction of economic revetments for protecting the banks of rivers and canals, *Proc. 22nd International Navigation Congress*, Section I, Subject 6, PIANC, Paris.

Potapov, V. M. (1955). *Ice Regime of Rural Power Stations*, (in Russian), Gosizdat literatury po strojitelstvu i architekture. Moscow.

Schäle, E., *et al.* (1968). Kanal- und Schiffahrtsversuche, Bamberg 1967, *Schiff und Hafen*, No. 4–9.

Sikora, A. (1962). *Winter Regime of Low Head Structures*, (in Slovak), Práce a štúdie No. 19, VÚVH, Bratislava.

Taus, K., Kutiš, L. and Brachtl, I. (1963). La méthode d'integration de mesure du débit des turbines, *Proc. 10th Congress IAHR, London*, Paper 4.25, pp. 187–197.

Tonini, M. (1965). L'effetto supporto nelle misure di portata in condotta con piu molinelli, *L'energia elettrica*, No. 4.

Index

Figures in italics refer to illustrations in the text.